*the*
# BIO-BREAKTHROUGH

## DECODE YOUR ILLNESS AND HEAL YOUR LIFE

## ISABELLE  BENAROUS

**Bioreprogramming® Press**
LOS ANGELES, CALIFORNIA

Although the author and publisher have made every effort to ensure the accuracy and completeness of information contained in this book, we assume no responsibility for errors, inaccuracies, omissions, or any inconsistency herein. Any slighting of people, places, or organizations is unintentional.

The ideas, concepts, and opinions expressed in *The Bio-Breakthrough* are intended for educational purposes only. This book is sold with the understanding that the author and publisher are not rendering medical advice of any kind, nor is this book intended to replace medical advice, nor to diagnose, prescribe, or treat any disease, condition, illness, or injury. The techniques, processes, and ideas offered in this book are not substitutes for consultations with your professional health-care provider. Reading this book does not constitute a professional relationship or professional advice or services. It is recommended that individuals who are experiencing unusual or concerning symptoms, or any symptoms, receive medical care from a licensed physician or other licensed health-care professional.

The author and publisher claim no responsibility to any person or entity for any liability, loss, or damage caused or alleged to be caused directly or indirectly as a result of the use, application, or interpretation of the material in this book.

1st printing 2020
ISBN: 978-0-9829157-9-0

www.bioreprogramming.net

# Contents

## PART III: THE BIO-BREAKTHROUGH DICTIONARY

# Foreword

I have never forgotten the time a friend walked on red-hot coals for 50 yards without getting so much as a blister. He was able to accomplish this by communicating with his brain, sending himself the message that the coals were not hot and thus would not burn his feet. It was a classic example of mind over matter. The mind is a powerful tool that we can use to our benefit or our detriment, for healing or for hurting. As a physician, I have become increasingly interested in discovering how we can more effectively engage the mind in the healing process.

In my medical training, I learned about the six underlying causes of every medical condition—nutrition, toxins, infection, structural issues, genetics, and emotions. In trying to comprehensively address these causes, I had already gained some familiarity with the concepts and observations of Dr. Hamer, the pioneering physician whose work is acknowledged in this book. With his intriguing idea that diseases often occur shortly after a perceived trauma, I began to ask my patients to talk about what was happening in their lives just prior to the onset of the condition that brought them to my office. To my surprise, many would describe a stressful event that had taken place not long before their disease symptoms manifested. Even more interesting was that many patients sensed or "felt" that there was a connection between the stressor and the onset of their condition. Dr. Hamer's observation about the link between unresolved emotional conflicts and illnesses became evident.

In its deep intelligence, the body seemed to be attempting to resolve psycho-emotional issues through physiological or structural mechanisms, and identifying this interplay was very helpful in diagnoses. However, knowing was not enough. The mere identification of the connection did not seem to help significantly, despite Hamer's prediction that it would. Bringing the emotional conflict from the subconscious realm into conscious awareness was not enough for many patients. They needed something more.

That is when I sought out strategies to help my patients address emotional causes and resolve them in an effective way. My investigation led me to Isabelle Benarous.

I went to Isabelle's office hoping to find something I could add to the healing process. I also believed that if it was worthwhile for patients, I should experience the process myself. I like to walk the talk. We all have hidden unresolved emotional conflicts, and I am no different. So I shared my own concerns and she walked me through the process of BioReprogramming®. Isabelle connected the dots and I understood the path. It was empowering, and it worked— giving me a new depth of understanding of the interaction between my thoughts, beliefs, feelings, life experiences, physical symptoms, and much more.

After a few weeks of seeing changes in myself, I realized that this was going to be a great tool for my patients. I began recommending Isabelle's first book, *Break the Code of Your Illness*, to my patients and staff.

Everyone has unresolved emotional conflicts and BioReprogramming® is an effective process for understanding and surpassing those conflicts, one that can be learned and implemented successfully with the proper training. It is rather simplistic to associate an event with a biological response. Yet understanding and clarifying the origin of such responses is one of the areas where BioReprogramming® shines. In some cases, the origins are derived from childhood, gestational or are trans-generational programs—as though the unresolved conflicts are embedded in the DNA. Other conflicts are predicted based on life cycles and timing. At times it is hard to believe, but the revelations that emerge from the investigations are impressive.

I encourage you to not just read *The Bio-Breakthrough*, but to prepare for it. Proceed with the intention of finding the purpose and deeper meaning of your challenges in order to benefit from the lessons of BioReprogramming®.

*The Bio-Breakthrough* makes BioReprogramming® available to everyone, providing a clear explanation of the mechanism between emotional stress and biological responses—essentially uncovering the missing link between psychology and biology. Isabelle references pertinent studies that support the theory that the physical body can be affected by the mind. She offers an understandable and concise discussion of complex theories for health professionals, as well as anyone interested in health and wellbeing.

*The Bio-Breakthrough Dictionary* contained in the final section will become a celebrated part of this book, as it provides an important reference guide for identifying the emotional root of a vast number of health disorders.

Perhaps most inspiring are the poignant accounts of individuals who overcame their emotional conflicts and changed their lives with Bioreprogramming®. Inside each of their stories are life-changing insights about the subconscious programs that created challenges in their lives and how they moved past those challenges. The solutions that they discovered are now available to you, too. This book is a guide for understanding that you have the power to change the subconscious programs that influence the choices you make in life and the health you experience. It provides a step-by-step plan for addressing and preventing health issues associated with past traumas. By thoroughly immersing yourself in its pages, you can unleash your true potential to grow, heal, and change.

We are entering a time when we need healing more than ever—our current medical system has some great attributes but it is woefully inadequate. In this book, Isabelle Benarous permits us to understand that we are not victims of circumstances but instead have the power to change the subconscious programs that influence our health and direction in life.

Jeremy E. Kaslow, M.D., F.A.C.P., F.A.C.A.A.I.
Diplomate, American Board of Internal Medicine
Diplomate, American Board of Allergy, Asthma,
and Clinical Immunology 1989-2009

# Introduction

People who have healed from cancer and other life-threatening illnesses are all around us. Although they may be exceptions, they challenge conventional medical theories and statistics. It stands to reason that if there is one exception to a theory, perhaps the theory is not entirely correct, no matter how long it has been accepted as truth.

It was this observation that fueled my quest for answers, when I helped a loved one who was confronted with stage-four lung cancer. I knew of people who had miraculously recovered despite the grim prognoses they had received. What caused those "miracles" to occur? What did it take to become an exception, even when the field of medicine claimed that the possibility of this was unlikely at best? Needing to find the answers to these questions was the starting point of my journey.

Self-knowledge can be life changing. Understanding the mechanism behind illness, as well as unlocking the subconscious programs that influence our destiny, is the focus of *The Bio-Breakthrough*. My purpose in writing this book is to give you the opportunity to look at health disorders, as well as your life path, with a new and empowering awareness. It will not only help you understand the root cause of health conditions, but will also allow you to change aspects of your life that you may find limiting.

For over sixteen years, I have dedicated myself to investigating new findings related to human evolution and the processes by which the species adapted to the challenges faced in the environment through cellular changes. Simultaneously, this study has involved a systematic examination of the psychological and emotional conflicts that correspond to those adaptive challenges. Being on a mission to understand the origin of illness and the true nature of disease has been an absolutely riveting process of discovery. I have been highly motivated by a belief that there is meaning in the crises we human beings face in body and mind—even if that meaning isn't immediately clear to us. I have wanted to get to the root cause of illness in general, in order to find solutions that are effective, thorough, and repeatable.

Illness seems to be the result of a survival mechanism that prevents the body from dying quickly from unmanageable stress. However, if an individual is unsuccessful at resolving the emotional conflict in a timely manner, an illness such as cancer may progress to a point of no return and become insurmountable. Yet it appears that this doesn't have to happen.

After witnessing many "exceptions"— people healing from cancer and other illnesses, against all odds—I became increasingly determined to dedicate myself to the type of approach I had been studying. That search ultimately led me to specialize in helping people resolve the emotional distress that underlies disease, as well as unlocking limiting programs that create obstacles in one's life path. From this investigative quest, a new modality of healing has emerged—BioReprogramming®—that rests upon a solid foundation of knowledge that formed the core principles of my work.

## A NEW APPROACH

Unfortunately, most medical doctors disregard the reasons why some people heal against all odds. Most times, the successes of such patients are labeled as "rare cases" and promptly disregarded.

Wouldn't it make sense to closely study those cases, in an attempt to decipher what was medically or methodologically different from other cases? Do we not stand to gain invaluable information and insights by doing so? Western medicine believes that the mind cannot be more effective than drugs.

Still, regardless of how many obstacles appear along the path to health and healing, we need not be deterred. As we seek to find solutions for the multitude of ailments that we contend with in our modern world, one of the most empowering actions is to ask *lots* of questions.

As you come to understand that everything we go through in life has a specific purpose, you will be able to look at your life story from a completely different perspective. As you allow yourself to open up and discover your subconscious programs and their true meanings, you will understand that the people you have attracted along your particular path play a specific role in the story of your life, according to your subconscious programs. These programs prevail for as long as we are unaware of their existence; they dutifully attempt to keep us alive by attracting events of the same nature through specific patterns and cycles. However, these patterns can be changed. You can make a shift. There is no need to remain frustrated, hurt, or victimized. It may be possible to overcome illness, or other life challenges, mainly by positioning yourself with a level of consciousness that supersedes the content of the story you are experiencing. This new awareness will allow you to free yourself and create the future you desire.

As you delve into this book, it will be useful to keep in mind that the ideas and processes introduced here are offered in a condensed and digestible form. As you proceed, I invite you to explore new concepts with an open mind, allowing yourself the natural oscillation between old and new belief systems regarding health, life, and evolution. Consider giving yourself ample time to evaluate this new information, utilize the self-help processes, and observe your life through a new lens of possibilities. To that end, there is a special Bio-Breakthrough Dictionary at the end of the book. It is essential to read the entire book before you refer to the dictionary. All the chapters lead to understanding, and applying, its contents.

As the healing-success stories included throughout the book will demonstrate, BioReprogramming® is meant to be a part of an integrative approach to wellness and not a panacea in and of itself. For individuals who are undergoing standard or complementary medical treatments, this method can provide additional support.

The knowledge presented in this book has changed my life as well as the lives of many others, and it can change yours, too, as you realize that you have the power and ability to awaken the inherent healing forces within you.

This is your starting point for a new relationship with life and healing.

# Part I: The Meaning of Illness

# 1

# Julia's Story

On a bright, sun-drenched morning, Julia was in her kitchen preparing breakfast for herself and her husband, Richard. She was in a particularly cheerful mood because her best friend of twenty-five years was getting married later that day.

When Richard came into the kitchen and sat down at the table, Julia noticed that he was on edge and somewhat disconnected. He ate his meal without uttering a word. When she asked if he had slept well, he shook his head no. Julia didn't say anything; she would not allow Richard's bad mood to spoil her day.

After breakfast, Richard went back into the bedroom, and an hour later he reappeared carrying a small suitcase and his coat, saying, "Julia, I am leaving you. I will never come back. Please don't ask me why. I am leaving now."

As he headed out the door, Julia ran after him, screaming his name, but he would not stop. He did not even acknowledge her. Julia was stunned, speechless, blindsided. She felt as if the ground had been ripped from beneath her feet. Her mind raced, searching for a reason, an answer, but this rupture in her marriage made no sense. She had thought that they were a happy couple and had not been aware of any specific problems. During her five-year marriage to Richard, she had been loving, affectionate, selflessly caring, and nurturing toward him.

As she sat in the open doorway watching Richard drive away, she trembled uncontrollably. Her heart was pounding so hard she felt it would explode out of her chest. Overwhelmed with nausea, she could not catch her breath or even cry. For Julia, time had stopped.

After perhaps twenty minutes of feeling stunned, cold, and unable to move, she gathered all her strength, got up, walked slowly back inside the house, and collapsed on the bed.

She did not go to her friend's wedding that afternoon. Instead, she spent the time repeatedly calling Richard's cell phone. There was no response. As days went by, all her efforts to reach him were in vain. Richard had quit his job and disappeared. His family and friends told Julia that they did not know where he was. She was very confused and worried about Richard's well-being.

Six months later, Julia willingly signed the divorce papers Richard's lawyer had sent her. She wanted to put this experience behind her. She now had something more important to take care of: her health. During a routine exam, Julia had found out she had a malignant tumor in her right breast. It was the first time anyone had been diagnosed with breast cancer in her family. She was only forty-two years old, did not smoke or drink, did not live a sedentary life, was not overweight, and had never used birth control pills. On the contrary, she ate healthy organic food, exercised regularly, drank plenty of water, and every day breathed fresh country air during her morning jogs.

What had happened to Julia? Bad luck? A horrible coincidence? How was it possible that cells in Julia's breast suddenly mutated and formed a tumor? Why then and not a year before, or two years before that, or even a year or two later? What an awful year it had been for Julia! Everything seemed to happen at the same time. She felt her life was falling apart, and this made no sense to her ... or maybe it did make sense.

Could Julia's disease be related to the only major event in her life that year that was out of the ordinary? Her husband had left one morning without an explanation and never came back, a terrible experience and a major shock for Julia. The emotional distress she felt was similar to the one she had experienced thirty-six years earlier, at the age of six, when her father left the house after a fight with her mother on their wedding anniversary. He had stormed out angrily, saying that he was never coming back. Julia loved and cared about her dad very much, and she ran after him, screaming for him not to go. He came back three days later with a hangover and stayed with Julia's mom for another fifteen years before he died.

The incident with her father was an emotionally searing and traumatic event for Julia, and although buried in her past, it was still part of her history.

This story illustrates how the subconscious mind can store away memories and that nothing is ever emotionally forgotten. Each experience has a specific feeling attached to it. This is referred to as the *felt experience*. As we go through life, we subconsciously link together emotional states of the same type. Our brain recalls experiences from our past that resurface in our present each time we go through emotions of the same nature.

For instance, when Julia's husband left her unexpectedly, it triggered an unconscious association in her mind with her father suddenly leaving her family. The emotion she felt at six years old was an unconscious stress that resurfaced with Richard's sudden departure. As psychiatrist Carl Jung observed, "Everything that does not rise into consciousness comes back as destiny." The same way Julia worried about her father for three painful days when she was six, she also worried about Richard. Only this time, her anguish and concern continued for weeks: How long was Richard going to stay away? Where was he sleeping? How could she know if he was safe? Did he leave her for another woman? Maybe Richard was endangered by a mental illness, or perhaps he was having an identity crisis. These were just some of the thoughts and questions that continuously cycled through her mind. She wanted to be there for him, help him, and comfort him. For several days, Julia could not eat or sleep normally. Her imagination was constantly at work, and her mind was on high alert as she sought answers to alleviate her stress. No matter what reasons had prompted Richard to leave her, she wanted him to come back so she could take care of him and make everything better. More than anything, Julia was consumed by her maternal instinct.

Symbolically, the organ associated specifically with nurturing is the breast. Its function is to produce milk for the nourishment of offspring.

In a broad sense, a concern related to anyone or anything a woman wants to mother and protect is referred to as a nest-worry conflict. Julia's extreme emotional distress about Richard unexpectedly leaving found its expression in her breast tissue. Subconsciously, Julia's brain triggered a manifestation in her body that precisely solicited the organ corresponding to her unique felt experience.

Six years later, Julia had overcome the illness. And although she had met another man, she hadn't remarried. She found out through an old friend that Richard was living in his hometown and did not want to have any contact with her. This was fine with Julia. She had been through too much in the intervening years and was now living a peaceful life. She liked her job and was happy with her boyfriend. She had stopped thinking of Richard and felt free.

Sometime during that year, Julia was invited to the wedding of the daughter of a longtime friend. After the church ceremony, everyone gathered at a fancy restaurant for the reception. Julia sat down with her boyfriend and a couple of old friends. Suddenly, she noticed Richard in the crowd of guests. She stood up and started to walk toward him. The second Richard saw her, he turned away, and he left the room before she could reach him. Once again, Julia was speechless, caught completely off guard, and shocked.

At that moment, Julia's past experiences and related emotional stresses resurfaced in her mind. Her emotional history was reawakened when she saw Richard. For an instant, she felt exactly the same way she had six years earlier when he left. As a result, an immediate response to her emotional distress manifested. Her brain retriggered the cellular memory related to nurturing, turning on the genes in her breast tissue responsible for the growth of a tumor. Five months after she saw Richard at the wedding, Julia's mammogram showed a recurrence of her cancer.

When I met Julia in 2003, she wanted to learn more about this new approach regarding illness. By this time, Julia was undergoing cancer treatment for the second time in her life. As she told me her story, we connected the two onsets of her illness with their emotional triggers. The revelation of the intimate link between her emotional life and her illness gave Julia the ability to recognize and unlock the subconscious stress that was directly related to the disease in her body.

During that meeting, tears of relief ran down Julia's cheeks. For the first time since the beginning of her journey with cancer, everything made sense to her. While Julia continued medical treatment, I saw her a few more times. She was able to achieve several personal breakthroughs as we worked on changing the limiting beliefs and perceptions at the root of her emotional distress. Although she had been given a bleak cancer prognosis, the illness resolved.

# 2

# Illness Is Not a Mistake

What is the real secret behind the origin of disease? According to Western medicine, genetic disposition is assumed to be largely responsible for the onset of our illnesses. But how did we arrive at this assumption—and is it true?

Our knowledge and understanding of illness have been deeply conditioned by conventional science, which is rapidly exposing one of the great paradoxes of our time. Although our collective passion for progress and technological advancement has resulted in many astounding medical breakthroughs, it has also resulted in an estrangement from our own bodies. For generations now, we have been conditioned to perceive any unusual biological expression as a pathology or malfunction. But the emerging paradigm is one of understanding illness as a meaningful, adaptive program of survival. We look to the experts to tell us what we should know and expect, but the sense of security we derive from this is short-lived. Instead, we are left feeling suspicious of every ache and pain and woefully disempowered as well. Looking no further than our own friends and loved ones, we can observe the growing tendency to live our life anxiously, in anticipation of health disorders striking out of nowhere.

Eventually, fear and suffering give rise to a deep desire to break free from the status quo and seek answers to the questions that can heal and empower us.

What is the true nature of disease? Is illness the result of random organic developments, or is it the product of specific biological programs that can be learned and understood?

Medical specialists frequently dismiss the intrinsic connection between body and mind. However, this attitude is no longer acceptable. As both practitioners and laypeople, we simply know too much now. Advances in integrative medicine and evolutionary healing methods are showing us that our unresolved emotional struggles can be at the root of health disorders.

There is now a new possibility, a different path that will propel you to a higher level of consciousness about the meaning of illness and disease. You will be empowered by a new knowledge that will allow you to take direct action and claim an authoritative role in the potential recovery of your health.

## THE RESEARCH

The most eloquent harbinger and precise teacher of this exciting new way of relating to illness is Dr. Ryke Geerd Hamer, formerly of the University of Munich and the University of Tübingen in Germany. In 1978, after he had been practicing internal medicine for fifteen years, a sudden and dramatic personal tragedy led him to an important discovery regarding the origin of illness. This was the year his seventeen-year-old son, Dirk, was accidentally shot while on a boat anchored off the Mediterranean island of Cavallo. Dirk never recovered from his injuries and died four months later.

Shortly after losing his son, Dr. Hamer was diagnosed with testicular cancer. Considering that he had been healthy all of his life, he suspected there might be a connection between the traumatic event of the death of his son and the onset of his illness.

Some time later, when Dr. Hamer became head internist of an oncology clinic in Munich, he decided to seek verification of his hypothesis by investigating traumas in the lives of his patients prior to a cancer diagnosis. Interestingly, he found that nearly all of his cancer patients had experienced a deeply felt trauma a few months before the appearance of their disease. Eventually, Dr. Hamer claimed that he could confirm his discoveries with over forty thousand cases studies.

After exhaustive research, he concluded that disease is the consequence of either a sudden, highly acute, and isolating shock or an intense and prolonged emotional stress. This conflict-shock dynamic seems to cause the appearance of a focus of activity in the brain that looks like sets of concentric rings, each centered on a precise point of the brain that can be seen in a computerized tomography (CT) scan.

Although it is controversial, Dr. Hamer's approach deserves attention as well as further exploration. His theory resulted from a set of findings linking the nature of disease to universal biological principles and their interaction between the three levels that make up the human organism: the psyche, the brain, and the organs. Dr. Hamer's research culminated in his conviction that diseases have a biological meaning and are not mistakes of nature.

Dr. Hamer's theory is not yet approved by conventional Western medicine, although a growing number of medical doctors are now giving legitimacy to his ideas through their own research and patient outcomes. Unfortunately, his findings have been used haphazardly in some instances, without proper safeguards or adequate methods to address and resolve emotional conflicts. Nevertheless, his work has instigated a revolutionary approach to addressing disease, especially cancer, which is generally considered to be cellular chaos.

Prior to Dr. Hamer's discovery, other researchers came to similar conclusions linking stress to disease. P. J. Rosch wrote in his essay "Stress and Cancer: A Disease of Adaptation?" (from *Cancer, Stress, and Death*, edited by J. Taché, H. Selye, and S. B. Day, New York, Plenum Publishing, 1979) that, "[i]n 1701, the English physician Gendron commented on the effect of 'disasters of life as occasion much trouble and grief' in the causation of cancer, and 80 years later Burrows attributed the disease to 'the uneasy passions of the mind with which the patient is strongly affected for a long time.' Other authors, such as Nunn in 1822, emphasized that emotional factors influenced the growth of tumors of the breast, and Stern noted that cancer of the cervix in married women was more common in sensitive and frustrated individuals. . . . Toward the end of the century, another English physician, Snow, reviewed 250 patients at the London Cancer Hospital and concluded that 'the loss of a near relative was an important factor in the development of cancer of the breast and uterus.'"

In the 1960s, Yugoslavian psychologist Ronald Grossarth-Maticek, from Heidelberg University in Germany, gained notoriety by reporting research results that seriously questioned standard medical beliefs. Specifically, he investigated the relation of psychosocial risk factors to mortality in a prospective study of 1,353 subjects during a ten-year period. He studied the psychological traits that could predispose an individual to illness, showing that despair and unexpressed emotions were related to the onset of certain diseases. Based on the subjects' emotional profiles (without any medical diagnoses), he was able to predict precisely which of them would one day trigger cancer or cardiovascular disease. Grossarth-Maticek's studies also point to the fact that there is a psychological dimension to disease. (Grossarth-Maticek, R. J. Bastiaans, and D. Kanazir. 1985. Psychosocial Factors as Strong Predictors of Mortality from Cancer, Ischaemic Heart Disease and Stroke: The Yugoslav Prospective Study. *J Psychosom Res* 29(2):167–76.)

Dr. Caroline Bedell Thomas, of Johns Hopkins University School of Medicine, followed more than 1,330 people over 30 years, analyzing the psychological factors implicated in five illnesses. In 1973, she concluded that cancer is the illness most clearly linked with psychological traits. Certain common characteristics predispose an individual to its development: poor bonding with one of your parents, feelings of despair in difficult situations, inability to express feelings, and a significant loss—of a partner or a job, for example—sustained one or two years before the diagnosis of cancer. Her research showed that such events shatter the individual's peace and security, and lead to a feeling of isolation from the world, alienation, or being cut off from one's roots. (Boukaram, C. *Le pouvoir Anticancer des Emotions*. Montreal: Edition de l'Homme, 2011.)

In the 1990s, Dr. Claude Sabbah expanded on the discovery of Dr. Hamer and created a first therapeutic approach, called Total Biology®, to resolve conflicts leading to illness. He developed healing metaphors that precisely connect diseases to their specific emotional sources and ingeniously combined various findings (such as the work of psychologists Marc Fréchet and Anne Ancelin Schützenberger) to help individuals understand and resolve their subconscious stresses.

Undeniably, Dr. Hamer's findings offer the most precise connections between organs and their emotional meanings. The type of illness an individual triggers depends on his or her felt experience during a stressful event or shock. However, I would like to mention that the BioReprogramming® Method differs from the philosophy and methods of Dr. Hamer in fundamental ways. One of the primary differences is based on the premise that gaining knowledge about the origin of the onset of illness is extremely important, but this knowledge alone will not necessarily produce the emotional shift needed to get results. BioReprogramming® particularly focuses on *how* to resolve emotional conflicts by using a combination of powerful tools and specific healing modalities, which I believe are essential to increase the chances of getting positive effects.

## THE BIOLOGICAL MEANING OF ILLNESS

To further explain this life-altering theory about illness, and to bring a new level of soulfulness to the science that underlies it, we will take a close look at this new approach resulting from findings that link the nature of disease to universal biological principles.

In essence, each organ in the body has a function and is connected to a specific group of neurons in the brain that monitor the cells within that particular organ. Therefore, the brain controls the behavior of our cells. For example, when a human being is experiencing a state of intense stress, the brain has the capacity to prompt an adaptive response to alleviate it. Such a response will generate a modification in the brain, and the organ controlled by that specific brain center will then register a functional transformation that directly corresponds to the way an experience is perceived and ultimately "felt" by an individual. This transformation in the body can manifest as a growth, as tissue loss, or even as a loss of function, such as paralysis.

Stress or shock is experienced simultaneously on three primary levels: the psyche, the brain, and the body.

◆ **The psyche** (the conscious mind) expresses the meaning of the traumatic event—the so-called "conflict," whether real, imaginary, symbolic, or virtual.

◆ **The brain** expresses the location of the disease through the isolation and alteration of the group of neurons correlated to the targeted organ, thus manufacturing a cellular change in the organ simultaneously.

◆ **The body** expresses the biological meaning of the "conflict" according to the type of embryonic layer to which it is connected, catalyzing a change that will manifest at a cellular level in a specific organ. (**Note:** Embryonic layers are a foundational aspect of this theory and will be explained in detail in Chapter 3.)

## BIOLOGICAL RESPONSE

When a conflict generating extreme stress within an individual is not resolved, the brain will order a specific biological response in the body that will express the emotional struggle. Apparently, the brain alleviates stresses that we experience as unmanageable by expressing solutions within our biology. It is as if we have a built-in "conflict resolution" system that functions without our having to think about it.

As human beings, we tend to define our emotional struggles in a metaphorical or figurative sense, subconsciously using primal language and animalistic sets of representations and emotions. Our unique perception of an experience will awaken our primary visceral maps; these are our most ingrained and instinctive patterns of response, connecting our internal sensations with their corresponding organs. For example, we might consider an experience to be "disgusting" (which corresponds to the colon), "suffocating" (lung), "staining" (skin dimension), "stinking" (sinuses), "indigestible" (stomach), and so on. An individual's verbal description of an experience has a high significance. As one expresses emotional stress, information can be gathered about the "felt sense" of the difficult or traumatic experience.

If we imagine four women going through the same sudden, isolating, traumatic shock, such as unexpected news that their child has a life-threatening illness, we may wonder: why don't they all respond emotionally to the news in the same way? And, if their trauma triggers a disease process, why don't they all manifest the same disease? This is where understanding the notion of *felt experience* is important. The felt experience is directly connected to the emotional significance that people, places, circumstances, and events hold for us. And although most of us experience the world through the same five senses, we have different ways of giving meaning to our experiences.

In the case of the four mothers, the determining factor of their individual perceptions and emotions related to their child's diagnosis is a matrix of influences that resides within their subconscious mind. The subconscious contains their life stories, including all of the beautiful and painful memories. It is the keeper of the beliefs and values that are aligned with their different religions, traditions, cultural influences, and personal conditioning, as well as the ancestral and gestational programs that I will be describing later in the book.

Each of us filters the environment in a way that allows us to succeed at waking up the latent internal conflicts we subconsciously seek to liberate. We are predisposed to our interpretations and our illnesses in a multitude of ways. Any distorted perceptions we may have about the circumstances we find ourselves in are often proportional to the limitations we experienced growing up. Just like the generations that preceded us, as children and adolescents we often lacked the choices and resources that would allow us to see life differently.

In the example involving the four women, if the first woman perceives the situation about her child's health as a "nest-worry conflict," which refers to a mother-child or a daughter-mother conflict, her emotional response might manifest a cell proliferation in her left or right mammary gland caused by the subconscious yearning to produce more milk to nurture and protect her child. Whether she is innately right-handed or left-handed will determine which mammary gland will be affected. Instinctively, a right-handed woman will hold her child in her left arm and feed the child with her left breast, thus permitting her right arm to be free, operational, and able to deflect danger. In this case, a "nest-worry conflict" will affect the left breast. The right breast (for right-handed women) is linked to concerns regarding someone or something that is mothered secondarily, such as a partner, family member, friend, or pet. These conditions would be reversed for a left-handed woman.

The second woman may be a person with strong religious principles who has spent her life following the Bible and "making sacrifices" for God. In this particular case, the woman feels extremely angry with God after receiving the news that her child is sick, and she cannot "digest" the fact that He is making her child suffer. She feels betrayed but suppresses her rage toward God. Her incapacity to process what she considers a vile action of God's might subsequently lead to a tumor in the colon. The tumor is a manifestation of the "morsel" she can't "digest." Rather than being a mistake of nature, the tumor will function to produce more mucus in the colon to "slide away" the undigested piece.

The third woman's perception may be an actual "death-fright" as she imagines that her child could stop breathing and die. Symbolically, she might want to take in more air for her child. Since staying alive is primarily contingent upon breathing and the lungs' capacity to process oxygen, the alveoli of the lung would be the targeted organ in this case. A proliferation of cells in the alveoli allows for a greater oxygen exchange, thus resulting in lung cancer.

The fourth woman may have a strong belief system and inner resources that allow her to handle the situation with much less emotional stress than the other three women. For example, she might believe that her child is protected no matter how bad the circumstances may seem. She might have an inherent, fervent, spiritual acceptance about life's challenges and their purpose; that is, a strong belief that the presence of disease or even death is meant to engender spiritual growth. The example of the fourth woman shows how a difference in the perception of a particular situation can prevent unmanageable stress. It is very possible that the fourth woman will remain free from any disease or symptoms related to her challenge.

Diseases are not triggered by circumstances; instead, they are triggered by our perception of the circumstances. Our thoughts, brain, and body do not operate independently. The synchronicity between the three is the key to understanding this new approach.

## THE HUMAN BEING

### The Psyche

In exploring how the human psyche operates, we can easily observe how it collects information from the outside world through the five senses (sight, sound, taste, smell, and touch). When an event occurs, we create a personalized evaluation in agreement with our values and belief system. Thereafter, the brain will adapt to the experience in accordance with our perceptions and emotional state. When we rely predominantly on our ability to reason, we're under the illusion that we can make decisions and direct our life through logic alone. The meanings we assign to our experiences, and the decisions we make, are based on subconscious programs. (This will be covered in more detail in later chapters.) Because as human beings we are prone to mental conditioning, these programs influence how we interpret our moment-by-moment experiences.

### The Brain

The brain is both a computer and a recorder, capable of processing about twenty million bits of environmental stimuli per second. It permanently stays alert to surroundings, continuously filtering the information gathered at conscious and subconscious levels. Subconsciously, we accept and absorb the opinions that are formed by the conscious mind. The brain has been molded by evolution to maintain the survival of the individual and its genetic progeny. It simultaneously maintains external and internal awareness, whether it is the blinking of an eye to avoid a projectile or the monitoring of the heart rate during exercise. Our brain always operates in the present moment as it works to control behavioral and biological systems. It is an autonomic system, which means that it configures and reconfigures itself in order to adapt to the environment, continually optimizing its abilities.

Astonishing in its capacities, the brain can be compared to a gigantic database of stored programs that contains your basic learned behaviors (including walking, talking, and writing), as well as the behaviors acquired since birth by observing and emulating those around us, like parents, siblings, peers, teachers, etc.

Beyond the conventional understanding of how it functions, the brain manages input that is most often ignored or denied any relevance in day-to-day life. It also contains built-in programs—the "hardwiring" that comes from the mental and emotional imprints received from parents during gestation, as well as encoded memories inherited from our ancestors. Since we are not consciously aware of these programs, the subconscious mind is essentially running the show.

Given how far we have come as a species, it can be difficult to understand why our will, determination, and focus are not sufficient to create the ideal future we dream about. This is because our subconscious mind does not reason with the same type of logic as our conscious mind. Instead, it operates independently, following its intrinsic and inherited imprints without question. It is quite similar to a machine that contains an incalculable load of prerecorded tapes that are ready for activation as soon as the appropriate environmental trigger presses the play button.

One of the classic illustrations of this mechanized process comes from the research of famed Russian scientist Ivan Pavlov and his experiments confirming the power of conditioning. Pavlov's research focused on ringing a bell each time his laboratory dogs were fed. Over time, merely the sound of the bell, without the presence of food, elicited a salivary response in the dogs. An auditory trigger had conditioned the dogs' neurology, and they were now programmed to elicit a biological reaction at the sound of a bell.

As human beings, we have also undergone Pavlovian conditioning through which our emotional states are similarly induced by repetitive stimuli. What we see, hear, feel, smell, and taste is stored in our memory, becoming our subconscious anchors as we experience life. We live in a world of continual stimuli involving millions of pieces of input that can potentially trigger responses in our thinking, feeling, and reacting. For example, a man who has a severe allergic reaction every time he eats peanut butter may be triggering a childhood memory. At the age of five, he was eating a peanut butter sandwich when he experienced a trauma: after his mother hung up the phone in the kitchen, she told him that his beloved grandmother had just died of a heart attack. During the moment of such shock, the subconscious mind recorded at least one of the environmental components present at the time of the experience. In this case, even a substance as harmless as peanut butter became associated with a shock. The subconscious mind programmed a strong allergic reaction to peanut butter, which is now associated with a conflict related to separation (loss of contact). Chronic allergies involve the epithelial tissues (primarily the skin). Any memory of a separation that has not been dealt with can be awakened by the stimulus of a component that is associated to the separation (in this case, the peanut butter).

For another person, a quiet walk through a garden of roses could trigger the subconscious memory of the loss of a loved one because roses were present at the funeral, which might represent the moment of shock. This link between roses and separation may be at the origin of an allergy to roses, even if the traumatic event happened many years ago and is nearly forgotten at the conscious level.

**Note:** The emotional crisis related to one's allergy or other illnesses can also find its cause in gestational or ancestral programs. (This will be covered in more detail in later chapters.)

Our brain is capable of achieving very complex operations. However, it reacts to the environment in an almost simplistic fashion by creating survival reactions, such as allergies (see page 229, in the Bio-Breakthrough Dictionary). Our felt experience guides our brain to select the most appropriate response, according to a particular emotional distress.

Behavioral and biological responses are based on our reality (what is true for us) as well as our mental constructions (what we imagine). The brain does not distinguish the difference between what we see externally and the images we create internally. It will react the same way to what is real, imaginary, virtual, or symbolic. Imagine a woman being awakened by an unusual noise in her house at 4 am. She automatically thinks that burglars have broken into her home, and the images she manufactures in her mind trigger a rush of adrenaline. As she goes down the stairs to investigate, she is anxious and afraid of what she might find, causing shortness of breath, a dry mouth, and trembling. Then she sees that the intruder is the neighbor's cat that has entered through an open window. The woman breathes a sigh of relief and immediately calms down. In this "fight or flight" situation, she has accepted both imaginary and real events as true and reacted accordingly on an emotional and biological level.

*Two Sides of the Same Coin*

The conscious and subconscious minds rely upon each other in order to function. The conscious mind uses the resources of the subconscious, so we don't have to continuously relearn behaviors and can instead operate automatically. The autonomic brain gets information from the conscious mind and triggers responses to adapt to an ever-changing environment.

As we process information from the outside world, we give meaning to our experiences and engage our thoughts, feelings, and emotions. In order to be able to respond quickly to dangers in the environment, the brain processes gathered information into metaphors and symbols. This archaic mechanism permits the subconscious to immediately interpret the type of situation we are facing, in order to activate the appropriate survival program. A symbol or a metaphor can carry a maximum of information on a minimum of data. If I tell you that my friend Paul is like a "rock," you probably get a clear image of Paul without a detailed description. Because I used the word "rock" as a symbol, you might presuppose that Paul is a solid and reliable man, a strong person who can withstand adversity. The subconscious mind is highly responsive to this form of communication because it saves time and energy, enabling a focus on biological monitoring and environmental dangers.

After gathering and analyzing the meaning of your thoughts, the subconscious mind acts independently from the conscious awareness, following its own trajectory in correlation with its ingrained blueprint.

In other words, no matter how positive our conscious thoughts are, the power of the subconscious will prevail and often override the conscious desires. For instance, a child who has been programmed to think he is worthless and does not deserve to be loved will carry a limiting mental and emotional imprint into adulthood. Even though as an adult he consciously realizes his significance and repeats affirmations to reinforce this belief, the fact remains that the deep imprint from childhood might persist, resulting in low self-esteem and eventually depression. Similarly, when an individual has a disease, positive affirmations often need to be supported by a subconscious deprogramming of the lifelong accumulation of negative imprints and their related stresses.

## The Body

The human body is made up of approximately one hundred trillion cells. Each cell works independently while simultaneously working on behalf of the entire body. Like a member of a well-run community, every cell contributes to the survival of the entire organism by executing the various programs transmitted by the brain. Internal receptors identify biological variations—such as heart rate, sugar levels, and nutrient and hormonal levels—and report them to the nervous system, which, in turn, regulates metabolic function. External receptors are located almost everywhere throughout the body, reporting fluctuations in the environment—such as the temperature, the humidity of the air, and the amount of light—so that the activity of organs can be regulated accordingly.

The nervous system maintains homeostasis, which is the intricate balance of the body's basic functions. In case of a crisis occurring within an organ, the brain generates a solution in an attempt to reestablish proper functioning of the body.

And, as amazing as it may seem, observations of nonhuman animals in their natural habitats may allow researchers to uncover the biological process behind the onset of the so-called "diseases" that seem to override these brilliantly designed stabilizing systems. That's what the next chapter will cover.

❖

# 3

# Our Survival—Understanding Biological Conflicts

U nlike humans, animals can only experience conflicts—the loss of off-spring, fear of attack, or territorial threats—in real terms and not in imaginary, metaphorical, or virtual terms. A bird being kicked out of its nest by another bird represents a real territorial conflict. But, as human beings, we may lose our territory literally or symbolically. For instance, a man may lose an election as the mayor of his town, and his felt experience may resonate deep within him as a territorial loss. The bird's conflict is real; the man's conflict is symbolic. Yet, by observing animals and how their systems handle dangerous situations, we can begin to understand how our own minds cope with threats, whether real, imaginary, or symbolic.

## THE STORY OF A FOX

Accidents can happen in nature, and animals often have the resources to overcome them. We can imagine a fox rapidly eating its prey, such as a rabbit, for fear of it being stolen by other predators. But if a large morsel composed of bone, nail, and fur travels down the digestive tract, regular digestion may not be able to break it down because of its size and composition. The "morsel" may therefore create a blockage in the fox's stomach, and the fox would be in trouble if it didn't have built-in mechanisms for handling the situation.

However, using its natural resources, the fox's body will create spasms and contractions in an attempt to regurgitate the morsel. If this process is not successful, the fox's brain will trigger another solution and launch a more suitable program to improve digestion and break down the material that is stuck. By instantly programming a cell-proliferation process, which creates a tumor in the mucosa of the stomach, the production of increased digestive enzymes will take place, thus permitting an intense and rapid digestion.

Why is this an important example? I'm using it to demonstrate how the brain provides the perfect solutions to sustain life as long as possible in any given biological context. For the fox, once the morsel is digested, the receptors in the stomach will inform the brain that the tumor is no longer necessary, and it will be eliminated. This example seems to suggest that cancer can be an intentional program of nature, which has a definite purpose in terms of prolonging life.

The human brain is still using an archaic mode of action to ensure the survival of the species. To adapt to the pressures of our environment, we sometimes still find ourselves responding as we have since the beginning of time. Just like every animal on this planet, we experience distress when our safety, security, and survival seem to be under threat. Even though our consciousness is more evolved, we produce the same type of archaic responses to stress as most other species do. The key to understanding this notion is by knowing that our perceptions and interpretations are subjective and that the associations we make between events and their meaning are subconscious. What we call "disease" appears to be the biological solution to the individual's mental conflict, whether its origins are personal, gestational, or ancestral.

## FRANK'S STORY

Frank is a small-business owner who is married, has two children, and owns a nice house in a good neighborhood. A couple of years ago, his best friend, Rick, went through a difficult divorce and lost everything, including his business. Because Rick was in such terrible financial shape, Frank hired him to work for his company. He also loaned him a substantial sum of money, which Rick used to rent an apartment and repay the numerous debts he had accumulated during his divorce. Because the two men had been friends since childhood, and Frank felt that they were more like brothers, he trusted Rick completely. Beyond the financial assistance, Frank had also supported his friend emotionally throughout the painful process of grieving his broken marriage.

Two years went by, and Rick recovered financially. It was now Frank who was going through a challenging time. He and his wife could not afford the new payment on their home, as a result of an increase in their interest rate. To make matters worse, Frank's wife lost her job. They were on the brink of losing their home, and Frank desperately needed to refinance with a larger down payment to modify his loan rate and monthly fee.

When Frank asked Rick if he could repay the money Frank had loaned him two years earlier, Rick said he would not be able to. He stated that he was starting a side business for which he needed to use all the money he had saved during the past year. Frank was stunned. After a few seconds of total shock, he left Rick's office without saying a word.

That night, Frank couldn't sleep. He was devastated, shocked, and so disgusted by Rick's reaction that he felt nauseated. He found Rick's unwillingness to repay him unacceptable and figuratively "indigestible." For three days, Frank spent every second dwelling on the situation and was unable to sleep or eat. He didn't want to speak to anyone about it, not even his wife. And despite his constant ruminations, Frank was unable to find a liberating solution of any kind. No matter how he looked at it, he could not "digest" the fact that Rick wouldn't pay him back.

Think about Frank and the fox: they seem to have a lot in common, as they both had a "morsel" too big to digest. The key difference is that for the fox, the morsel was physically real, and for Frank, the morsel was symbolic. Frank's conflict originated in the mind, while the fox's conflict originated in the stomach. Frank's felt experience was interpreted metaphorically by his brain, which responded as if a real "morsel" was stuck in his stomach and needed to be broken down to pass through. The content of the mental conflict was translated as a metaphor, which simply indicated that there was a "morsel" in his stomach that was too big to be digested and processed. Given the intensity of the internal conflict and stress, a possible outcome could be that Frank's perception would consequently awaken and manifest one of the programs of adaptation related to digestion.

When no solution is found by the mind, the brain transfers the conflict from the psychological sphere into the biological domain, where a solution can be expressed. The brain will target the organ that corresponds exactly to the felt experience. *The questions we might ask ourselves are these*: why would cancer in Frank's stomach be considered the ultimate solution by the brain, versus letting Frank struggle with his mental battle? How is an illness such as cancer in any way profitable to a human being as a response to an emotional struggle? The logical answer becomes clearer as soon as we understand the functioning of the nervous system. To set the stage for the processes you will discover later in the book to address your own health issues, it's important to make this point abundantly clear: most often, when our circumstances involve unmanageable stress, our brain will implement an archaic solution that modifies our physiology. This modification in our body will occur according to recorded evolutionary programs.

## THE AUTONOMIC NERVOUS SYSTEM

The sympathetic nervous system (SNS) is part of the autonomic nervous system. The SNS activates the neuronal and hormonal stress response commonly known as the *fight-or-flight response*. When the nervous system recognizes the signals of a threatening environmental stress, the hypothalamus and the pituitary gland team up to prepare the body's organs for action by informing the adrenal glands of the need to initiate the fight-or-flight response. Subsequently, the quick release of adrenaline in the body will modify our physiology, giving us instant access to the high-powered fuel we need to fend off or flee danger.

As human beings, we experience a certain amount of stress in our daily lives, whether it's driving in traffic, arriving places on time, paying our bills, meeting work deadlines, maintaining a harmonious relationship, or raising children. Fortunately, we're quite adept at anticipating and adapting to these ordinary stresses, including coping with the momentary anxieties and fears that often accompany them. We find creative solutions to meet our vital needs as we navigate through our days. Although the chronic nature of our stresses can be extremely challenging, most are not acute enough to threaten our survival. Provided we find satisfactory solutions relatively quickly, we are able to recover emotionally as our stress starts to calm down. Under the control of the parasympathetic nervous system, our bodies are allowed biological recuperation.

The parasympathetic nervous system, which is also part of the autonomic nervous system, complements the sympathetic nervous system by regulating internal organs and muscle contractions, thus allowing us to rest and digest after a phase of stress. Essentially, we are under the control of the parasympathetic nervous system every time we fully rest, sleep, and recover.

## UNMANAGEABLE STRESS

Unfortunately, sometimes the level of stress can exceed the limits of what we can humanly bear, such as the death of a loved one, a divorce or separation, the loss of a job and security, or a betrayal by someone we trust. An event we did not anticipate that creates an acute, isolating shock (meaning an experience we cannot fully process or express to others) can trigger a peak state of stress.

We stay under the control of the sympathetic nervous system for as long as we perceive a situation as a threat. In case of danger, our body is ready to expend a maximum of energy, so we can survive and prevail in battle or during escape. The longer we're subjected to such stress, the longer we will experience an acceleration of our heart rate and a constriction of the blood vessels of the digestive tract. Subsequently, optimal absorption of nutrients will be suppressed. The adrenal stress hormone will also constrict the blood vessels in the forebrain (the center of reasoning), temporarily preventing us from accessing an analytic thinking process. (Lipton, B., Ph.D., *The Biology of Belief*, Santa Rosa: Mountain of Love/Elite Books, 2005.) This corroborates the fact that the human brain is designed to automatically find the quickest route to safety, soliciting primal instincts in the face of danger versus relying on an intellectual process.

Imagine you're on a camping trip in the mountains, having a wonderfully peaceful time, when suddenly a bear appears in your path. Since the brain records the situation as dangerous, it will quickly gather information from the surrounding environment that will immediately be used to inform a behavioral reaction. Your instinct might be to run away from the bear as fast as you can and to jump in a lake. If instead you started to "evaluate the situation" by trying to remember a strategy you learned on a television program, it might be to your disadvantage.

However, this instinctive operating system doesn't always work to our greatest advantage. Students who are frightened and mentally paralyzed by academic tests frequently mark wrong answers because they cannot properly access the needed information. These students are also in fight-or-flight mode. The higher the stress, the more we lose access to logic and evolved intelligence in order to maintain a state of instinctual alertness. The lower the stress, the more capable we are of arriving at solutions through the reasoning intellect.

As long as a situation is *perceived* as dangerous, the brain will activate the sympathetic nervous system and the fight-or-flight response. Therefore, even if the source of the conflict is related to stress in your personal life (such as a painful separation or the loss of a loved one), the brain will react and stay alert to the environment from a primal perspective. If your conscious mind cannot find a way out of the problem, and instead dwells on it day and night in order to resolve it, stress will persist. As expected, during such a state there exists very limited access to mental resources and well-thought-out solutions.

While in a period of acute stress, we have trouble meeting our most basic survival requirements. We can't sleep or eat, and we feel cold. If the intensity of the stress persists, the consequences can be dire. Whenever we are physically, mentally, or emotionally exhausted, our level of conscious awareness is diminished. We could die of exhaustion or inadvertence (lack of awareness), since our attention span is limited to looking for a solution to the conflict we are compulsively thinking about. This is when we find ourselves at risk from environmental dangers, such as cars or buses, which replace the archaic dangers that living beings were exposed to throughout evolution.

Because the evolutionary process has molded human behavior, our neurological pathways have been selected to increase and ensure the survival of the individual. As richly complex as we are as human beings, the human brain can only act on our biology in the present moment. Unlike our conscious mind, our subconscious mind, which accesses stored data to make choices moment to moment, is not concerned with the future. If a level of unmanageable stress is reached, the subconscious will gather the information provided by the conscious mind: input perceived through our five senses, as well as the thoughts and feelings associated with the present conflict. In turn, this will trigger a neurological response that is independent of the conscious mind and designed to increase chances of survival.

The outcome of this chain of events is that a new program will be expressed biologically, one that perfectly matches the content of the felt experience. Even without our conscious knowledge or understanding of this adaptive program, our biology will masterfully orchestrate a way to address the extreme stress. A modification will immediately start in the targeted organ for the purpose of metaphorically solving the conflict.

Interestingly, as soon as the conflict is expressed in the organ, the level of stress lowers to where it becomes manageable. The blood constriction in the forebrain is alleviated, which once again gives us access to more coherent reasoning in our thinking process. We begin to eat, sleep, and function better. As we become more alert to what's happening in our environment, our safety and well-being increase.

Because the conflict is still mentally unresolved at this point, part of the memory of it will be hidden in the depths of the subconscious. Eventually resulting in a so-called "blind spot," or the obscuring of memory, this movement of the mind serves an important purpose: it mercifully allows us to lose awareness of our conflict in order to stop being confronted by the stress it triggers. The stress level has now become compatible with life. What is actually occurring may seem counterintuitive at first;

however, the stories and examples that you will read in the pages ahead will substantiate this further.

**Note:** It appears that our biological system allows us more moments of life by expressing an illness in place of the extreme stress that could prompt death more rapidly.

For as long as a solution to a conflict has not been attained, the biological response (dis-ease) will be maintained. Fortunately, sometimes through a change of circumstances or a shift in perception, emotional conflicts can resolve naturally, even when an individual is unaware of the emotional content their body-mind is processing. This can explain many spontaneous recoveries.

## EVOLUTION: FROM UNICELLULAR ORGANISMS TO HUMANKIND

Over the course of evolution, living beings have had to adapt to challenges presented by the environment. In the oceans about six hundred million years ago, a succession of minute biological changes gradually led to the development of reproductively isolated populations. Almost imperceptibly, each new generation transformed into a life form slightly different from the preceding one. The way living beings have evolved is directly related to the law of cause and effect. Mutations within individual organisms have provided advantages under certain environmental conditions or "stresses." It's fascinating to note that organisms with mutations have increased in number faster than those without them. Adaptation has been necessary for lineages to survive in the ever-changing environment of life on earth.

The biologist Jean-Baptiste Lamarck (1744–1829) stated that the physiology and behaviors of animals can change according to their environment and the animals' survival needs. (Kolvalchuk, I., and O. Kolvalchuk, *Epigenetics in Health and Disease: A Historical Perspective*. New Jersey: FT Press, 2012.) He also hypothesized that the newly adapted characteristics can be transmitted from one generation to the next. For instance, he proposed that the neck of the giraffe becomes longer each generation as a result of needing to reach the upper leaves of the trees.

Lamarck also stated that every living organism, including human beings, has an innate drive to reach a greater level of perfection.

Organisms, since the beginning of life on the planet, have continued to evolve in response to their environments. Disease, within the context of evolutionary history, may be redefined as a meaningful biological emergency program. Today all of those primordial programs remain part of our basic imprints. They can resurface according to the solution our brain needs to extrapolate from its evolutionary memories.

Essentially, each organ in the body can be solicited for its *basic functioning* as well as its *modified functioning*. For instance, we use about nine percent of our lung capacity when at rest (*basic functioning*), but if we run as fast as we can to catch a bus, we will use close to one hundred percent of our lung capacity (*modified functioning*). We have a reserve of lung cells in case we need more capacity to breathe. However, if one's need for oxygen is superior to what the one hundred percent of cells available in the lung can grasp, *extreme functioning* of the lung will be triggered. This process will manifest through a cell proliferation of the pulmonary alveoli (tumor), which will symbolically provide "extra lung" to increase lung capacity during an unmanageable stress related to "being unable to breathe" (such as the fear of death). Simply put, we subconsciously use our biology to adapt to what we perceive as insurmountable.

## OUR HUMAN NEEDS

We've all been there. Something happens in our life that momentarily suspends the ability to reason. We are taken over by our emotions, which prevent us from coping logically. We have an emotional distress, which signals to our subconscious that we are not meeting our needs. When a need is not being satisfied, our stress level rises instantly, thus soliciting a biological solution in order to help us cope. We get ill based on our inability to attain our needs at a moment in time. There is a link between the illnesses we trigger and our human evolution, which has been characterized by a multitude of small biological changes since the beginning of life. Cellular changes appeared so our evolutionary ancestors could adapt. Today the same laws apply. When our needs are not being met, we adapt through cellular changes, thus leading to health disorders.

In 1943, the renowned psychologist Abraham Maslow introduced the concept of the hierarchy of needs, which suggests that people are motivated to fulfill basic human requirements before they attempt to satisfy other needs of importance. Maslow's pyramid of needs is in perfect alignment with the evolution of our species. If we observe the development of the organs of living beings, we can see how each biological modification relates to a need of adaptation to the environment, which, in turn, correlates to the embryonic layers of the brain (which will be covered in the next section).

Today, the needs that are related to our animal memory are at the core of our biological makeup and at the root of our emotional struggles.

**Note:** It appears that any conflict or illness we may experience is directly related to the inability to meet one or more of our basic needs.

The foundation of our human life is supported by the fulfillment of four types of needs. This foundation starts with physical basic requirements, such as being able to breathe, eat, drink, regulate body temperature, eliminate waste, and reproduce. Today, when we struggle with attaining our basic needs in a literal or figurative sense, our subconscious mind seeks solutions to such conflicts through our vital organs.

Once physiological needs are fulfilled, the next level of needs pertains to protection and security, which can be attained through acquiring a job, making money, and having shelter. Our subconscious connects our need for security to enveloping organs that are responsible for the protection of internal vital organs.

Maslow's hierarchy of needs is depicted as a pyramid to be ascended. As people progress up the pyramid, needs become increasingly of a psychological and social nature. Specifically, the needs for relationships, love, and belonging emerge, as well as needs related to self-esteem and importance in relation to others.

When any of the above four categories of needs is not met, there is a sense of deprivation. These needs are called Deficiency needs (D-needs). Viewing the needs hierarchically, above the D-needs arises a different type of needs called Being needs (B-needs). Related to personal growth and transcendence, B-needs are more intellectual in nature. The B-needs are connected to a sense of purpose and fulfilling the desire to contribute and grow as human beings.

Our level of stress becomes unmanageable when we perceive or interact with the world in a way that does not allow us to meet one or more of our D-needs. In response, the subconscious can instigate a biological modification to temporize the stress related to such a deficiency.

Coming to a greater understanding of what happens at the biological level when our vital needs are not met, could we allow ourselves to extrapolate and wonder if it may be possible to free ourselves from disease? How would our biology be positively affected if our perceptions allowed for our vital needs to be constantly fulfilled? Could we develop a philosophy of life that would allow us to meet our needs no matter what the circumstances?

## EMBRYONIC LAYERS

We are not aware of the moment when, in a fraction of a second, an organ becomes the communicator of our needs. The emotion is transferred from the psyche into the body within an instant. It appears that the story of an illness starts with an unsatisfied need. Through the intimate link that connects the psyche, brain, and body, a need winds up being fulfilled by a *bio-logical* function when your psyche is unable to find a way to ensure emotional satisfaction. Needs are attained through cellular changes, utilizing evolutionary archaic programs.

Biological lineages have gone through remarkable evolutionary changes, developing new organs to meet adaptive needs. Among those changes is the development of four embryonic layers in the brain, each layer in synchronicity with the development of the organs in the body.

The following explanation of these embryonic layers will provide a brief look at a fascinating aspect of our human biology, one that offers a greater understanding of the biological conflicts that trigger illness. Dr. Hamer's findings have brought to light and demonstrated the origin of illness as an adaptive mechanism. Although some of the terms may seem, at first glance, highly scientific, real-life examples are included that offer context and meaning. I suggest that you think of this section simply as an exploration; you do not need to fully grasp all the nuances related to the embryonic layers in order to proceed forward in your healing journey. A fuller understanding of how unmet needs impact on the most primal, physical level simply serves to clarify the story of how we get sick and what we might need in order for balance to return.

An overview of the embryonic layers begins with the *endoderm*. The *endoderm* layer, controlled by the archaic *brain stem*, is linked to *vital organs* and their related basic functions, such as breathing, eating, digesting, eliminating, and reproducing. Ancient aquatic creatures needed to ensure their vital needs, such as the intake of oxygen and catching morsels of food. As our ancestors evolved, they left their aquatic domain and became terrestrial. At this point, the need arose for the protection of a stronger skin layer in order to cope with rough terrain, a harsh environment, and extremes in weather and temperature.

The *old brain mesoderm* layer, controlled by the part of the brain called the *cerebellum*, is linked to enveloping organs and functions to protect against assaults or attacks. Later in the evolutionary development of the human brain, the *new brain mesoderm* appeared. Controlled by the *cerebral medulla*, the *new brain mesoderm* enabled movement through the development of a muscular and skeletal system, permitting hunting capacities to expand.

The youngest of our four embryonic layers is called the *ectoderm* and is controlled by the *cerebral cortex*. It relates to social and territorial needs. As evolution continued, living creatures began to exist in social groups and form bonds with other individuals of the same species. Along with those bonds came a need for connection as well as boundaries. The need for safety and stability of territory, along with the fear of losing them, became new parts of the equation. As individuals began to identify with each other and with specific places, the need to mark the territory and maintain familiar systems for living also evolved. The *ectoderm* layer controls organs whose functions permit us to mark and fight for the preservation of territory. It also commands organs that originated from the need to more accurately see, hear, and feel for the purpose of anticipating potential dangers.

## THE FOUR FAMILIES OF BIOLOGICAL CONFLICTS

In most animals, *embryogenesis* starts as soon as fertilization of the egg occurs. In human beings, the four embryonic (germ) layers (endoderm, old and new brain mesoderm, and ectoderm) develop within the first twenty-one days of the embryonic life. A fetus at its earliest stage of development will undergo all the evolutionary stages of the species with a tremendously accelerated speed and progress from a single-cell organism to a human being.

From those four stages of development, it is possible to deduce four families of biological conflicts:

**The endoderm.** The endoderm (inner germ layer), controlled by the brain stem, is the oldest layer, which forms and commands *vital organs* such as the mouth, lower part of the esophagus, lungs, liver, pancreas, stomach, colon, kidney collecting tubule, prostate, and uterus.

The biological conflicts related to endodermal tissues are associated with the individual's vital needs, such as the ability to breathe, have enough to eat, or process food. In a figurative sense, if a person is subjected to a "death-fright conflict" after being given a negative prognosis, the genes of his or her pulmonary alveoli might mutate, enabling a cell proliferation in the lung for the purpose of being able to get more oxygen and continue breathing.

Other examples may include:

- A concern about lack of money and food can represent a conflict related to the fear of starvation. It is the role of liver cells, hepatocytes, to maximize digestion. The proliferation of such cells, resulting in a tumor in the liver, may express a subconscious need to make the most out of a small amount of food while subconsciously fearing famine.

- A profound tragedy, such as the loss of a child, might affect the mother's ovary by triggering a cell proliferation to achieve faster reproduction and metaphorically allow replacement of the child who has died.

**The old brain mesoderm.** The old brain mesoderm, part of the middle germ layer which is controlled by the cerebellum, forms and commands organs linked to the *protection* of the organism, also described as *enveloping organs*, such as the corium skin, pleura, peritoneum, pericardium, and breast glands.

The biological conflicts related to the old brain mesoderm are connected to emotional stresses that concern attacks against one's integrity and can, as always with conflicts, be experienced literally and figuratively. For instance, an individual can be vulnerable to a verbal attack just as if real arrows were being shot at his heart. In this case, thickening of the pericardium (the double-walled sac that protects the heart) would safeguard the individual against further attacks. Pericardial mesothelioma, a rare cancer that develops in the membrane surrounding the heart, is related to such emotional conflict.

Other examples may include:

- Facing lung surgery, a man might perceive the procedure as an attack against his chest, and the pleura, the two-layered membrane that protects the lung, would be the targeted organ to express such conflict. This could result in a mesothelioma of the pleura.

- When one's integrity and boundaries are breached by unwelcome physical contact, a feeling of being "stained" will emerge. This might affect the skin and trigger the development of a melanoma (cancer of the skin).

- An inability to meet the need to protect and nurture her children or partner could affect a woman's breast glands and trigger the proliferation of "milk-producing cells" that could result in breast cancer. The extra cells allow the woman to symbolically "nurture" by providing more milk for the benefit of her loved ones.

**The new brain mesoderm.** The new brain mesoderm (part of the middle germ layer), controlled by the *cerebral medulla*, forms and commands organs related to movement, such as bones, tendons, ligaments, connective tissue, muscles, most of the lymphatic system, blood vessels (with the exception of the coronary vessels), and the adrenal cortex.

The biological conflicts related to the new brain mesoderm are predominantly associated with self-depreciation, such as feeling insignificant in comparison with others. For instance, in an athletic environment, a gymnast specializing in still rings might feel devalued after the arrival of a seemingly more talented teammate and could develop tendonitis in his arms as a result of such conflict.

Other examples may include:

◆ A woman who feels her femininity and attractiveness have vanished and considers herself worthless as a sexual partner might suffer from a self-devaluation conflict that affects her pubic bone with osteoporosis or even cancer, depending on the intensity of her "felt experience."

◆ A man whose salary has been significantly reduced because of severe company budget cuts is humiliated to face each day, believing that he's not living up to his wife's expectations or his own. Feeling stripped of power while simultaneously being criticized by his spouse leads to a reaction in the lymph nodes and perhaps the onset of lymphoma. The lymphatic system, which transports immune cells to and from the lymph nodes, figuratively represents our defense mechanisms. When one feels attacked (literally or figuratively), ulcerations within the lymphatic system permits a greater pathway for lymphocytes and monocytes to do their work to "defend" the organism.

The new brain mesoderm is also linked to conflict related to one's "direction" in life. A conflict of "having been thrown off course" or of "having gone in the wrong direction" might lead to a decrease in adrenal function, which in turn could elicit a level of exhaustion that forces an individual to stop pursuing the wrong path.

**The ectoderm.** The ectoderm (part of the outer germ layer), controlled by the *cerebral cortex*, forms and commands organs such as the epidermis, nasal and sinus membranes, inner ear, retina, bronchia, lining of the milk ducts, cervix, vagina, lining of the lower part of the rectum, lining of the bladder, and the coronary vessels. The ectoderm is also linked to meaningful functional impairments, such as diabetes and motor paralysis.

The biological conflicts of the ectoderm are related to conflicts that are territorial, sexual, existential, motor, and about separation.

For example, an elderly man may have a difficult time "marking" his territory since his son and family moved into his house. For practical purposes, the man moves his bed into the living room. To resolve his conflict, the old man subconsciously triggers the ulceration of the tissue lining of his bladder. In this case, the biological meaning of the tissue loss is to allow the bladder to expand so that more urine can be contained and used to mark his territory, thus forcing the recognition of his position and boundaries.

In a different example, a woman might have to endure a job she despises. While she "resists" a repugnant situation, constant muscle tension in her body will require a greater glucose supply. Over time, her sugar levels may rise in the bloodstream, thus leading to diabetes.

In most cases, illness appears according to a distress and provides a solution to it through the organ. A new awareness about how biology really works will permit you to face health disorders with more accurate information and, therefore, more power to overcome them.

# 4

# Deconstructing Illness

As surprising as it may sound, instead of being regarded as an enemy to be feared, disease may be looked upon as a useful biological change that ensures adaptation during situations of danger. All our adaptation systems, such as tissue and organ modifications that developed over millions of years of evolution, are stored in our brains and in our genes. During a phase of high stress, when individuals are subjected to the action of the sympathetic nervous system, organ function can be modified. To facilitate the resolution of the emotional conflict, the functional of an organ is either enhanced or decreased by a cell proliferation, a cell meltdown, or a specific functional change.

## THE ROLE OF GERMS

Western medicine focuses on organs in an isolated fashion and attributes their malfunctions to environmental toxicity, mechanical causes, or viruses and bacterial "attacks." It has viewed infections as illnesses on their own rather than important manifestations of the healing process. The events that occur after sustaining a simple skin laceration illustrate the role microorganisms (germs) play in our basic biology. Immediately after a laceration takes place, platelets stick together to create a scab and protect the afflicted area. Underneath the scab, new skin cells multiply with the help of germs that optimize the reconstruction of a new layer of skin. Once the wound is repaired and a new layer is completed, the scab falls off. What is happening outside of the body is similar to what is happening inside. The body knows how to repair itself, and it appears that bacteria play a specific role in our biology and are necessary for the restoration of our tissues.

While looking for the source of illness everywhere other than the ultimate personal computer—the brain—the priority of Western medicine has been to strengthen the immune system by destroying germs. Does that really make sense? Microbes were the first form of life to develop on earth and have supported the development of plant and animal life throughout the course of evolution. These organisms operate as decomposers and expellers of foreign bodies within the biological system. They are present at all times in the human flora, as well as in the cells. Interestingly, it was not considered that microbes might become *purposely* virulent in one's body in response to precise organic needs; nor was it considered that the source of their flare-ups and occasional proliferation might actually have been initiated by the host system!

Pierre Béchamp (1816–1908), a professor of medical chemistry and pharmacy at the University of Montpellier, discovered microorganisms and showed that germs are part of our system and constitute what he called "the terrain" in our biology. Conversely, Louis Pasteur (1822–1895), who was Béchamp's contemporary, stated in his famed writings on germ theory that germs invade our body from the outside world. Unfortunately, this hypothesis has long been accepted as true. Pasteur not only plagiarized what Béchamp had discovered six years earlier, but also perverted the facts and influenced the foundation of Western medicine with distorted and inaccurate information. Pasteur actually admitted this on his deathbed. A direct challenge to the germ theory took place when a man who wanted to prove the theory wrong deliberately drank a glass of water containing a substantial amount of *Vibrio cholerae*, a pathogen scientists assumed was responsible for acute intestinal infection. The man remained unaffected by the infectious agent. The scientists did not investigate this event further and his experiment was disregarded. (DiRita, V. J., 2000.)

Viruses and bacteria play an important role during the healing phase of certain diseases and act according to the solicitation of our system.

According to Dr. Hamer, mycobacteria such as tuberculosis multiply at a rate parallel to a growing tumor, so that the moment the conflict is resolved, the exact amount of tubercular bacteria will be available to decompose and remove the tumor.

In another example, the fact that the flu virus will manifest itself every year within only a small percentage of individuals is not related to the strength of immune systems in the population, but rather the types of conflict that flu exposed individuals might be resolving. The flu virus optimizes the repair phase of the bronchial mucosa, which can be affected when a minor human conflict is being experienced, such as a dispute of a territorial nature related to family or work. The bronchi correspond specifically to *aerial* territory. Symbolically, aerial territory relates to expression and the air between us and other people. It also corresponds to the meaning, value, and even the power we derive through communication. Feelings such as "you don't accept my words" or "my opinion doesn't matter" are indicators of this kind of conflict. In the midst of the tension, it can feel like someone is symbolically "eating up" the air of the other. Another feature is when we hold fast to being right about something, especially when being right becomes a self-righteous and uncompromising position. These common types of conflicts are, perhaps, why thousands of individuals wind up with the flu every year if the virus is present in their environment.

## THE TWO PHASES OF ILLNESS

When a conflict is resolved, the resulting illness develops in two phases: the *active phase* and the *healing phase.* The active phase starts at the time of the conflict shock and continues for as long as the individual has not resolved the emotional conflict related to the disease. For instance, the size of a tumor might depend on the intensity and duration of the conflict.

At the moment the emotional conflict is resolved, the healing phase starts instantly and allows the body to access the repair phase under the control of the parasympathetic system. The healing phase is elicited through two distinct pathways. The first pathway, called the "practical solution," is directly related to a change within the environment, which creates a context where the conflict no longer exists. For instance, in Frank's case, his best friend apologizes and gives back the money he owed. In this situation, the environment itself provides the solution.

Is the problem truly resolved after the environment provides a solution? No. When not accompanied by internal changes in one's thoughts, perceptions, and feelings, a solution may only be momentary. Ultimately, if the original circumstances were to reoccur, the risk of a relapse would be significant.

The second pathway toward healing is through the "surpassing solution"—one that goes beyond the problem by expanding one's way of thinking. When an individual is able to find (through a change of perception) a liberating solution to the distress, the healing phase can be set in motion. Ideally, this state of health will continue no matter what fluctuations the environment brings in the future.

In order to access the surpassing solution, it is necessary for an individual to shift emotionally. This often involves putting an end to blaming others for our conflicts and starting to look at life as the unfolding of circumstances that invite us to grow and change. Of course, this is easier said than done, when our subconscious programs are running the show by influencing our perceptions and dictating our responses to the environment. Fortunately, certain therapies, particularly Neuro-Linguistic Programming (NLP), support us in the exploration of new perceptions about our challenges and provide us with the necessary tools to take charge of our life.

During the two phases of disease, biological changes will take place according to the type of embryonic layer the emotional conflict solicits. Organs and tissues controlled by the brain stem and cerebellum respond in opposite fashion compared to organs and tissues controlled by the cerebral medulla and the cerebral cortex.

### The Conflict-Active Phase of Illness

During the conflict-active phase, also called the "cold phase," the individual organism is under the control of the sympathetic nervous system. The higher the stress, the more an individual will undergo symptoms such as sleeplessness, lack of appetite, coldness, and elevated heart rate.

Organs controlled by the *endoderm* and *old brain mesoderm* germ layers will generate cell proliferation during the active phase of a conflict. For example, during the active phase of a *nest-worry conflict*, milk-producing cells can proliferate and create a tumor in a woman's breast glands (*old brain mesoderm*).

Organs controlled by the *new brain mesoderm* and *ectoderm* germ layers will undergo tissue loss during the active phase of a conflict (the ectoderm is also linked to the loss of function of certain organs). For instance, during the active phase of a *separation conflict*, an individual will develop microscopic skin ulcerations (epidermal ulcers) in order to reduce skin sensitivity. Figuratively, being desensitized and unable to "feel" allows an individual to bear the absence of another human being—such as a family member or close friend—or any other absent element and sustain the distress related to separation.

### The Healing Phase of Illness

Growths and tumors controlled by the *endoderm* and *old brain mesoderm* germ layers (which developed at the active cold phase) are degraded with the help of fungi or bacteria during the healing phase, or "warm phase," of the conflict. For example, during the healing phase of a *nest-worry conflict*, a special biological program will be activated in order to decompose the tumor of the breast gland, with the help of tuberculosis bacteria (if they are available in one's system).

Tissue loss, which occurs in organs controlled by the *new brain mesoderm* and *ectoderm* germ layers during the active phase, will be replenished with the proliferation of new cells and the intervention of bacteria and viruses (if available) during the healing phase. For example, during the resolution phase of a *separation conflict*, an individual can experience eczema, which corresponds to the skin restoration phase through ulcer replenishment. Such a condition becomes chronic only when a periodic relapse of the conflict of separation occurs.

## THE ONTOGENETIC SYSTEM OF TUMORS & CANCER EQUIVALENT DISEASES (According to Dr. Hamer)

| TYPE OF EMBRYONIC LAYER | ENDODERM | OLD MESODERM | NEW MESODERM | ECTODERM |
|---|---|---|---|---|
| **COMMAND RELAYS** | BRAIN STEM | CEREBELLUM | CEREBRAL MEDULLA | CEREBRAL CORTEX |
| **CORRESPONDING TYPES OF ORGANS & CONFLICTS** | -Vital organs • *Conflicts of the "Morsel" of oxygen or food (catching, digesting, assimilating, evacuating)* -Reproductive system • *Conflicts of reproduction* | -Organs related to protection& integrity • *Attack Conflicts* -Organs related to life preservation • *Nest conflicts* | -Organs related to locomotion & circulatory organs • *Conflicts of devaluation* -Some reproductive organs • *Loss conflicts* | -Organs related to communication (five senses) • *Conflicts of Separation* -Organs related to territory&boundaries • *Territorial conflicts (Also motor conflicts & sexual/reproductive conflicts)* |
| **EXAMPLES OF ORGANS IN CORROLATION WITH EVOLUTIONNARY STAGES** | • Appendix • Bladder (submucosal) • Colon • Duodenum • Esophagus (lower) • Fallopian Tubes • Intestines • Kidney collecting tubule • Liver • Lung (Alveoli) • Mouth • Ovarian and Testicular teratoma* • Palate • Pancreas • Parathyroid gland • Parotid gland • Pharynx • Prostate Gland | • Breast (Milk gland) • Dermis • Meninges of the brain • Omentum • Pericardium of the heart • Peritoneum of the intestines • Pleura of the lungs • Shingles* | • Adrenal glands • Arterial blood vessels • Bladder sphincter • Blood vessels • Cartilage • Connective & fat tissue • Dentine • Kidney parenchyma • Lymph nodes • Muscles • Ovarian parenchyma • Rectum sphincter • Skeleton • Spleen • Tendons/Ligaments • Testicular parenchyma | • Alopecia* • Blader mucosa • Breast (intraductal) • Bronchi • Cervix • Coronary arteries • Cornea • Diabetes* • Epidermis • Esophagus (upper) • Glaucoma* • Hypoglycemia* • Larynx • Mouth (upper mucosa) • Multiple sclerosis* • Nervous system • Pancreatic ducts • Parotid Gland duct • Rectum (lower) |

| | | | |
|---|---|---|---|
| •Rectum (Sigmoid)<br>•Salivary gland<br>•Stomach (exept small curvature)<br>•Thyroid (Old)<br>•Tonsils<br>•Uterus | | | •Stomach mucosa<br>•Thyroid (new)<br>•Urethral mucosa<br>•Vagina<br>•Vertigo* |
| **CONFLICT ACTIVE PHASE** | CELL MULTIPLICATION Mass formation | CELL MULTIPLICATION Mass formation | CELL REDUCTION Necrosis (tissue loss/holes) | CELL REDUCTION Ulceration (tissue loss) or loss of function (blocking) |
| **CONFLICT RESOLUTION PHASE (Recovery)** | CELL REDUCTION Necrosis / Ulceration | CELL REDUCTION Necrosis / Ulceration | CELL MULTIPLICATION | CELL MULTIPLICATION |

## ONTOGENETIC SYSTEM OF MICROBES

| | FUNGI | MYCOBACTERIA | BACTERIA | VIRUSES |
|---|---|---|---|---|
| **ACTIVE MICROBES DURING REPAIR PHASE (Infecticus state)** | Cell decomposition through caseous necrotization | Cell decomposition through caseous necrotization Ex : BK/Tuberculosis | Repair and restoration of ulcers | Repair and restoration of ulcers |

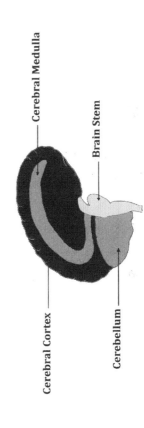

Cerebral Cortex

Cerebral Medulla

Brain Stem

Cerebellum

As soon as the conflict is resolved in the psychological realm (in one's mind), the individual feels a great emotional relief, and the healing phase (warm phase) begins. At this point, the autonomic nervous system reverts to the control of the parasympathetic system, thus permitting the individual to rest, regain appetite, and recuperate. However, symptoms such as fever, swelling, inflammation, infection, pain, fatigue, and headaches can occur simultaneously, making this natural healing process difficult to bear and sometimes dangerous.

Illness can be a reversible process, but the healing phase is rarely asymptomatic. Because of a lack of information, most individuals misinterpret the meaning of its course and interrupt it instead of gently monitoring some of its unpleasant symptoms.

Still, it is essential to remember that the natural healing phase of certain conflicts can be challenging. Individuals will benefit from the advanced techniques of Western medicine to assist them through the acute stages.

**Healing phase of a territorial conflict.** There are three main types of territorial conflicts. The conflict related to "territorial loss" can affect the heart (coronary arteries), the conflict linked to "marking territory" can affect the bladder or rectum, and the human conflict related to "aerial territory" (disputes and fear of being invaded by the enemy) can affect the bronchi. The following example pertains to the coronary arteries.

Observing animals' combat over territory offers a different way of understanding the origin of heart disease. Every year during the mating period for bull elk, the dominant bull elk is challenged by young rivals for the right to mate. If the dominant bull wins the fight, he will remain the dominant elk in his population and will be the only male allowed to mate with the females of his herd, thereby ensuring his genetic contribution to the next generation. During such extreme fighting with the challenging young elk, intense strength (muscle power) is needed for a short period of time. Throughout the combat, the inner lining of the elk's coronary arteries will ulcerate, thus permitting the enlargement of the arterial channels. This increase in the diameter of the coronary arteries will allow for a greater quantity of blood and oxygen to be available for distribution throughout the entire body.

This biological solution increases the chances for each male elk to win the fight related to territory. It is by far more vital for the dominant bull elk to keep his position and triumph over his rival than the other way around. He has everything to lose compared to the young buck that has not yet "owned" territory and a harem (a group of females sharing a single mate). In this case, the dominant bull elk will keep fighting until complete exhaustion, even in cases when he is losing the battle.

At the end of combat, a new biological response will take place so that the lining of the coronary arteries (intima) can be repaired. The restoration of the intima will involve an increase in cholesterol, which acts to replenish the micro-ulcerations of the coronary arteries during the healing phase. Interestingly, even though the male bull elk does not eat greasy food and exercises every day, his arteries can still present an overload of cholesterol. However, the reason why dominant bull elks die of heart failure is not directly related to the blockages cholesterol plaque might create.

According to Western medicine, heart attacks are related to blockages in the arteries, impairing blood supply and preventing enough oxygen from getting to the heart. From a biological point of view, it seems that heart failure is directly related to the conflict of territorial loss and the variations the brain is subjected to during the healing phase of such conflict. When the healing phase starts, the organ and its brain relay (the relay being the part of the brain that controls the transmittal of information to a specific organ) are undergoing repairs simultaneously with the appearance of edema (interstitial fluid). The size of the edema encompassing the brain relay related to the coronaries (within the cortex) can create danger. Its size is proportional to the duration of the territorial distress and can sometimes become relatively large. The process of elimination of such edema, which occurs in the middle of the repair phase, will create a momentary disturbance that can affect surrounding regions of the brain, thus stimulating relays that are connected to the functioning of the heart. One neurological relay in particular might be triggered, thus provoking bradycardia (the heart beating too slowly) or even cardiac arrest.

The origin of heart failure hides behind the mechanism, which takes place during the healing phase of a territorial conflict. But if nature is so clever, why does the so-called "healing phase" lead to death after an intense territorial conflict? Again, the answer lies within the survival archetypes of the species.

It appears that it is in the best interest of the species that the older bull elk does not return to his herd after he loses his fight, since it would disturb the young bucks that would be fighting again instead of mating. Such interference would lower the amount of offspring being conceived. Female elk have a short estrus cycle of only a couple of days where successful mating can occur. In order to ensure the next generation, mating needs to happen in a timely way and in alignment with the seasons. This will allow the calves to benefit from the camouflage the forest provides so they will not easily be seen by predators. After the dominant elk loses, his death through a massive heart attack becomes the perfect solution for the propagation of the species.

Nature provides two types of survival programs in general. This case illustrates that one program is that of personal survival, giving both participants a chance to win by enlarging the diameter of their coronary arteries, thus giving them greater strength to fight. The other program is related to the survival of the herd, when the ideal solution for the species prevails and leads the older bull elk to die of heart failure after the fight.

If the young buck loses, he does not insist on fighting relentlessly and will stop before exhausting himself. Although his need for territory is instinctual, it is not as strong as the need of the dominant bull elk, which already has the habit of owning his own territory and females. When recuperating after the fight, the healing phase for the young buck will be smooth, thus allowing his survival. The young elk will fight again the following year to win his territory. As years go by and the dominant elk becomes older and weaker, the chances for the growing buck to become dominant will progressively increase.

When human beings lose their territory, the same biological program experienced by the bull elk will be triggered. Their coronary arteries will ulcerate for as long as the fight for territory is sustained, whether that fight is real or figurative. For instance, when a man loses an essential component of his environment, such as his job, house, wife, or group of friends, he might "fight" to get his position back. This will trigger ulcerations for more blood flow in his coronary arteries while he is fighting.

When an issue perceived as territorial loss goes on for too long, the amplitude of the healing phase can be massive and can lead to heart failure. A heart attack is generally related to a conflict of territorial loss and prompted during the repair phase of the coronaries' brain relay. This can explain why people who exercise, eat nutritious foods, and lead a generally healthy life can suddenly have a heart attack if they experience intense stress related to territory.

It's not unusual for a man to have a heart attack a few months after retiring from his job. This is because he has lost his "territory," perhaps to a younger worker. Or a football player can experience a massive heart attack during a game as he fights for his team to win. Also, we've seen a dramatic rise in heart disease in women as their social positions in the world have expanded in masculine ways, such as holding more authoritative roles, gaining more and more rights, earning more money, and therefore acquiring more territory that they can lose.

Still, these phenomena are related to our individual perceptions, which is why every person who loses a job, spouse, or house won't experience a territorial loss in their psyche and trigger a heart problem.

Just like the heart, other organs controlled (or partially controlled) by the ectoderm—such as the rectum, bladder, cervix, and esophagus—can also manifest symptoms that are unpleasant and distressing during the reparation phase. It is often through symptoms such as bleeding that illness is discovered and perceived as aggressive, which understandably tends to be frightening for most people.

Consider the case of an older man who was undergoing rectal swelling and bleeding. Three months prior to this event, he was fired from his job without a clear explanation and was shocked by how his boss treated him after more then twenty years of being an excellent employee. This struggle in his psyche led him to an unmanageable stress. He felt as if he didn't know where he belonged after years in the same position in the company. In a fundamental way, he could no longer "mark" or find his position in the territory.

During the active phase of such conflict, which relates to territory and identity, the lower rectum (ectodermic tissue) will be subjected to a painless ulcerative widening that subconsciously allows more room for defecation. This phenomenon figuratively permits an individual to "mark" his territorial position according to archaic programs (in nature, some mammals use scent-marking to signal the limit of their territories by defecation).

**Note:** The territorial conflict related to identity is of a feminine type. However, this conflict can be experienced by men when they have low testosterone levels.

One day, he ran into his former boss at the supermarket and finally had a conversation in which he could express his feelings. At the same time, the boss found an opportunity to apologize and explain the situation. The man then understood that his firing was not at all personal; it was a necessity for the company to lay off a couple of employees in order to survive, and his position had not been refilled. The boss even promised to rehire him if the situation improved. Symbolically, the man still "owned" his position in the company after this conversation.

Immediately following this conversation, the man subconsciously let go of the conflict. That meant that he resolved his emotional distress. There was no reason for the illness to continue, and the ulcerations in the rectum were no longer necessary. The brain then switched its program to the healing phase, allowing the body to recuperate under the control of the parasympathetic system. The swelling of the rectal mucosa during the healing phase corresponded to the restoration of the ulcerated tissue, and therefore thin blood was present in the stool. At last, the man was diagnosed with hemorrhoids.

If we validate the two phases of an illness (the conflict-active and healing phases), the various types of symptoms we are subjected to during the course of a disease can finally be explained and anticipated. Once an individual resolves an emotional conflict, the biological modification that momentarily took place during the conflict needs to be reversed. The organs need to be restored to their original healthy state. For this to happen, growths and tumors need to be encased or decomposed, while ulcerations need to be repaired and replenished with new cells. During the healing phase of an illness, microorganisms such as fungi, microbes, bacteria, and viruses will be used by the system as optimizers to rehabilitate the proper functioning of the organs. As a result, as soon as the healing phase begins, infection, fever, and inflammation will arise as secondary symptoms.

It is important to know that a healing phase can be interrupted if a high-stress state recurs. The brain will halt the healing phase in favor of dealing with the new stress and mobilizing energy to "fend off or flee" danger, eventually triggering a new biological conflict. For instance, a woman might be in a healing phase of intraductal cancer (breast cancer of the milk ducts) because she has resolved a separation conflict (related to the nest) with her husband, whom she is no longer divorcing. But when her doctor tells her that her prognosis is bad, she is overwhelmed by an extreme fear of dying. The impact of frightening predictions could produce an unmanageable *death-fright conflict*, leading her to develop a secondary cancer, this time in the lung. A proliferation of alveoli cells figuratively permits her to grasp more air.

Therefore it is necessary to look at the connection between secondary stresses and secondary tumors and to reevaluate their origins accordingly.

## POSSIBLE ORIGIN OF METASTASES

According to Western medicine, cancer cells break away from primary tumors, enter the lymphatic system, and circulate through the bloodstream, subsequently affecting other organs and their tissues, where they will further proliferate. Modern medicine has never satisfactorily explained why the metastases of most cancers seem to be "organized." If it is true that cancer cells migrate erratically, why would these cells so often systematically follow the same course for the same type of cancer? For instance, breast cancer is often found in the liver, bones, and lungs. Colon cancer may also appear in the liver, while prostate cancer will frequently manifest exclusively in the bone as a secondary location.

Could it be possible that the course a cancer takes is determined by a logical combination of emotional conflicts, which often create the same domino effect, resulting in the same systematic layout of secondary locations?

Oncologists are not able to precisely define the cause of cancer or the mechanism behind secondary locations of most cancers. Oftentimes, medical prognoses are based solely on statistics. Consequently, in cases where there is unexpected cell activity, there are even fewer answers. Finding a metastasis of lung cancer in the spleen, for instance, is considered rare and out of the norm.

According to Dr. Hamer, the spread of cancer to secondary locations does not manifest in the way Western medicine describes: i.e., through blood and lymphatic circulation. Could it be possible that several conflicts can manifest in conjunction with one another, as the perception related to one dramatic experience might awaken multidimensional emotions? In that case, during the occurrence of a dramatic experience, several areas of the brain may be impacted at the same time, resulting in multiple conflict shocks and the manifestation of various simultaneous diseases.

Say a woman goes through a divorce and finds out her husband is planning on leaving her penniless, with absolutely no consideration for her needs. She perceives her husband's behavior toward her as vile and disgusting, which could trigger colon cancer. At the same time, she is worried that she might be unable to feed herself and her children. This perception may elicit a *starvation conflict*, which could lead to the manifestation of liver cancer. Her intense feeling of *worthlessness* could possibly trigger bone cancer, since she feels the distress of total self-devaluation. In that case, the bone cancer would produce a skeletal manifestation such as osteolysis (cell decrease), symbolically matching the woman's perception of being *nothing* and her subconscious intent to disintegrate.

Although all traumas do not seem to provoke an illness or symptom at the time they occur, the brain memorizes them, and consequently they become subconscious imprints. Nothing is ever forgotten emotionally; therefore, past stresses are often precursor programs to illnesses.

Some individuals who have been close to death recall seeing their entire life pass before their eyes, just like an accelerated film replaying all their experiences. In those few seconds, since death appears imminent, the subconscious mind rapidly searches for a solution, trying to access a stored program that exists in some part of that person's life experience that could possibly be reactivated to assure survival. The primary function of our brain is to keep us alive, and that is why it will keep in "storage" every biological solution and useful behavioral strategy, whether archaic, ancestral, parental, or personal, and whether pleasant or unpleasant.

## THE FOUR MODES OF SUBCONSCIOUS INTERPRETATIONS

When we are working on resolving an emotional struggle linked to a physical illness, it is important to investigate what has transpired within our subconscious mind. It is essential to understand how we operate internally as we process the world around us.

As you already know, one of the most important factors to understand when considering these questions is that the primitive human brain reacts to emotions based on our perception of reality during an event. When you examine a situation that happened in the past, the way you perceived the situation then is what really matters and what needs to be modified in present time.

In this context, the word "conflict" has an important and specific meaning. It refers to an internal struggle, which is the consequence of a perception that stops one from meeting his or her needs. Known in BioReprogramming® as "the invariant of the conflict," the underlying pattern between one's felt experience and its biological expression needs to be understood on four levels. There are four primary ways emotional conflicts can be experienced and interpreted in your mind. They are the conflicts:

◆ Toward another

◆ From another toward oneself

◆ With oneself

◆ From oneself toward all others

Let's use the example of diabetes to illustrate the four different ways a conflict can be experienced.

The nature of the conflict related to diabetes involves a feeling of resistance (being ready to fight) and having to endure a repugnant situation; i.e., "I resist something that disgusts me." (See the expanded definition of the conflict corresponding to diabetes in the Bio-Breakthrough Dictionary, p. 259.)

### Diabetes and the Four Modes of Subconscious Interpretations

**A conflict toward another**

One is resisting and enduring the actions of another in a state of repugnance. For example, one has to endure the insults of an abusive employer.

**A conflict from another toward oneself**

One feels that another person is in a state of resistance and repugnance toward oneself. For example, a man feels that his wife is rejecting him sexually. He believes that she feels disgust toward him while she has to endure intimate sexual relations.

**A conflict with oneself**

One is resisting a part of the self that he or she perceives as repugnant. For example, one is rejecting the fact that he or she is overweight and feels a state of constant rejection toward oneself.

**A conflict from oneself toward all others**

One is resisting the environment (meaning other people, the world, and/or God) because of the repugnant things he or she thinks are associated with it, such as injustice, violence, abuse, rape, poverty, or war.

The subconscious only records the nature of the conflict (in this case, resistance due to repugnance). It isn't concerned with where the resistance is coming from or where it is being directed. It is the *felt experience* that influences the subconscious and primitive brain.

## THE FEAR OF THE CONSEQUENCE

When working to resolve a conflict, you need to remember: there is "the thing" (the stressful event) and the consequence of "the thing" (the secondary problems that you imagine may occur because of the event). A person may reach a level of unmanageable stress as he projects his thoughts into the future, imagining an unfavorable or even disastrous outcome, like:

*"What if...?"*
*"What next...?"*
*"What about...?"*

For example, a man goes through a breakup, which creates an emotional struggle. At the same time, he projects in his mind the potential consequences of that event, such as imagining being alone for the rest of his life.

The mind can travel into the future, assembling information and going to a place of fear in an instant. As human beings, the intensity of our struggles is often related to the anticipation of what might happen. In reality, however, how many times do we expect the worst (the consequence of "the thing") but later realize that the problem did not create any of the anticipated consequences?

## THE PROGRAMMING AND TRIGGERING EVENTS OF ILLNESS

There are three principal ways a person can trigger a disease through the impact of individual experiences.

**First possibility: The programming of an illness and its trigger are simultaneous.** The disease trigger involves a specific type of stress that occurs for the very first time in a person's life, where there is no previous imprint of the same nature. At the age of fifty-nine, Caroline is experiencing extreme emotional distress related to her grandchild's accidental death at the playground. The stress triggers breast cancer. It is the first time in her life that Caroline experienced a *nest-worry conflict*, and her brain is imprinting a stress and triggering an illness simultaneously.

**Second possibility: The programming of an illness and its trigger are at a distance in time.** The human brain acts in many ways like a camcorder, vividly recording events. While a specific event may not be retrieved by the individual's conscious mind, it continues to exist in the subconscious. Both the *event* and the *feelings* associated with it are stored in the memory of the brain, thus creating imprints at a subconscious and cellular level simultaneously.

At the age of twenty-six, Sandy loses her two-year-old daughter in a car accident and is experiencing a *profound loss conflict* (first shock), which affects one of her ovaries (a cell proliferation that metaphorically allows a woman to achieve faster reproduction to replace the deceased offspring). She becomes pregnant three weeks after the loss of her child. Sandy believes in reincarnation and attributes her new pregnancy to the return of her daughter. Her soothing perception permits her to find a satisfying solution to her stress and resolve her profound loss conflict. The start of the cell proliferation in the ovary is interrupted and remains unnoticed. However, an imprint of the emotional impact of profound loss and all it entails remains, thus establishing a "first program," or first emotional imprint, in her subconscious mind.

When Sandy's second daughter is diagnosed with leukemia at age five, Sandy re-experiences a *profound loss conflict* (second shock) as she anticipates the death of this beloved child. Since her doctor does not give her the certainty that her daughter is going to live, Sandy stays in a state of unmanageable stress for too long. Her subconscious mind automatically ensures survival on its own terms by awakening the program she imprinted five years earlier when she lost her first child. Both conflicts are of the same nature and, this time, lead to ovarian cancer.

Sometimes several stresses of the same nature can accumulate during one's lifetime before a disease is triggered and manifested.

**Third possibility: A big stress awakens past stresses that are not correlated in terms of "meaning" and "conflict content."** At the age of fifty-one, Jeffrey, who lives alone, loses his house to a fire. Shortly afterward, his vision is severely impaired by an acute eye inflammation. Since he saw his house burn, there is an inclination to think that his eye problem occurred because subconsciously he didn't want to experience seeing his house being destroyed in front of his eyes. But this is not the case. When his stress level was at a peak as he watched the dramatic event unfold, Jeffrey's subconscious brain was actively searching for a stored solution that would lower his high level of stress. Since there were no stored memories that immediately resonated with this unexpected, distressing experience, Jeffrey's brain awakened a response that corresponded to another stress of similar intensity but different in its content.

It turned out that when he was seven years old, instead of giving him his usual cleaning eye drops, his mother mistakenly gave him a different medication that belonged to his dad. Although this medication did not burn young Jeffrey's eyes, it created temporary blindness, resulting in a state of fear and a peak level of stress. This event was followed by a terrible eye inflammation, restoring the damage caused by the medication. Decades later, when his house burned down, Jeffrey's subconscious mind awakened the biological response associated with the stressful experience forty-four years prior, namely the eye inflammation. The brain, operating just like a computer's search engine, connected together two events that were completely different in terms of "meaning" but equivalent in terms of stress and intensity. A big stress can awaken any past stress and its corresponding biological response.

The better the real mechanism behind the mind-body processes is understood, the greater your capacity will be to deliver new and useful information to your subconscious, thus leading you to optimal health and a more fulfilling life. The BioReprogramming® Method, with its understanding of the metaphorical language of the subconscious brain, plays a crucial role in deciphering these multidimensional processes.

# 5

# What Is Influencing
# Our Destiny?

There is no question that parents influence the lives of their children. However, where BioReprogramming® is concerned, another aspect of that effect is explored. The impact parents have on their offspring during gestation, uncovered by the clinical psychologist Dr. Marc Fréchet, is called the *project purpose*. As human beings, we carry within our subconscious mind the memories of all the stages that living beings have experienced throughout the course of evolution, thus enabling us to not only subsist on the planet but to progress forward as well. Since the beginning of life, subconscious programs have been passed on from generation to generation, particularly from parents to their children, in order to preserve the learning acquired during each experience in which survival was at stake.

A rather poignant experiment with earthworms is a perfect illustration of the impact emotional distress can have on the next generation. In this experiment, an earthworm was poked with a needle every time its container was subjected to direct sunlight. So every time the worm was exposed to light, it felt pain and therefore associated light with danger. In an effort to save its life, the earthworm sought a place in the shadows, hiding in the corner of the container, seeking to end the pain. As a consequence of this emotional distress, the worm's offspring, as early as birth, repeated the same behavior of straying from light and finding refuge in the shadows, even though the offspring were never poked. This demonstrates that the psychological conflict of the parent truly becomes "bio-logical" in the progeny.

Through the subconscious memory shared among generations, information is passed on in order to save the species the time to "relearn" the strategies necessary for survival. Any stress experienced by the parents can have an impact on the offspring's biology, behavior, and life path. As human beings, we will express throughout our lifetime the solution or purpose we were meant to fulfill. *More specifically, this is the solution or purpose related to the stresses, as well as the subconscious plans, of one or both of our parents.* For instance, if a pregnant woman feels a strong desire to divorce her husband but cannot fulfill her *project* because of the financial difficulties she would have to face without the security offered by her husband's job, her unborn daughter might be predisposed to a certain path. The daughter may be programmed to express the "winning solution" that would ultimately liberate her mother's struggle. Along with growing up to become financially independent, the daughter would be subconsciously programmed to attract the ideal partner whom she would wind up divorcing in order to express the solution connected to the project of her mother: finding financial independence and ending an unfulfilling marriage.

We are predisposed to recreating the *climate* that permeated the life of our parents during the time between our conception and the age of at least one year old. Whether the climate during gestation is one of poverty and loneliness or abundance and joy could produce very different progeny. Certain imprints related to shocks endured by the parents during gestation and up until one year after the child's birth can be at the origin of health disorders.

What we might consciously want to change in our life does not stop our subconscious mind from completing its intrinsic programs of survival, consequently influencing our future and destiny. Since all of us are subject to biological laws, we are not victims of our parents but rather the recipients of information that will be processed and used according to the logic of our archaic brain. It is essential to remember that our parents cannot be held guilty for the programs they transmitted to us during or after gestation, since they had no awareness of these imprints.

The moment of birth is unique and represents the first traumatic experience in life. After nine months of experiencing the warmth and safety of the uterus, an infant is suddenly exposed to the outer world. The physical elements surrounding the first moments of life outside the womb, such as sounds, smells, and physical contacts, will be deeply imprinted. But the strongest impact of all will be the emotional milieu. The tears of the parents—as well as their wants, needs, and overall emotional states of mind—will be embedded within the blueprint of a newborn.

A mother might hope for her child not to be born before her husband returns from a business trip, so that he may witness the birth. Her emotional stress is related to the timing of the birth and wanting to slow down a natural process that is imminent. As the child grows up, he or she may become a person who frequently arrives late, subconsciously expressing loyalty to the emotional need of the mother during labor.

Our subconscious mind contains a considerable amount of data and memories besides our archaic biological codes of behavior. Everything that happens to us while we're alive, good or bad, is considered by our brain to provide the essential information needed to create survival strategies for the extension of our life. For that purpose only, even negative and shocking events such as accidents and illnesses tend to reoccur in a cyclical manner during our lifetime.

## LIFE CYCLES

Have you ever wondered whether there is an explanation for the recurrence of similar types of events in your life? Whether experienced as traumas or triumphs, have you been mystified by the return of strangely similar situations?

The existence of *bio-memorized cellular cycles*, discovered by the psychologist Marc Fréchet, demonstrates that there is an inherent tendency for individuals to repetitively experience certain events according to predictable intervals. Those events, which are memorized in the holographic system of the brain, cause the return of similar emotions and decisions during one's life and reappear according to cycles that can be recognized and anticipated. The time line and duration of one specific type of life cycle is determined by the age at which an individual becomes autonomous and capable of providing for his or her needs. This specific moment of independence is considered by the brain to be a recurrence of birth.

When we are born, we move away from the security of the womb. Similarly, when we become autonomous, we move away from the security of home and go out in the world. Although this important time is a symbolic "birth," the brain records it as a literal or actual event. A young woman who starts her first job at the age of 19 years and 3 months, rents her own apartment, and is in all respects completely independent from that time on will experience subsequent cycles of 19 years and 3 months. Her subconscious mind might attract circumstances to replay significant events from the "recorded tape" (that is, events imprinted by the brain during the first cycle), from the time of birth until the age of 19 years and 3 months.

## Illustration of Bio-Memorized Cellular Cycles

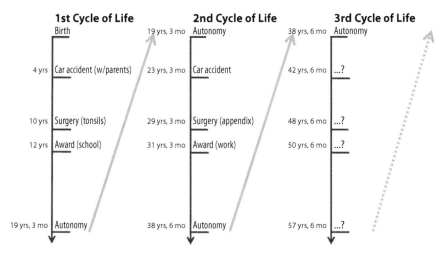

If she was in a car accident with her parents at the age of 4, she might again have a car accident at 23 years and 3 months (19 years and 3 months plus 4 years). If she had surgery at 10 years of age, she might have another surgery at 29 years and 3 months old (19 years and 3 months plus 10 years). If at 12 years old she received an award as the top student in her class, she might relive a similar experience at 31 years and 3 months (19 years and 3 months plus 12 years), when given an award for Salesperson of the Year by her company.

## THE DOUBLE POINT CYCLE

Other types of cyclical patterns can be explored throughout one's personal time line, such as those recurring at the double point of a person's age. I have verified this outcome with many clients, and the following story illustrates such a cycle.

Cathy was forty-six years old when she first walked into my office. She had eczema on her chest and arms. The condition first appeared two months prior to our meeting, and while she tried almost everything to help relieve her skin issue, nothing had worked for her. During our sessions, I helped her uncover the emotional conflict related to her eczema, which corresponds to an issue of separation.

Cathy and her boyfriend of four years had broken up a couple of months before her symptoms first appeared. She felt heartbroken and blindsided when her relationship ended. She never expected it would take such a turn, because she had thought that she'd met the man who would be with her for the rest of her life. Although working on Cathy's health issue (eczema) and helping her grieve the ending of her relationship was a must, the key to her healing would be her understanding of the programs that led her to attract this particular situation.

Interestingly, Cathy had gone through a very similar situation at exactly twenty-three years old. At that time, she was engaged to a man she thought she would spend her life with. When her fiancé broke up with her after a six-month engagement, she experienced a devastating sense of separation.

Working our way backwards, I asked Cathy about what happened to her at eleven and a half years of age. She remembered it clearly. That was the point when her father left her mother and moved away from their town. When her parents got divorced, Cathy and her younger brother were raised mostly by their mother, seeing their father only occasionally during the holidays. At almost six years old (half of eleven and a half), Cathy's grandfather, whom she was very close to, passed away.

We can see that separation from important men in Cathy's life, which she experienced as traumatic events, recurred in her life at specific time intervals. Once brought to her conscious awareness, the recent separation with her boyfriend made sense. Her skin condition was related to a cycle that once brought to consciousness, could be eliminated from her subconscious mapping. This realization brought relief to Cathy, and she was able to look at her situation from a different perspective. In addition to her eczema clearing within two weeks of our sessions, she felt empowered and excited about the future.

This amazing discovery of the cyclical recurrence of life events, which has been verified by hundreds of therapists and their clients, shows us that such repetitions in our life are not random but rather a "co-incidence" of events related to certain dates imprinted within our cellular memory. Once you become aware of such cycles, it is possible to free yourself from the repetition of unwanted events while still preserving positive reiterations. Please note that not all significant events or traumas are associated with a specific cycle on your time line. Beyond the influence of your personal life experiences, including time in the womb, there is also the influence of programs passed on from previous generations.

## TRANSGENERATIONAL TRANSMISSION

Since childhood, Natalie, in her late twenties, possessed a constant fear that involved contracting an incurable illness. She also experienced continual anxiety that one of her parents might die early. These ever-present fears fueled a feeling of heavy, seemingly incurable sadness. However, while investigating the life of her ancestors, she discovered that her despair might be directly related to the grief her grandmother experienced when she lost her five-year-old daughter (Natalie's aunt) to leukemia. Natalie's grandmother had struggled with the fact that she could not save her daughter from an incurable illness and thus was forced to watch her die at such an early age. Interestingly enough, Natalie went on to graduate with a Ph.D. in biology and chose to specialize in cancer research. Was she subconsciously attempting to find a solution to her grandmother's distress by becoming an expert in the field of cancer?

Transgenerational transmission has been widely explored by psychologist Anne Ancelin Schützenberger. Her work describes how programs are passed on from one generation to the next and how our life often reflects circumstances, traumas, and dates of events belonging to antecedent members of our clan. It appears we are not as free as we think, and we often express an invisible loyalty to our ancestors. What we call coincidences—such as the repetition of deaths at a certain age, separations, divorces, births, illnesses, and professional failures—are often related to unresolved stresses that reappear in our life. What's more, these same unresolved stresses will reappear in the lives of subsequent generations in order to be liberated. Freud addressed a similar phenomenon when he interpreted the repetitive nightmares of descendants of war survivors and the horrors they endured, describing them as "the return of elements that should have been surmounted a long time ago by our ancestors" (in his essay "Das Unheimliche," 1919).

In a recent study, researchers Brian Dias and Kerry Ressler, both of Emory University, showed that specific information about a traumatic experience linked with a smell can modify the architecture of the nervous systems in later generations. The study reveals how "memories" in mice can be passed from a male down to his offspring. During the first experiment, the mice received a shock to their feet while simultaneously being exposed to the scent of the compound acetophenone (the simplest aromatic ketone). This led to the alteration of the structure of mice's olfactory neurons, in a way that increases the capacity to detect the smell of acetophenone. Following that experiment, offspring were reproduced via artificial insemination (and kept separate from their parents while being raised by unrelated mice). They reacted two hundred times more strongly when exposed to the acetophenone scent than other mice, even though they had never been exposed to the smell before. That sensitivity to the scent of the compound acetophenone was passed down the generations. (Eastman, Quinn. December 2, 2013. Mice Can Inherit Learned Sensitivity to a Smell. *Emory News Center*.)

The neurological changes that Ressler noted during the first experiment manifested in both the first and second generations. It appears that this information came not through social communication, but through inheritance. Regarding this discovery, Gregg Henriques, Ph.D., stated, "At a more abstract level, the possibilities become truly remarkable—things like generational psychological legacies and notions such as Carl Jung's collective unconscious archetypes, which might have seemed far-fetched in the past, become more scientifically plausible." (Henriques, Gregg. December 12, 2013. A Revolution in Evolution: A Return to Lamarck? *Theory of Knowledge/Psychology Today*.)

Throughout the course of our life, we often express behavioral reactions or biological responses that are correlated to the stress of a parent or ancestor. The transmission of the emotional stress of a parent, a grandparent, or even an aunt or an uncle may lead to specific health issues in an offspring. An illness can be linked to the emotional conflict or trauma our predecessors could not express or resolve, whether or not they triggered an illness based on that conflict during their lifetime. For example, a man who feels forced to symbolically "swallow" the fact that his brother received a larger portion of the inheritance after their father's death might predispose a descendant to esophageal disease. A grandmother who could not "digest the filth" related to her husband's affair might transmit a program that will affect the colon in a member of the next generation. The psychological conflict of an ancestor and its emotional meaning can be passed on to the next generation who will express it biologically.

Even when ancestral conflicts circulate within the clan, healing is often possible through accessing an awareness of such unresolved emotional stresses. This type of awareness allows us to understand how illness is often rooted at a more inherent level than the personal circumstances of an individual during his or her lifetime. It seems none of our circumstances happens by either accident or luck, but in fact our circumstances are infused by our subconscious. By understanding this model, we are now able to see the origins of predispositions to certain illnesses, behaviors, or life paths.

Symbols that are attached to birth, such as the choice of a name, can also influence our life. Names that are chosen according to religion, tradition, politics, sports, theater, or to honor a deceased member of the family will remain emotionally charged by the memory and the intention they represent. For instance, a boy named after his brother who died right before the boy's birth might carry a burden of having to *replace the dead child* and never feel that he is good enough for his inconsolable parents.

Helen, a young woman I know, was named after her grandmother, who died when Helen's mother was ten. Helen felt that she somehow took on the role of being the *mother of her mother* by providing emotional support to her at an early age. For as long as she could remember, Helen felt that it was her "job" to take care of her mother.

New concepts in transgenerational therapy suggest that it is possible for organic healing to begin as long as one member of the clan can bring to consciousness his or her inherited and subconscious memories of trauma, drama, death, injustice, incest, rape, miscarriage, crime, and unfulfilled desires. Like an ancestral cleansing of sorts, this will "purify" the shared memories of all concerned. Addressing the issues of family members, such as parents, aunts, uncles, and grandparents, can be an act of compassion and generosity rather than a quest for separation and detachment from the clan. With the Bio-Reprogramming® Method, it can be approached as a profound opportunity to liberate our ancestors and descendants, while healing ourselves in the process.

## WHAT IS ILLNESS, AFTER ALL?

Disease can be compared to a biological emergency measure that increases or decreases the function of an organ in correspondence to an unresolved emotional crisis. Then again, not every individual may have the chance to fully resolve his or her distress. As most of us know, it's not always easy to overcome an emotional conflict, and there's no guarantee that life will provide an ideal change of circumstances. Nonetheless, for many, a resolution can be achieved, whether through personal transformation or an environmental change.

However, environmental changes come with a word of caution. Although a solution based on a shift in the environment might be momentarily strong, one's problems could easily be transferred to a new set of circumstances. Just as recovery can't be assured by a change of scenery or situation, it also can't depend upon changes that other people make. One person cannot be made responsible for the health of another. True healing comes from a change within oneself.

If our belief system, and not our genes, controls our health, how could biological healing manifest when we hold on to the same limiting beliefs and perceptions about our issues or traumas? For instance if a man cannot "digest" a situation, what perception has made him feel that he can't digest it, and how much of that perception is a distortion on his part? How does he filter the world, and what are the subconscious imprints that predisposed him to such beliefs and perceptions? Aside from any self-generated imprints, how many other imprints are directly related to his parents' stresses during gestation, or even belong to his ancestors? How can he free himself from those hidden stresses, if he perceives the environment and circumstances as responsible for his misfortune?

If a woman heals breast cancer based on her reconciliation with her husband after he left her for another woman, what is going to happen if, one day down the road, he has another affair? In order to liberate herself from emotional stress, the woman will need resources that are stronger than a mere intellectual understanding of her conflict and its expression in the body. If she continues to perceive her husband and his affair in the same way as before, it simply means she did not surpass the problem. However, if she learns how to detach, take responsibility, and manifest emotional independence, she could resolve her struggle for good. The external problem would still exist but it would not affect her emotionally anymore.

Think of our relationship to gravity. When you hold an object in your hands, you can toss it to someone, put it on a table, continue to hold it, or drop it on the ground. Without even thinking about it, you know that the law of gravity has an impact on what happens to the object. But as impressive as it is, that law doesn't operate in isolation when it comes to where the object ends up. It's what you choose to do with the object that determines the outcome. In most instances it is what you do that matters and not what you know. In the same way, it is not just what you know about your biological conflict that will create a shift in your biology and permit healing, but rather what you do about it.

# 6

# Questioning Old and New Paradigms

In times of great change and transition, constructive inquiry assists us in creating new maps into uncharted territory.

The answers proposed below, in response to commonly asked questions, offer possibilities to consider and interesting directions to explore. Of course, there is much to understand before making any definitive statements, especially in relation to biology and illness. So please understand that these answers offer a sum of new findings that will require further investigation.

**If cancer is related to an emotional conflict, why, then, do smokers develop lung cancer? Aren't cigarettes the cause of such disease?**

The emotional conflict related to the fear of death (for oneself or a loved one) creates at a subconscious level the need for more oxygen in order to improve respiratory function and avoid death. The role of the alveoli in the lungs is to acquire oxygen. The meaning of lung cancer, for instance through the proliferation of alveolar cells, is to allow the grasping of more oxygen in order to distribute it to the organs.

It's interesting to consider that the act of smoking gives an individual the illusion of getting more air into his or her lungs. Those who smoke give themselves emotional relief each time they inhale—a momentary respite from their worries or dread. Ultimately, it is their *latent* emotional stress that leads them to smoke. One day they might trigger lung cancer because of a conflict shock related to breathing that manifests according to their particular predisposition to the conflict arising from the fear of death (involving the alveoli). Or they might trigger lung cancer stemming from a conflict linked to the fear of their territory being invaded by someone who is seen as "the enemy" (involving the bronchi), someone who might be perceived as "eating up their air."

As always, the conflict might be real, imaginary, virtual, or symbolic. Although cigarettes metaphorically offer a practical solution to the two subconscious stresses just mentioned, they might not be the exact root cause of the cancer that smokers develop. The fact that two elements are simultaneously present in a certain context, in this case smoking and lung cancer, does not mean they are related in the anticipated way.

A stirring example is the story of Dana Reeve, the wife of actor Christopher Reeve. Although she had never smoked cigarettes, Dana was diagnosed with lung cancer on August 9, 2005, ten months after the death of her husband, on October 10, 2004. Let's assume that, in a unique way, breath and breathing were intensely meaningful in their life together. From the time of his accident in 1995, when he fell from a horse and became paralyzed, Christopher's one form of movement was his breath. As deeply bonded as they were, when Christopher passed away and could no longer breathe, did Dana subconsciously try to breathe for him? Was the proliferation of cells in her lungs the biological solution to this urgent need?

**What evidence suggests that metastases are not the result of cancer cells migrating from one organ to the other?**

Even though the idea that cancer cells can be transported to distant sites in the body has been generally accepted, has it yet been proven?

According to Dr. Hamer's theory, when a person has cancer in multiple areas in his or her body, modifications centered on precise points of the brain can be identified through a set of concentric rings (see page 23). These alterations, *which correspond to the areas of the affected organs*, can be observed through CT scans. However, these modifications, which are observed during an investigative procedure, are often considered "artifacts" by radiologists. The location of the "focus," which is the alteration in the brain that is visible on the scan, seems to be found in the area of the brain controlling the affected organ. Although these observations regarding the presence of concentric rings in the brain are conflicting, they also lead to the question of why the so-called artifacts appear in correspondence with the affected organs in the body.

If the cause of secondary cancers was related to a "spill" from primary tumors or an uncontrollable migration of cells, why would CT scans show a visible mark indicating the presence of *cerebral alterations* in perfect correlation with the primary—as well as secondary—locations of cancer in the body?

It seems an alteration systematically manifests in the cerebral relay related to each newly affected organ, which clearly tends to indicate a correlation between new stresses and secondary cancers.

Could the reason why cancer that is found in secondary organs has the same histology (cancer type) as the primary cancer be related to the nature of the initial conflict? If a cancer of the same type is found within other organs, what we could be observing is the biological materialization of different shocks related to the original conflict. In other words, the identity of the original conflict remains present within the expression of another conflict in another organ, with each new cancer being a solution to a new stress. For example, a person with breast cancer (nest conflict) might develop a tumor in the lung (with the same cell characteristics as the breast tumor) because of her fear of death due to her breast cancer.

**Is the cause of illness always related to emotional distress? Aren't environmental factors such as pollution, nutritional deficiencies, and toxins also contributing to disease?**

The World Health Organization estimates that twenty percent of deaths in the developing world are attributed to environmental factors: pollutants including lead, mercury, hexavalent chromium, and arsenic. Most often, pollution and chemical toxins are held responsible for health issues such as cancer, cognitive impairment, and respiratory problems. Conventional medicine is not certain about the real cause of cancer. It seems researchers and practitioners of Western medicine look to external factors in order to gain some sort of understanding about the cause of cancer.

The question is this: If pollution were the primary cause of cancer, wouldn't most of us get sick, and not just a small percentage of the population? Cancer existed before the modern world, when the air was still pure and pollutants were nonexistent. So what was the cause of cancer then? If we accept the premise that cancer is the result of the biological expression of an emotional conflict, which involves the action of the brain from where a specific program is coordinated, it seems apparent that toxins may not be at the origin of cellular mutation.

It appears it is only when toxicity reaches a level that humans cannot bear that the body will respond through a cellular reaction in order to process and combat the excess of poison. During the Chernobyl disaster in Ukraine, most fatalities from the accident were caused by radiation poisoning, because toxicity levels were elevated beyond the threshold a human being could absorb. For as long as the level of toxicity can be processed and eliminated by the body, it is unlikely that disease will manifest as a consequence of environmental factors.

And although we are subjected to unhealthy substances, our life span is consistently increasing because we continue to adapt to the environment. Granted, the amount of pollution in big cities is unnatural and unhealthy, but is it enough to explain all the different types of cancers? Using the same reasoning, we could also ask ourselves why unhealthy food would be the cause of health issues for some and not for others. Almost all of us know people who don't eat well and who smoke and drink, yet they stay free of disease.

While there are reasons to believe that illness is related to emotional conflicts, it is also true that prevention of disease starts with healthy living, including exercise and avoiding sugar, greasy food, alcohol, drugs, and cigarettes. Those who are depleted energetically will be emotionally ill equipped to manage their feelings when caught off guard by a highly stressful or traumatic event, and therefore more susceptible to a conflict shock. A healthy and conscious lifestyle promotes a strong and balanced mind. A study at Ohio State University demonstrated that women who focused on nutrition, physical activity, and certain relaxation methods were sixty-eight percent less likely to die from their cancer in the following eleven years, compared to women who did not improve their lifestyle during and after treatment. Several studies also suggest that emotional states can have an impact on cancer statistics. (Andersen et al. 2004, 2008; Blake-Mortimer et al. 1999; Fawzy et al. 1990, 1993; Monti et al. 2006; Spiegel et al. 1989.)

A positive and healthy lifestyle helps us to access more resourceful emotional states. As emotional conflicts are matters of perception, a lucid mental state can allow for greater understanding toward others and perhaps an ability to let go of the very conflict that is at the root of the illness. Sometimes it's easier to alter the way of looking at an event when we have the support of a healthy mind and body.

**Why are some children born with illnesses when they have not yet been exposed to life and stresses?**

During the intrauterine period, the fetus is imprinting the emotional conflicts of both parents. A combination of the parents' emotions and their stresses creates a powerful equation. When both parents undergo the same type of stress at the same time, the imprint is even more potent. The solution to the stress will often emerge instantly through the embryo at a cellular level. A disorder often starts *in utero*, in alignment with the emotions that both parents share. This allows for an immediate biological solution to be expressed through the developing child. In a peculiar way, the parents' unmanageable stress is alleviated through a download that is literally transmitted directly from their brains to the offspring. In order to understand this phenomenon, it is important to remember that during pregnancy the survival of the parents prevails, and that is why the parents' well-being is primary. Hence their emotional distress is lowered by subconsciously downloading the stress to the embryo (or infant).

As an example, one of my clients in Paris came to me for the purpose of improving her relationship with her husband. She had brought her son along with her to the session. He was twelve years old and had been born deaf. The woman had always wondered why her son had been afflicted with such a condition. I asked her to tell me what had happened during her pregnancy that was related to hearing. It turns out that when she was pregnant she had ear infections and did not take care of them properly.

When she finally went to a doctor, her infections were so bad that he thought she might lose her hearing. For several days during her pregnancy, both this woman and her husband feared that she might become deaf.

As always, the subconscious will express the perfect solution to eliminate stress. If one is on a bike with an intense fear of falling, this will trigger a general discharge of the sympathetic nervous system. Consequently, the brain will need to provide the ultimate solution to interrupt the stress. The solution to the fear of falling off a bike is to actually fall! Once on the ground, the fear of falling no longer exists. In a similar way, during that intense phase of stress related to the fear of becoming deaf, the embryo manifested a solution to alleviate this particular fear. Consequently, the infant developed an ear impairment and was born deaf.

It has been observed that when the parents undergo the same distress simultaneously, the child might be born with a biological dysfunction that corresponds precisely to the emotional conflict the parents struggled with during pregnancy. However, if only one parent has a conflict, then a related disease might manifest later on in the child's life.

In seeking to understand the origin of illness and alter the subconscious programs that have been passed along from one generation to the next, it is so important that parents not feel guilty in any way. What is being described here are simply the laws of biology to which each of us is subject. Therefore, it is my hope that guilt will be dissolved in the face of new knowledge and growing compassion. There is every reason for optimism to overtake negative feelings, such as reproach or regret, that may creep in. Now more than ever, we are empowered with the ability to do something about the patterns that were set in motion ages ago. We can alter the future right here in present time. We can learn the facts that will liberate us—and all those who will come after us.

**Why do our pets get sick?**

Domesticated animals can develop illnesses related to their owner's stresses, whether real, imaginary, virtual, or symbolic. A pet can, in fact, act as an extension of its master's brain, absorbing its owner's distress like a sponge and expressing the related illness. For instance, a female dog might suffer from ovarian cancer after her owner experiences the stress of the profound loss of her husband. The animal's sensitivity and devotion can elicit a transfer of the emotional struggle of its master into its own biology. However, if the master resolves her psychological conflict, the health of the animal can improve simultaneously.

### Isn't Western medicine progressing and helping more and more cancer patients?

Although billions of dollars are given to research, the number of cancer deaths is increasing. What does this mean? For as long as Western medicine adheres to the same paradigm about the origin of cancer and only recognizes surgery, chemotherapy, radiation, and immunotherapy, a breakthrough is unlikely to arise. Unfortunately, astronomical amounts of money are allocated to these favored forms of treatment. It seems that modern medicine is not on the right track to curing cancer. In addition to an increase in emotional conflicts and distress stemming from the pressures of modern life, the notion of cancer itself creates even more stress and continues to strike fear in the minds of so many.

Cancer rates have been climbing steadily in the U.S. since 1940, in synchronicity with the increased use of screening tests. In the UK, research published on July 9, 2009, in the British Medical Journal revealed that as many as one in every three breast cancers diagnosed by mammogram screening would never have become life threatening and could naturally have regressed on their own without treatment. Could the increase in the cancer rate be related to overdiagnoses from imaging resources detecting tumors that were not actually malignant?

An article in the *Los Angeles Times* reveals that "autopsy studies have found undetected breast cancer in about 37% of women who died from other causes ... and a study of 42,238 Norwegian women calculated that 22% of symptom-free cancers found on a screening mammogram naturally regressed on their own." (Aschwanden, Christie. Aug. 17, 2009. Cut back on mammograms? *Los Angeles Times*.)

What happens when healthy individuals are thrown into the category of cancer patients and subjected to painful, toxic, and often frightening treatments? Could some early deaths be related to such unnecessary and extreme therapies and not to cancer itself?

89

When considering the new findings about illness, we begin to understand why cancer can regress on its own, since it is related to an emotional distress that can be resolved. Also, it could help radiologists and oncologists interpret scans and mammograms very differently if they were made aware of the two phases of disease: the conflict-active phase (cold phase) and the healing phase (warm phase). (See page 53.) At the same time, individuals would be protected from an unnecessary threat, the ultimate invasion of their bodies, and the oftentimes devastating psychological impact of the diagnosis.

Is it possible that cancer is on the rise in proportion to the conscious and subconscious expectation that most individuals now have, that disease will strike them one day? The threat of cancer—its magnitude and seemingly unstoppable progression—bombards us on a daily basis. In particular, the "pink ribbon" campaign for breast cancer has taken on a life of its own, with an astounding amount of pink paraphernalia being sold on behalf of related charities. With the ubiquitous cancer-awareness walks, runs, and so on, it seems as though cancer is fully accepted as a fact of life. Is all of this apparently benign awareness turning into a self-fulfilling prophecy? We all know of someone who has died of cancer, and the fear related to it is so deeply ingrained within the population that, for many, when cancer is diagnosed, it might as well be a death sentence.

For some, a "do-it-yourself proposition" may be the only option left, one that can open the doors to the dangers of unreliable "cancer cures." Likewise, understanding the link between emotional distress and disease does not constitute a cure. Rather, it is the base of knowledge from which we can understand and resolve the conflicts that lead to illness. If scientists and researchers accepted the idea that the cells of our bodies are affected by our thoughts, a new style of mind-therapy could be further developed and incorporated. In response, doctors could modify their treatment protocols according to whether an individual is in either an active or a healing phase. This would result in evolved forms of treatment that respect the laws of nature and promote emotional as well as physical health.

## CAN WE LOOK FORWARD TO A HEALTHY FUTURE?

*"To heal, it is necessary and sufficient to remove
the source of conflict within one's self."*

—Dr. Claude Sabbah

We are living in one of the most fascinating eras in human history, when brilliant new knowledge regarding illness is finally surfacing and is being made available to everyone.

So how can you benefit the most from this enlightening era?

Knowledge about the origin of illness does not guarantee healing; therefore, efforts need to be made in the direction of finding ways to influence the subconscious to let go of limiting programs. We need to resolve our emotional conflicts in order to heal and step beyond the "primal programs" that have been running unchecked. In my experience, it is *fundamental* to work on resolving these core conflicts that manifest as imbalances or disease.

Embracing this idea will support the one thing that matters most: that you get the *results* you need and want.

The in-depth theory in the first six chapters is meant to provide a basis that supports the next section of the book. Based on my experience of what works (the information, processes, and techniques that get results), the self-help section that follows is the heart and soul of this book. It is the material that I have carefully researched and put into practice with clients over the past fourteen years, so that they would be fully empowered to heal. This section can support you and your loved ones in a number of important ways. Foremost, by offering a new philosophy of life—one based on freedom from the past and independence for the future—it can help prevent illnesses that have not taken shape and resolve the conflicts behind illnesses that have.

If you or someone you care about has lost hope because of a diagnosis, I want you to know that there is another way. There is the certainty of possibility. And this is precisely why this book is in your hands—so that as you gain independence from opinions you might have been programmed to believe, you will be able to see new possibilities for yourself.

This is one of the first steps to healing.

In the self-help segment that follows, you will get an opportunity to modify the limiting beliefs and behaviors that may be standing between you and your ultimate health, happiness, and peace.

You can be free to thrive in a world of wellness that *you* have created for yourself, and that is the blessing that awaits you.

# Part II: Breakthrough Methods for Resolving Emotional Conflicts

# 7

# Recovering Power

If you are reading this book with the intention of mastering your health, the next most important step you can take is to evaluate your thoughts. Do you focus on your illness, or do you focus on the state of health you want to create? Do you envision an unhealthy organ in your body, or do you see yourself in the future with a healthy, well-functioning organ? Do you hold a clear image of what your healthy organ and body would look like? Do you imagine what it would feel like to be healthy again? Do you dare to allow yourself to picture this, or are you so consumed with fear that all you can think about is a catastrophic scenario? Are you really clear about what you want?

Thoughts trigger emotions, and the mind reacts accordingly. The role of the subconscious is not to judge whether the images you produce are good or bad, right or wrong. Its role is to comply with your command, which you may be unwittingly exerting through the focus of your attention and the intensity of your emotions.

Did you ever notice the power of your mind, when left to its own devices? Did you ever have the experience of daydreaming while driving somewhere and then actually ending up at the destination you have been daydreaming about instead of the place you planned to drive to? This exact scenario happened to me not long ago. Last summer, I was driving back to my home in Silver Lake after a long day of work. While driving I had a lingering thought, which was that I was thankful that I was no longer residing at my old apartment near the Hollywood Bowl in Los Angeles. There was a big summer concert happening that evening. And as I thought about the inevitable traffic jam that would soon begin to mount, I kept imagining how hard it would be to park in my old neighborhood.

Well, guess where I ended up.

I was on the road that would take me back to my old neighborhood near the Hollywood Bowl. Subconsciously, my command was answered based on my mental observation, and my brain, with its influence over my destination, took me where my imagination was lingering. Although I didn't want to be in my old neighborhood, my brain responded to the precise images I was conjuring. The subconscious mind is the observer of the conscious mind. It does not judge thoughts; rather, it simply operates according to mental representations, even the ones we think we have consciously overridden.

Where do you go with your thoughts? Toward health or illness? Life or death? The direction your thoughts are taking is directly related to what you believe about your illness. The primary reason a negative prognosis can be extremely harmful is the power of beliefs, because a belief can easily become a self-fulfilling prophecy. If you don't create a conscious plan for your own life, you will be influenced by the suggestions and commonly held beliefs with which the environment is bombarding you. Your mind will hear and react to the messages and meanings that you have tacitly agreed to. In order to stay on the path to health, you need to have clarity about what your objective is, and you need to support this objective with an adequate belief system.

If you received a dire prognosis, you may lose hope. If so, you must pull yourself out of the pit of despair, because it is essential to confront your habits of thinking head-on. Why would you let yourself be controlled by a social belief based on statistics? So many social beliefs have been proven incorrect throughout history. Reality is often far from what outward appearances seem to convey.

Imagine a group of scientists seeing an iceberg for the first time. To them, it looks like a mountain of floating ice on the surface of the ocean. The reality cannot be observed, but it still exists. The appearance only reveals ten percent of the reality of the size of the iceberg, while the hidden part of the iceberg represents ninety percent of reality.

Today, even when observing one hundred percent of an iceberg, the "absolute" reality cannot be seen. There is always more to discover, because the big picture of things is infinite. Consider that when you observe an object that appears to be immobile, it is subject to the rotation of the planet at the speed of 1,666.66 km/hour. It is also subject to the orbit of the earth around the sun, as well as the rotation of our solar system in the galaxy, which is itself moving through the universe.

During the seventeenth century, Galileo confirmed that the earth was not flat but round and that it was not situated at the center of the universe. By observing the universe through a telescope, he was able to prove the Copernican theory that the earth revolves around the sun. The official science of the time held firm to the flat-earth theory, and Galileo's concepts were perceived as heresy. He was widely persecuted and ordered to stand trial in 1633. He was forced to recant his beliefs in order to stay alive. This was a grand case of scientific obscuration.

As the German philosopher Arthur Schopenhauer stated, all truth goes through three steps: first it is ridiculed, then it is violently opposed, and finally it is accepted as evident.

It is imperative to expand your awareness of reality, since the subconscious mind is functioning with the laws of the universe and is fully connected to the real reality. It is our conscious mind that creates obstacles to accessing a higher level of awareness. Ultimately, what we think we know maintains the status quo. What you think you know keeps you in a state of "blindness," depriving you from accessing the true knowledge that could liberate you. To believe requires a conscious thought accepted as containing some "truth" value. Although many would argue that beliefs supported by scientific evidence possess the greatest value, paradoxically, they can also act as barriers to further understanding.

Interestingly, through the ages even the most prolific scientists and philosophers have held beliefs that prevented them from seeing beyond their own discoveries and inventions. Sir Isaac Newton's belief about absolute time prevented him from formulating a workable theory about relativity, although he had begun to think about it long before Einstein did.

Although it seems astonishing to consider disease the perfect solution for keeping us alive during a moment of high stress, this concept becomes evident once we get access to the information necessary to understand this paradigm.

There are no failures in life, only results. Today you are living the results of your programs. Despite appearances, nothing happens at random in the universe. Your path, your behaviors, your health disorders: all have meaning. The inherent meaning can be found in the intimately woven compilation of programs of survival. Some of these programs have been subconsciously rendered since your birth, others are the expression of a solution for your parents during your gestation, while still others are the lingering conflicts of your ancestors. The path you are experiencing, and the people you are attracting in your life, are all aligned with your subconscious road map. If your experience is one of conflict and limitation, your limiting programs can be brought to consciousness and altered. *You don't have to let the programming of your past dictate your future.*

Illnesses are clearly related to primal programs that have permitted our species to continuously evolve. We would not be here today without our ancestors and parents, all of whom faced their own struggles and ultimately passed their programs on to us in an evolutionary cascade. There is no purpose in blaming your predecessors for their influence on your life. Instead, as your awareness increases, your own role becomes instrumental in permitting the entire clan to evolve.

It is possible to repair the traumas of the past, liberate yourself from old programs, and dramatically increase your free will to make different choices right now.

## PREPARING FOR YOUR NEW REALITY

Once you open yourself to *learn* about a new reality, you will be able to attract all circumstances to experience this new reality. Remember: nothing has meaning in life except the meaning you give it.

In preparation for the transformative chapters ahead, I encourage you to begin now to get clear about the limiting beliefs that you are holding about your health. It is time to challenge these beliefs.

Write down the beliefs that you feel are most limiting to your health at this point in your life:

*I believe*_____.

*I believe*_____.

*I believe*_____.

*I believe*_____.

*I believe*_____.

*I believe*_____.

Now, with each one of the limiting beliefs that you have identified, ask yourself the following questions:

- When did I adopt this belief?
- Does this belief belong to me or to someone else?
- How do I know that this belief is true?
- Do I think that this belief is true beyond the shadow of a doubt?
- Why would I act as if this belief were true, even though it may not be absolutely true?
- Is this belief the most useful one for me right now?
- What price am I going to pay if I continue to believe this?
- Considering that this belief may not even be true, can I imagine myself without it?
- How could it change my life if I did not believe this?
- What other belief could I adopt that would be more powerful in helping me attain my objective?
- What new action am I going to take, based on my new belief?

**Example:** *I believe that my illness is incurable.*

- When did I adopt this belief?
  *When I got my doctor's prognosis.*

- Does this belief belong to me or to someone else?
  *It belongs to my doctor.*

- How do I know that this belief is true?
  *Because my doctor informed me of the statistics related to my illness.*

- Do I think that this belief is true beyond the shadow of a doubt?
  *No.*

- Why would I act as if this belief were true, even though it may not be absolutely true?
  *Because most people believe it's true. Because I don't want to create false hope for myself and be disappointed. Also because I am afraid that my family and friends won't agree with me if I challenge conventional beliefs.*

- Is this belief the most useful one for me right now?
  *No, it is not.*

- What price am I going to pay if I continue to believe this?
  *It may become a self-fulfilling prophecy.*

- Considering that this belief may not even be true, can I imagine myself without it?
  *It is possible.*

- How could it change my life if I did not believe this?
  *I would have more strength. I would have less stress and more power to deal with the situation. I would be able to tap into more of my internal resources. I would have a chance to recover.*

- What other belief could I adopt that would be more powerful in helping me attain my objective?
  *I can be an exception to the social expectations, because I have access to a different approach. I am not a statistic. I have a role to play in the outcome. This is my life.*

◆ What new action am I going to take, based on my new belief?
*I will do everything in my power to become healthy with the help of my doctor and to work on understanding and resolving my emotional conflict. I will support my body with a proper diet and lifestyle.*

## THE POWER OF CLARITY

At an early age, I had the chance to study ballet. My teacher, Monica, was an amazing dancer who took me under her wing and taught me the discipline, courage, and perseverance needed to become a professional dancer. I remember being six years old when I asked her how she had become so good. She told me it was all about observing the best dancers and studying how they moved. Her strategy was to focus on excellence and how she could constantly improve, instead of focusing on her limitations or mistakes. "Observe good dancers," she told me. "Play with the ideal movement in your imagination, see yourself achieve it in your head, and dance in your mind. Feel it, and you will become a great dancer."

Years later, having followed her advice with great determination, I fulfilled my dream by being hired by the top modern jazz choreographer in Paris and dancing in his productions.

Later on in life, as I was studying Neuro-Linguistic Programming and acquiring knowledge on the functioning of the brain and the power of the mind, I understood that Monica was absolutely spot-on. It is what we focus on that influences the speed of our progress and permits us to attain our dreams. An observation occurring repeatedly, good or bad, eventually becomes our reality. In order to master any area of our life, including health, it is a question of how we will control our focus and utilize it to achieve what we really want.

In order to heal, you must first clearly evaluate your present state. What is your situation? What is the state of your health right now? As you ask yourself these questions, you can immediately begin to alleviate emotional stress by realizing that this is an opportunity to grow and live a better life.

To change your situation swiftly and efficiently, you will need to clearly inform your subconscious mind about what your objective is.

Your formulation must be clear and precise. Also, your intention needs to be positive and supported by a strong interest. *The purpose behind your objective of becoming healthy is the engine that will propel you to health or other objectives.*

Going even further, you need to have purpose that extends beyond just recovering from an illness or imbalance. For instance, if a woman desires to lose weight, it will certainly be important to clearly define the ideal weight she wants to be. But, in fact, "losing weight" represents only a path, not an objective. For the subconscious, the word "losing" presupposes something has been lost that will need to be found. This type of verbal formulation can influence whether someone will remain successful or periodically gain back the weight they "lost." Through this simple example, I want to show you the importance of words and how subconscious interpretations can create obstacles to success. A formulation such as "I want to be thin and fit" will show the mind the correct direction to take.

Now, if I ask a woman about her interest in being thin and fit, and her only interest is to be able to fit into her clothes again, it will likely not be enough motivation to unleash the power of her mind. It won't influence the action of the subconscious. On the other hand, if this objective is supported by strong values such as health, attractiveness, longevity, and femininity, it will trigger a more powerful subconscious reaction. The positive outcome attached to attaining the objective is the most powerful force she can focus on in order to obtain positive results. If she has numerous strong reasons, she will definitely be supported by the power of her emotions and the pleasure she associates with being thin.

Now it is your turn. Think about the condition you want to address. Define your objective in clear and positive terms. Name the organ that is affected and define the ideal state you want to attain. Write down your desired objective simply and clearly, so that your mind can connect to an image corresponding to your healthy organ.

Here are some examples:

> *I desire for my liver to be healthy and to function in harmony with all other organs.*

*I desire for my breast to be clear and perfectly healthy.*

*I desire for my legs and arms to be strong and move freely.*

Then, after each stated desire, write down the purpose that fuels that objective. For example:

*I desire for my liver to be healthy and to function in harmony with all other organs.*

*This is my underlying purpose: to be healthy, have energy, create abundance in my life, live in harmony with others, enjoy time with my family and friends, have joy in my life, do something I love, and contribute to the world in the best ways I can.*

## TRUSTING THE PROCESS

After you state your objective, the following paragraph will provide extra power to your subconscious to start moving into action. You do not need to force anything consciously. The most important thing is to be clear at all times about the outcome you want to produce and to keep your thoughts focused on the right target. Trusting the masterful workings of your mind will in itself initiate a shift. And while you work passionately on your programs during the next few chapters, your subconscious will ingeniously use the information you gather.

If possible, read the following passage out loud, and refer back to it as often as you wish:

*At this moment, I do not need to know how or when my subconscious mind is going to shift so that I will regain a state of health. I will focus on my intention and express my profound desire to be healthy. With humility, I will investigate the meaning of my condition so that I can evolve away from its presence. And with the assistance of my subconscious, I will unlock the programs associated with it. I will eliminate the stress I may have created within myself because of my perceptions. I have the power and intelligence to change the meaning I give to my experience. I will find freedom outside the bounds of certain programs. I am now ready to create a state of balance within my body. This condition will no longer represent a solution for me or anyone else in my clan. I have all the resources necessary to undo what has momentarily served a purpose in my being. I will be guided with the intuition needed to help me resolve this health disorder. Healing will emerge from the transformation I allow within myself. I thank my organs for helping me at a distressed moment in time. I thank myself for allowing the transformation of my thoughts. Healing can now take place in my body.*

# 8

# Defining the Meaning of Your Illness

Undesired realities that prompt traumas or shocks can precipitate diseases according to the type of emotions they trigger. Our emotions are directly connected to our organs. Each invisible emotion is a precious thread that can connect us to the physical organ to which it is intimately linked. There are a number of meaningful metaphors that speak to the important roles our organs govern, in addition to their pure biological functioning. We could say that our organs are the parents of our emotions, the wells of our deepest feelings, and the roots of our sensations. As we've seen by exploring the origin of illness in the preceding chapters, it is evident that an emotion can awaken the expression of its source—that source being the organ.

## ORGANS OF EMOTIONS

An organ can tell a story. It can represent the distress we could not communicate and solve at a specific moment. When we are finally able to gain awareness, we may find that illness has much to relay to us. Illness speaks of the fears we faced when alone and isolated from others. It acknowledges the loss, sadness, and despair of losing a loved one. It tells of the betrayal we could not accept, the injustice we could not express, and the anger we could not exhibit and kept locked inside. It exposes the anguish about the child we could not have or the relationship we could not keep.

It tells of the attacks from which we could not protect ourselves. It confesses the secrets that belong to our childhood or to others in the family, even secrets that transpired before we were born.

Health disorders, from the most harmless to the so-called incurable, are not whims of fate. When we get sick, it means something happened emotionally that translated deep into our biology, somewhere inside the stomach, the lung, the heart, the bone, the breast, and so on. The organ is the messenger, the manager that takes over the problem and resolves it the only way it can, through cellular changes. When we experience existential difficulties that we are unable to resolve through thought or action, a biological response will emerge. Illness is the indication of an emotional need that a biological function has attempted to satisfy through an archaic solution.

**Note:** Malnutrition, intoxication, poisoning, and radiation can also trigger illness.

## THE BIOLOGICAL MEANING BEHIND YOUR CONDITION

In order to define the type of emotional struggle you are dealing with, the first step is to precisely understand the role the affected organ plays in your body. For example, the role of the breast is to nurture and protect, the role of the throat is to swallow, the role of the stomach is to digest, the role of the intestines is to assimilate, and so forth. Understanding the function of the organ will inform you of the nature of the conflict it can express.

Remember that every cell of the body possesses intelligence and is responding to your emotional needs.

A cellular modification has been triggered as a solution to your emotional distress, and now illness has occurred. The illness is signaling that an opportunity is presenting itself. Now you can choose to view your disorder as a chance to heal the part of yourself that has been emotionally challenged. It may be time to change your vision about certain aspects of your life or to create a stronger alignment within yourself and greater congruence with your core values. The moment you understand the meaning of your condition, you may find it meaningless to hold on to the emotional struggle that triggered it. Sometimes it is possible to get rid of a disease merely by being aware of the exact nature of the conflict.

An event has happened, and as you filtered the experience through your five senses (sight, sound, touch, taste, and smell), you assigned a particular meaning to it, which has prompted stress. The event that happened in the environment is not the cause of your distress, as it is only external. The meaning you attributed to the event is the source of the problem, and it is personal. Emerging from your subconscious programming and conditioning, the perception belongs to you. Your felt experience originated from within yourself in relation to the environment. *The good news is that you can modify your perception of the event, so you can let go of the conflict.* That is what we are going to explore together as you learn to shift the way you perceive certain events—no matter how long ago they occurred.

> *"If you are distressed by anything external,*
> *the pain is not due to the thing itself but to*
> *your own estimate of it; and this*
> *you have the power to revoke at any moment."*
>
> —Marcus Aurelius, Roman emperor

It is important to understand the source of our distortions and how our personal experiences can lead to a particular sensitivity to certain situations. Throughout our life, we adopt values and beliefs, and we make decisions according to our needs. We carry subconscious imprints, which are the mind maps we hold on to in order to navigate and survive.

Having to adapt to challenging circumstances since conception, each of us developed our own elaborate emotional map. We carry our own "model of the world" that is uniquely shaped according to our experiences. For instance, a client of mine named Lisa had stomach problems almost every weekend. She could not "digest" the fact that her husband watched football games on Sunday afternoons. While she worked in the kitchen, hearing the sounds of the game in the background made her angry. She felt like she was forced to accept this situation every weekend. Her next-door neighbor, on the other hand, loved to grab a couple of beers, sit down next to her boyfriend, and enjoy a relaxing time as they watched the game together.

Lisa was particularly sensitive to the *sound* of the game on TV, as it reminded her of her childhood sadness when her father refused to take the family out on a Sunday walk or a drive. He chose instead to stay home and watch the game. Her sensations as an adult were linked to the old emotions of disappointment and sadness she felt years earlier. The up-setting feelings resurfaced as if nothing had changed. She was instantly transported to the time when she had to bear staying indoors most of the day, a time that was filled with loneliness and boredom. At the time, she could not accept her father's behavior; she believed that he was selfish, saw her mother suffer from it, and could not "digest" that he chose sports over them.

As a girl, Lisa didn't have the maturity to perceive her father as a tired man who worked two jobs, six days a week. She didn't realize that his positive intention in watching the game on Sunday was to recuperate and get recharged for the week ahead. As an adult, the conflict Lisa had on Sundays with her husband was directly related to her past memory. The "problem" was inside Lisa, not outside.

Very often, we might believe that if our circumstances were to change, our stresses would be eliminated. Not surprisingly, we might also tend to react strongly to situations in the environment because they awaken old wounds. As human beings, we expend a great deal of energy fight-ing with or defending ourselves against the outer world, particularly the circumstances of our own life. But once we accept that the solution is to look inside ourselves and modify our beliefs, we get the chance to repair wounds of the past. Healing takes place as we embrace self-responsibility, flexibility, and awareness.

More specifically, illness is nothing less than the opportunity to evolve by behaving differently from your parents and ancestors, at least in certain areas. It is also an opportunity to heal your younger self, the child inside you who is still waiting for resources he or she could not ac-cess during stressful times. The people around you acted in certain ways because they did not have access to biological codes other than the ones imprinted in their subconscious mind. As human beings, our behaviors are driven by our instinctive reactions based on survival, not intellectual calculation. It is a lot easier to forgive others once this principle is understood. A health challenge is often rooted in a misinterpretation about others or what the circumstances around you mean. Our experiences are transformed in our mind, which modifies them to match the model we know.

## IDENTIFYING THE STORY YOUR BODY IS TELLING

If you are being challenged by an illness, you are expressing within your biology an emotion you could not articulate during a stressful event; thus you are fulfilling a subconscious need. Your emotional sensation is being translated in your biology and is telling a story that needs to be told. The body is fulfilling one of its purposes: to liberate the mind from a particular struggle. Maybe you felt the struggle of a maternal concern (breast) or of not being able to figuratively digest a "morsel" (stomach). Maybe you felt separated from someone you loved (skin), or maybe you felt that you could not verbally respond to an attack (bronchi). Your primitive brain, whose logic must be understood as a clever and useful mechanism, manages your condition. It has helped you alleviate your stress and express an emotional conflict that you may have been unaware of until now.

To begin to unwind from the struggle, the first step is to identify the story that triggered your emotional conflict. The second step is to describe the conflict to someone or to yourself on paper (we will get to this in a moment). During the stressful event, what did you conclude, believe, and feel? What did you want to say that you could not say at the time the problem occurred? What did you want to do that you could not do?

Once you start expressing the stressful event, it will no longer be locked up inside you, and you will have a chance to explore the roots of your felt experience from a more neutral state. You will become the observer. It will then be possible to revisit the event from a different point of view in order to let go of the conflict.

Remember that your primitive brain reacted to your emotions based on your reality during an event. The way you perceived the situation then is what really matters and needs to be modified. Even if you think that this event is in the past and that you got over it long ago, a part of you may still feel unsettled about it. This is the part that is holding on to the conflict in your deepest self.

The following exercise will help you define the nature of your condition and find the triggering event related to it.

**Note:** Origins of some health disorders may be found before birth, either during intrauterine life or during the life of your parents or ancestors. It is possible that the onset of a disease may be triggered subconsciously according to particular dates, ages, symbols, or memorized cycles (personal or ancestral). In those cases, you won't necessarily have access to a memory of a stressful event just prior to your health issue, as it is possible that the trigger may have been fully subconscious. However, most times there is a triggering event prior to the onset of illness.

## DEFINING THE NATURE OF YOUR CONFLICT

After a precise medical diagnosis, the next step is to educate yourself about the type of emotional conflict that is related to your condition. The Bio-Breakthrough Dictionary (starting on page 223) will be your resource guide for informing yourself and evaluating the nature of your conflict. Fortunately, you don't need to study medicine or biology to understand the emotional meaning of your illness. After acquiring some basic knowledge, you can use your mind's logic and trust your common sense.

*Based on your diagnosis and referencing the Bio-Breakthrough Dictionary, provide the following information:*

Name of illness_____

Date of first symptom_____

Organ affected_____

Organ function in the body_____

Embryonic origin _____

Type of emotional conflict_____

**Note regarding the embryonic origin:** If you are unable to locate the embryonic origin of your disorder in the Bio-Breakthrough Dictionary, simply continue with the process. You can still work on your issue, whether or not you have this piece of information.

*Example:*

Name of illness: breast cancer (glandular)

Date of first symptom:

Organ affected: left breast

Organ function in the body: feeding/nurturing

Embryonic origin: new brain mesoderm

Type of emotional conflict: nest conflict (related to the child for a right-handed woman); need to nurture and protect

In general, the following questions can help you clarify the information you're seeking: What is the purpose of the affected organ in the body? What is the behavior of the organ? Is its function increased? Decreased? Blocked (e.g., paralysis)? Uncontrollable (e.g., Parkinson's)? What are my cells expressing specifically?

There is a purpose to your biological imbalance, which is expressing your struggle in metaphorical terms. You are expressing a bio-logical solution to what you could not solve in your psyche. For instance, paralysis provides a solution to the fear of movement. Breast cancer represents a solution to the need to nurture (i.e., maternal impossibility). Bladder cancer may be related to a need for marking the territory with more urine (figuratively) and creating boundaries. A hyperthyroid problem will accelerate the metabolism and pertains to a struggle related to speed: a need to act faster in order to allow one to catch a "morsel."

## THE TRIGGERING EVENT

From shock to illness, there is a path that connects psychological circumstances to biology. Let's follow Linda, a fifty-year-old married woman, along the seven steps of her path, from event to interpretation and biological reaction.

**First:** There is a triggering event in Linda's life.

*Linda arrives home early. As she enters her bedroom, she finds her husband in the arms of another woman, making love.*

**Second:** Linda gathers information about that event through her sensory system (visual, auditory, kinesthetic, olfactory, gustatory).

*Linda is caught off guard. A negative sensation is emerging as she sees her husband and his mistress in each other's arms. She recognizes the other woman, who is a long-term client of her husband's. She hears their voices and even smells the perfume of the other woman.*

**Third:** Without knowing it, a subconscious association is made. Within a split second, the event resonates somewhere along the time line of her personal history. She instantly evaluates the experience according to her imprints, conditioning, values, belief system, upbringing, culture, traditions, religion, and programming. Then as now, a need is no longer being satisfied, and something feels indigestible.

*Some of Linda's deepest values, such as love, trust, and respect, are violated. It is a devastating betrayal. She concludes that her husband's affair may have started a long time ago. What bothers her most is the thought that her husband and another woman probably made love in her bed several times before; it feels like a disgusting affair to her. The situation reminds her of other times she suspected her husband of being unfaithful. It also reminds her of her high school sweetheart, when he went out with her best friend behind her back. She was seventeen years old when she saw them kissing in a parking lot. She was devastated then too, and her felt experience was colored by a sense of betrayal and disgust.*

**Fourth:** Powerful and painful emotions arise.

*Linda is shocked and disgusted by the situation. Seeing her husband with the other woman in her own bed feels dirty, gross, vile, and deeply unfair.*

**Fifth:** Stress will rise according to the magnitude of the emotional struggle and the consequences anticipated by the individual.

> *Dwelling on the situation and experiencing an internal storm of emotions, Linda can't sleep or eat properly for days. She can't digest the filth of this affair.*

**Sixth:** Linda will either be able to express her struggle and find a satisfying solution or she won't.

> *Linda does not know how to solve her issue with her husband and can't even express her emotions of disgust and anger. She spends time away, choosing to stay alone in their country house. Continuing to dwell on the problem, she does not want to communicate with anyone.*

**Seventh:** If it is impossible to find a satisfying solution to her struggle and attain her vital needs, Linda's felt sensation will ultimately awaken a biological solution. Thereafter, for as long as the situation remains unresolved in her psyche, her cells will express a subconscious, archaic solution to her issue.

> *Linda expresses her emotional conflict through colon cancer, which is related to a need to digest and evacuate a "dirty morsel." According to the distress of her "felt experience," it is in her tissues that the solution to her issue will metaphorically manifest.*

> *Note: an illness can be triggered either instantly (during the moment of shock) or after a period of time when the emotional stress remains unresolved (intense permanent stress).*

## CONSCIOUSNESS AWAKENING

There was a *before*, when your body was in balance; there is an *after*, when, at a specific moment in time, your biology shifted.

What do your *before* and *after* look like? What are the particulars?

You may now work on recalling the triggering event that is directly related to your symptoms. Depending on your condition, this event may have happened a few days, weeks, or months prior to your first symptom, but usually within a year before you became aware of your condition or were diagnosed with the disease.

**Note:** You may believe that it takes years to create cancer. It never made sense to me that cancer would take years to develop and all of a sudden be found, and from then on progress rapidly and become life threatening within a few months. Dr. Hamer's findings suggest that cancer is often found within a year after a shock or period of intense permanent stress.

As you are processing this information, you may have already recalled the shock related to your health issue, and your mind may have instinctually made the right connection.

If your problem is related to your digestion, you might remember a situation in which you could not figuratively digest something. If your issue concerns your breast, the conflict is related to the nest or nurturing. You may remember a worry you had about your child, or someone else you cared about, a few months before your breast manifested a lump. If one of your lungs is affected, you may remember not being able to breathe in a situation in which you feared death, literally or figuratively. If your knee is affected, you may remember not being able to bend to an authority figure. If you have put on weight, you may recall feeling abandoned or isolated after a breakup.

Write down the event you instinctively feel is connected to your condition. If your disease is cancer, you most likely went through a problem that was of great significance, and you experienced a high level of stress. Your autonomic brain provided a biological solution because you could not resolve the problem soon enough to interrupt the phase of high stress.

The purpose of this section is to allow you to express certain emotions, perhaps intimate ones that you have encapsulated and not permitted yourself to process. The status of your health is directly related to such emotions, which you can allow yourself to contact, express, and be liberated from.

**Note:** As you feel confident that you have accessed your condition's triggering event, know that you are preparing yourself for the steps that come later in this chapter.

It's possible that you might have difficulty recalling the experience related to your condition. You could be confused because you may have recalled a few stressful events of the same nature and aren't sure which one connects to your condition. Most times, it is difficult to recall precisely the triggering factors of an illness. The reason is that often, the subconscious brain stores away stressful memories so we don't revisit them. This is a natural protective mechanism that guards us from the painful details of the story that prompted the illness. This is why I suggest that you connect directly with your subconscious to unlock the memory associated with your condition.

In order to access the source of your emotional struggle with precision, I will show you how to utilize the power of your own words, which are emotionally charged. Emotions are complex and connected to specific thoughts and behaviors. The dictionary defines the noun feeling as "a psychological and physical reaction, subjectively experienced, which involves physiological changes that prepare the body for vigorous action."

Throughout our life, we make associations that link our feelings in the present to similar ones from the past. Our feelings and psychological responses to stimuli are the result of recorded experiences. Physical and psychological feelings occur in conjunction with one another. The smell of a particular perfume might make you feel sensual, reminding you of someone you were in love with. The sound of an alarm clock may create feelings of fear and urgency, reminding you of the time when you had to get up early for school. The taste of a homemade soup might make you feel comfort and remind you of your childhood and your grandmother. The vision of miles of highway traffic ahead of you can bring about anxiety and remind you of feeling trapped.

Your illness is connected to a specific recorded experience. The words that define how you feel about your illness can be used as stimuli to recall the experience associated with it. Sometimes the words you will use to describe your feelings may not sound as primal as the emotion you really feel, but nevertheless, your choice of words is intimately connected with your story.

*The words you utilize to express the sensations related to your illness are directly related to the experience that triggered your illness.*

In this linking process, you're using the technique of *sensory memory*, just like an actor. Defining your illness through words and sensations will allow you to retrieve the original trigger. If you describe to yourself, in all honesty, what your illness means to you and how you feel about it, you will find an avenue that directs you to the subjective experience related to the problem.

Words can be used as anchors to recall memories, and they possess the capacity to reach your psyche and awaken hidden imprints. Trust the spontaneous feelings and words connected to your illness, as they will induce an intuitive response. Your words and feelings will be your instruments for opening the doorway to your subconscious. The way you feel about your illness, and your unique linguistic choices for expressing it, provide essential information regarding the root of the problem.

A young man who had terrible back pain consulted me a couple of years ago. I asked him what the pain was like and how it made him feel. He said he could not physically hold himself straight and that he felt disempowered. He felt as if he could collapse at any time, which created a sense of despair. The experience of this young man's back pain was unique to him, and the words he spoke in order to describe and define it belonged only to him as well.

I asked him what he had experienced in his life, prior to having the back pain, that also felt "disempowering," when something could not "hold" and felt as if it were "collapsing" and was accompanied by an emotion of "despair." He explained that he was in the midst of losing the photocopy store he had created with his sister. The business was going down, as he could no longer support it financially. And his sister, a single mother with two children, wasn't in a financial position to help either. He felt powerless to turn the situation around and intense despair about not being the pillar of strength for himself and his sister's family. The words he used to describe his back pain permitted us to locate with precision the stressful event connected to the onset of his condition.

## JEANNE'S STORY

Jeanne had difficulties understanding the emotional distress associated with the cancer in her left breast. Already familiar with the approach of decoding the emotional aspect of biology, she was well informed about the type of conflict related to her disease. Before she came to see me, Jeanne had consulted with several therapists in an attempt to resolve her emotional issues. I could hear the sound of despair in her voice when she called me for the first time, as her last scans had revealed that the cancer had progressed to her lymph nodes. During our first meeting, she explained that she knew her distress was related to a "nest-worry conflict" and that she had endured the pain of several "nest" related stresses within a few months preceding the diagnosis of a tumor in her breast.

Jeanne had prepared a list of all the events she was able to remember that had created stress in relationship to the nest. She had gone through a divorce the year prior to being diagnosed with breast cancer. She also remembered how worried she had been during that same period, discovering that her sixteen-year-old son was smoking marijuana and secretly drinking every weekend with his friends. At the time, she did everything she could to stop him. Then, just a few months prior to her diagnosis, her mother died. Jeanne had taken care of her until she lost the battle with a heart condition. As a result of taking care of her mother, Jeanne also lost her high-paying job. She had been a chef in a well-known restaurant while she simultaneously attempted to juggle caretaking and parenting. After several instances of arriving to work late, leaving early, and having to be absent on occasion, her behavior became unacceptable to her employer.

Like an excellent detective, Jeanne had made the connections related to concerns that primarily pertained to the nest. Each of these situations was accompanied by immense stress. She felt overwhelmed and isolated during each experience. Jeanne thought that any of those stresses could be linked to her illness, but unfortunately she was not making progress in resolving her issue.

I asked Jeanne to think about her illness for a moment and connect to it with honesty and precision. I asked her to remember a particular instance when having breast cancer felt overwhelming. Jeanne first looked down and then closed her eyes as she retrieved a specific memory. I then asked her what it meant to her to have breast cancer and what it felt like having to deal with it in that moment. As tears rolled down her cheeks, Jeanne said her illness meant disappointment and sadness. It meant that her life would never be the same. It represented the absence of a future. It felt discouraging and lonely. It felt as if she could no longer count on anything.

I then asked Jeanne to stop thinking about the cancer. I asked her to travel back in time a few months before she felt a lump in her breast, and I asked her the following questions: "Jeanne, when did circumstances in your life mean disappointment and sadness? When did you think your life would never be the same? What represented the absence of a future? What happened that made you feel discouraged and lonely? When did you feel that you could no longer count on anything?"

As I repeated her words exactly, Jeanne became conscious of the connection between her illness and an event she had pushed aside, something she hadn't been able to cope with. The words describing her illness evoked a memory, an emotional recall with the same meaning. Jeanne started to remember the moment when she decided to let go of her house. After a last-ditch effort to get financial help from her ex-husband, she had come to the conclusion that she would have to sell her house. In the back of her mind, she had always thought her ex-husband would help her if necessary. The day of their final conversation about the house, they had a big fight. He harshly reminded her that she should have been more careful to keep her job. After several weeks of being unreliable because she had to deal with her mother's condition, she had received a phone call from her boss early one morning saying she did not need to come to work that day. The day she was fired was stressful but somewhat expected. It was the consequence of losing her job that was about to create unmanageable stress.

Jeanne did not know how she was going to continue making the mortgage payments on her house and called her ex-husband for help. This was the house where she had watched her son grow up. This was the place she had loved to live in and had enjoyed decorating over the years. During her divorce, she had fought very hard to keep it, as it represented the family nest. This was where she felt safe living with her son now. But since the divorce, in order to make the high mortgage payments, she had to be on a tight budget, and she was barely making it. She was shocked at her ex-husband's reaction; she had been certain he would offer to help until she could find another job. She knew it could take a while to find a comparable position in her field, and she had thought that since she was living with their son, he would surely help. On the day they discussed it, she realized that selling the house and moving to an apartment was going to be the only option.

In this specific case, and in order to understand Jeanne's conflict, it is important to remember that for many creatures, such as birds and certain mammals, the nest is the precursor to the birth and nurturing of the offspring. The breast is intimately connected to the nest itself, which from an archaic perspective comes first in preparation for the offspring. As soon as the nest is ready, the female hormone estrogen increases to permit reproduction. Breast cancer can sometimes be the expression of a conflict directly related to what represents the nest itself, like a house or an apartment.

As for Jeanne, her feelings about her illness precisely described how she felt the moment she knew she was going to lose her nest. Being fired and not getting help from her ex-husband created a situation that would deprive her of the house she loved. The moment Jeanne found out her ex-husband would not help her was the moment Jeanne could no longer meet her needs and felt the resulting shock (notice that until then, she had thought she had a solution).

In the wake of this crisis, for Jeanne it meant:
*disappointment and sadness;*
*that her life would never be the same;*
*the absence of a future;*

It felt:
*discouraging and lonely;*
*as if she could no longer count on anything.*

119

Jeanne was now able to connect with the trigger of her illness in a way that was supported by her personal inner logic, rather than by any external suggestions about the source of her conflict. This realization felt very liberating to Jeanne. She was now able to reconnect with the circumstances surrounding the painful moment when she felt that there was no way out of the conflict. She reconnected with the day she had the pivotal fight with her ex-husband. She vividly remembered fine details of the moment—the weather, what she was wearing, where she was standing in her house, the pattern on the wallpaper, and the sound of her ex-husband's voice—when he told her that he would not be able to help and that her only option was to let go of the house. The memory of that painful moment was finally released to her conscious awareness. She remembered how terrible she felt that day—flooded with uncontrollable emotions that affected her to the core. She had fought during her divorce to keep the house, only to realize a few months later that she would not be able to keep it after all. It was with great sadness that she sold it eight weeks after she had run out of options, having made the decision that she would move into a small apartment with her son.

Jeanne felt a lump in her breast four months after she decided to sell her home. She had yet to fully grieve the loss of her house. She felt that she had been able to grieve her mother's death, the divorce, and the loss of her job. The worry about her son had also stopped, since he had changed his behavior. However, Jeanne kept going in and out of conflict about the house, very often feeling strong regret. And now it was abundantly clear that the only event she hadn't resolved—one that she never anticipated and would be at the root of her illness—was about being forced to let go of her cherished home.

The psychological circumstances around that stressful event matched the syntax of her illness, the hidden language behind her breast cancer. The nature of Jeanne's conflict was related to the nest and was felt in a way that was unique to her perception. Jeanne's reasoning prevented her from facing and coping with the situation. She thought that she would never be able to afford to live in a house again, and even if she did, *this* was the one she loved and would always miss. Not only were memories of her son growing up ingrained in her feelings about this house, but she had also lost the place where she thought she would be able to live while creating a new future for herself. Jeanne no longer had her "nest."

## STRUCTURES OF ILLNESS AND MEANING

During a traumatic event, there is a moment of loss of control over our reasoning. This moment can last for as long as we lack resources, leaving us feeling trapped and unable to cope with the situation. The representation of the event that we see in our mind has been gathered through our five senses (visual, auditory, kinesthetic, olfactory, gustatory). Once this sensory information is collected, it is internalized by the nervous system. Neurological representations are precursors to the meaning given to the experience, using linguistic maps such as symbols, metaphors, and words. Health disorders are merely the transformations of neurological representations, and their linguistic counterparts, into biological metaphors.

An illness is the *surface structure* statement of a deeper map (the *deep structure*) in which the meaning of the illness is contained. The *referential structure* of an illness is the experience that was originally perceived through the five senses and instantly transformed according to one's personal filtering system.

In Jeanne's case, after listening to her *surface structure* statement (the name of her illness, breast cancer), I started exploring the linguistic representation of her illness (*deep structure*) by listening to the words she used to describe it. I then reformulated Jeanne's words so she would have direct access to the experience associated with those words and corresponding emotions (*referential structure*). Her emotions were connected to a story that pertained to the nest. Jeanne perceived the experience based on the limitations of her beliefs at the time. What caused her to perceive her house with such importance? What beliefs supported her emotions? How did she interpret the experience of having to let go of her house in such a way that it created stress for her?

By uncovering the triggering experience, Jeanne's distortions could now be challenged, thus allowing the expansion of her personal map. By engaging in a reframing process, a new perception would emerge that could liberate her emotional stress.

After working with me on modifying her beliefs about what the house meant to her, including her rigidly held rule that this house was the ultimate one, Jeanne allowed herself to grieve. The process of grieving is based on learning how to re-create in another context the same value, role, and identity that a person, pet, or object we have lost permitted us to express. As Jeanne did this, we were also able to make significant connections with her past. When she was three, her parents left their home to move to another city where her dad had found a better job. At that time, the family had to start over, away from the comfort of their familiar nest. After processing this old and unresolved memory, Jeanne realized that her strong attachment to the house (where she had raised her son) was related to her childhood felt experience, because leaving their home had been heartbreaking for her parents as well.

Jeanne allowed herself to imagine a future possibility of owning another house, but this time with more detachment and realism. She was able to accept her situation in the apartment as momentary, realizing it would only be a matter of time before she could resettle in a new home if she so desired.

Her distress was resolved and, simultaneously, her health improved. She also continued her medical treatment for a short while. Within three months of our first meetings, Jeanne's scans were normal. She started a new job as a teacher in a culinary school and promised herself that she would look for a house when the time was right. Jeanne also promised herself that she would stay mindful of the emotional attachments and nest conflicts that could arise, and that she would approach her home situation with her newly expanded lens of perception.

## THE BIO-SYNTAX

The same meaning links your illness and your felt experience, as one is the expression of the other. You can now observe the following structures of language to gain a clearer understanding of this linkage. The linguistics model that I have mapped out below connects one's intimate meaning of illness to one's personal language. It is inspired by the premises of Neuro-Linguistic Programming, Transformational Grammar, and General Semantics.

NLP initially focused on the power of therapeutic language. When we speak, we produce statements that are the result of the transformation of deeper and more extensive meanings, which are part of the "deep structure" of language. This last structure refers to a fuller linguistic and neurological model that the "surface structure" is attempting to convey. When we speak, we abstract elements, leaving out information that would provide a better explanation of our experience if it were included (the referential structure). Because of our filtered way of perceiving, we cannot always access the complete experience we are attempting to describe. The more details and sensory information we provide (deep structure), the better others can understand us.

In the context of illness, we can refer to the name of the illness as the "surface structure" of the biological language. The description and personal meaning one can verbalize about one's illness, and the emotions associated with it, are connected to the "deep structure" of the biological language. Once the deep structure is expressed, it can lead to the "referential structure," which is the experience associated with the triggering event.

1. **Surface Structure:** The illness or symptom.

2. **Deep Structure:** The full linguistic and emotional definition connected to the illness; the personal meanings and feelings related to the illness.

3. **Referential structure:** The experience corresponding to the shock or struggle that is linked to the health disorder.

*Jeanne's example:*
Surface structure: The words naming the illness.
*Q: What illness or symptom do you have?*
*A: Breast cancer.*

Deep structure: The personal meaning of the illness; the words and feelings associated with it.

> *Q: Think about your illness for a moment and connect with it. What does having breast cancer mean to you? What is it like for you to have this condition? What does that make you feel?*
>
> *A: Disappointment and sadness that my life will never be the same. It represents the absence of a future. It feels discouraging and lonely. It feels as if I can no longer count on anything.*

Referential structure: The event related to the words and feelings described in the deep structure.

> *Q: Go back in time, a few weeks or months before being diagnosed. When did circumstances represent disappointment and sadness? When did you think your life would never be the same? What represented the absence of a future? What felt discouraging and lonely? What made you feel as if you could no longer count on anything?*
>
> *A: Having to let go of my house when my ex-husband refused to help me financially after I was fired.*

**Note:** The description Jeanne gives about the meaning of her illness does not contain words such as "nurturing" or " protection" or " nest," although her experience directly pertains to a nest conflict. However, very often a person uses words or predicates that contain a meaning directly related to their condition. For instance, expressions such as "I was *touched*" may be related to the skin; "that was *nerve-racking*" may connect with the nerves; and "this was a major *loss*" may relate to the ovary. It is important to listen to the words while keeping an open mind, since there are no rules to guarantee how a person is going to describe the meaning of his or her illness or the event related to his or her conflict.

## A PATHWAY TO YOUR SUBCONSCIOUS

The purpose of the following technique is to help you connect to the triggering event related to your condition, using the power of your words and emotions.

It requires that you take time alone, away from any distractions. Choose a time and place that support your intention for centeredness and increased awareness. Allow yourself to freely explore your private emotions regarding your condition. (I suggest that you write your thoughts and feelings in a journal.)

## Bio-Syntax Technique

**Step 1:** Think about your condition for a moment and allow yourself to connect with its presence in your body. As you elicit feelings related to your condition, ask yourself the following questions: What does this illness elicit in me when I feel its presence or symptoms? What does this illness represent? What does this illness mean to me? What do I go through because of its presence in my life? What does it feel like emotionally to have this condition?

Write down the words and emotions that come to you as you connect with the sense of your illness. Allow yourself to identify the underlying meaning of your condition.

**Step 2:** Go back in time and remember what was happening in your life just prior to becoming aware of your condition, or prior to having the first symptom (generally within a few weeks and up to a year before). For a moment, put aside your thoughts and feelings related to the illness and think in terms of circumstances. Ask yourself: What happened in my life prior to my first symptoms that connects precisely to the definition and feelings I expressed in Step 1? What happened that resonates with the words I used to describe the meaning of my illness and my associated feelings?

Let your subconscious do the work. As you repeat the words and feelings, let the images of the triggering event come to your consciousness.

As you recall a specific memory, go further in your investigation by asking yourself: What moment bothered me the most during this event?

**Step 3:** If you have successfully accessed the triggering event, define the moment that bothered or upset you the most. Write about the particular moment that resonates the most with the words describing the meaning of your illness. Take your time, as emotions that have been repressed may emerge from the depths of your subconscious. Allow yourself to receive and accept your true feelings. This experience is organic and oftentimes emotionally liberating. Trust yourself in this process.

Now express in detail the circumstances, emotions, sensations, struggle, and lack of resources you were experiencing at the time of the triggering event. Were you caught off guard? Shocked? Confused? Overwhelmed? Isolated? What did you believe about what was happening? What did you say to yourself? What went through your mind? How did you react?

This is your opportunity to express yourself in an uncensored and unrestricted way. It is an opportunity to free yourself from the stress you have been holding inside. As you write, honor yourself by not denying, diminishing, blocking, or hiding your feelings. Now is the time to empty your mind from the distress you experienced and continue to carry within yourself.

Listen to all voices inside of you. Allow them to surface. In the safety of your own healing process, you are free to express them all. Write down your perceptions of the stressful event until you feel that you have released all emotions and have accessed a state of liberation. Once those feelings are expressed on paper, they are no longer trapped in your mind.

**Note:** If you connected with an experience that you feel is older than your triggering event, go through the same process and write down your feelings from that time.

**Step 4:** Once you have expressed your feelings, step back from your notes and take a quiet moment for yourself. Thank yourself for allowing this opportunity to express the pain you may have been holding inside or may have repressed at the time of the event. You may realize that your circumstances have changed since the event and recognize that you now have greater resources to deal with it. One can heal emotionally, only when facing reality. You may decide that it's time to look at this event from another perspective, choosing to resolve the conflict it represents so that your mind can have the opportunity to be liberated.

Do not fear change. You are about to experience a remarkable journey of transformation within the story of your life. ...

In the next chapter, you will reap the benefits of the deep inner work you have accomplished with the previous steps. If you are now willing to explore new interpretations, you will be able to work on changing your perceptions. The significance of this cannot be measured, as a change in perception is at the heart of healing and transformation.

# The Notebook Shift

Examining and questioning our experiences, and looking at situations through a new lens of perception, can give us a kind of psychological neutrality. What I came to call "gymnastics of the mind" is extremely valuable in my work. Our truth is not *the* truth. It's just our truth based on our programs and the limitations of our model of the world. Unless we are willing to acknowledge this, we remain at an impasse.

My ten-year training as an actor—and especially in the psychology of character through HB Studio, the school of renowned drama teacher Uta Hagen—has been invaluable in helping me to understand the characters in the stories of our real life. Of course, back then I had no way of knowing that the drama school's teachings about using sensory memory and Gestalt psychology would become instrumental in my work in the field of emotional healing. And perhaps the most important influence of this training was the way it taught me how to explore perceptions. Acting gave me an affinity for looking at life as I would a play: Who are the characters? What are their intentions? Maybe their intentions aren't what we think they are. I use this tool today with my clients to help them step into the shoes of the different "characters" in their life, thus allowing them to see another reality—one they haven't been able to see on their own.

After working with hundreds of people over the past decade, I have observed that when people are willing to look beyond the problem, they can heal. I don't think that anyone heals while staying in the same place, with his or her beliefs and perceptions unchanged. It is the meaning we attach to the personally significant events of our life that determines our emotional path.

When perceptions lead to stress, the memory of a stressful event is encoded in our cells. We often feel emotional pain in relation to a conflict with another person. We stay trapped within the confines of bad feelings, distressing conclusions, and limiting decisions that ultimately shape our behavior. It is rarely our first choice to place ourselves in others' shoes when we feel that they have hurt us. But, when it is investigated, we can find that the origin of many illnesses involve conflicts with others, whether a parent, sibling, extended family member, colleague, boss, friend, or neighbor. When we are unknowingly led by unresolved or painful emotions, we can rarely grasp another's point of view or the limitations that person may be dealing with. It is challenging to access a true state of empathy toward anyone else when we're clinging to our own point of view, beliefs, and values—using them as a protective shield against life's uncertainties.

Ideally, as we grow we can strive for compassion and move toward a level of consciousness that includes an understanding that all of us are led by a personal matrix of subconscious programs. A behavior, no matter how destructive, was at some point in time adopted by the person as a survival mechanism. A behavior may also represent a solution to subconsciously alleviate the struggle of an ancestor. We make the best choices we can, according to our particular constraints, and most often we adopt limiting behaviors because of a lack of resources. This doesn't mean that we aren't responsible for our actions, but it can be helpful to be aware that any behavior has a purpose in terms of survival. For instance, the behavior of lying may represent a subconscious solution to past experiences when a person needed to avoid being severely punished as a child. Similarly, someone who is always defensive and prone to yelling or attacking may subconsciously anticipate a possible assault. This stance of self-defense is connected to childhood memories of abuse and humiliation.

All of us arrive in the world with subconscious imprints and certain predispositions that are enhanced and revealed through our life stories. The paths we follow, and the behaviors we engage in along the way, are influenced by the invisible forces of our numerous subconscious programs:

the ancestral memories we carry, the gestational programs we have absorbed, the programs we have acquired since birth, and the influence of our upbringing, religion, culture, values, and beliefs.

If we could enter into the consciousness of another human being, it would probably be a puzzling experience. We might observe that while we interact in the same world, we hold very different beliefs and values and operate at different levels of consciousness. Yet, at the same time, we are all united by the fact that we all live, breathe, and love. We are all trying to survive and satisfy our needs.

There is something else we share. When our values are deeply violated by someone's behavior, the first choice is rarely to explore the positive intentions of that person. Instead, we often stay imprisoned within our own mental model, waiting for the other person to understand, apologize, and change. We assume, or secretly wish, that the other person will filter the world through lenses much like our own. If this does not happen, we may enter into a conflict and hold on to it in our mind.

We often want others to hold the same values that we do. Values represent what is most important to us; they are the driving forces that motivate and propel us forward. Our values are adopted subconsciously according to the pain-and-pleasure principle. We make decisions along our own life path according to our multitude of experiences and how they make us feel. More specifically, during a given experience, our brain records our emotional state and whether it is one of pleasure or pain. Assessing which experiences might lead to pain and stress, and then attempting to avoid them, can become the doctrine by which we live our life. It determines the choices we make on a daily basis and the priorities we hold.

If your family was very poor when you were a child and unable to provide for your vital needs, money may be especially important to you today. If you felt that no matter how hard you tried to excel, your mother or father put you down, recognition and acceptance may be a continual quest for you.

Again, our personal values motivate us in life and give direction to our path. A person may not choose work as an important value because of past circumstances. One poignant example of this is a man whose father held a demanding job for many years at the same company. His father was fired and two weeks later committed suicide. As he witnessed his father's emotional struggle, work quickly became associated with tremendous pain. When his father died, he symbolically associated work with death. He made a decision (consciously or unconsciously) that he would not live his life the way his father had. From that point forward, he acted in agreement with the model of survival he created for himself. On the other hand, his wife, who did not suffer the same stress, complains about his lack of interest in finding a job or pursuing a career. On the surface, this man appears to be lazy, but at a deeper level he is expressing a solution to a struggle. This solution influenced his way of thinking to ensure that he would stay away from the value "work," which he won't master unless he changes the *meaning* he attributed to his father's suicide and its connection to being employed.

Since our direction in life is determined by the values we choose, and since our choices are often related to avoiding pain, it can be transformative to look closely at the circumstances that led us to these choices.

We may still remember tough moments with our parents and siblings while growing up, and we may continue to hold on to the same beliefs about the cause of their actions. Often, a lack of information about past situations alters our perception in a way that narrows it down to just what is obvious. A young boy, finding out from his mother that his father has abruptly moved out without saying good-bye, may conclude that his father does not care about him. Devastated, the boy feels worthless and unloved. However, the truth may be that the father cared about him so much that he could not bear saying good-bye and had no way of explaining this adult situation to his five-year-old son. We develop a lot of distorted perceptions during childhood based on missing information, and later on we tend to subconsciously regulate or delete information so that our perception continues to match our model of the world. We modify information according to our unique filtering system. Often, the original facts need to be retrieved in order to gain a full understanding about the situation and adjust and expand our perceptions.

When we seek to resolve a conflict with others, it is only through the understanding of *their* model of the world that we can find a place of true empathy within ourselves and ultimately let go of the conflict. Equipped with new knowledge regarding the origin of illness, and the influence our subconscious programs have on our behaviors, we can train our mind to instantly look at a bigger picture before judging other human beings for their actions. Instead of asking, "Why did they do this to me?" we can ask more expansive questions like: "How do they see this event from their point of view? What are their limitations and positive intentions? What are their circumstances? What programs might they be operating from? What am I not seeing from where I stand, because my model is different?"

And when we have a conflict with someone, we might also have the audacity to ask, "What kind of program inside of me led me into this situation with this person?"

It is fascinating to observe how the situations we attract may correlate to ingrained programs. There is always meaning to our encounters and an opportunity to look inside ourselves to identify programs we may need to eliminate. Our subconscious programs are solely our responsibility. There are no accidents, and our greatest challenges are the experiences that permit us to gain insight into what we need to learn.

A major step toward emotional healing takes place when we become willing to question long-held perceptions of ourselves, others, and the world.

As human beings we are emotionally equipped to feel empathy. Because we are biologically driven to sense the nonverbal emotional signals of others, we are wired for compassion, providing our ego doesn't get in the way. When we allow ourselves to truly feel what another human being is experiencing, we are in a state of empathy.

It is magnificent to observe how the wisdom of interconnectedness and compassion allows us to navigate our mind away from conflicts and emotional stress. If empathy were to become a dominant force in our evolution, we would have a chance to eliminate our one-sided perceptions, which ultimately are the distortions that create struggles in our life.

## LUCY'S STORY

Several years ago, I was helping a sixty-five-year-old woman named Lucy understand the root cause of her weight gain. She had started to put on weight when she was twelve, although she had been a normal-sized kid until then. After searching for the triggering event related to her condition, which would have happened right before she started to put on weight, Lucy's situation quickly came into focus. It appeared that her dramatic weight gain was directly related to a series of traumatic experiences with her father. He had abused her sexually several times over a six-month period during that year. Interestingly, when we made that connection, she seemed to feel angrier with her mother than her father. She described her feelings about this experience as if all that mattered was that her mother could have prevented it. Her anger toward her mother was intense.

Lucy never told her mother about the situation with her father but was certain that her mother knew anyway. In fact, she hadn't talked to her mother for a period of thirty years, until just before she passed away. Although her mother was often loving toward her, she had some behaviors and attitudes that Lucy could not understand at the time. She explained that every Saturday morning, her mother would go shopping at the local supermarket. She would leave very early and would only take Lucy with her if she was ready; if she wasn't, her mother wouldn't wait for her. Lucy had a hard time waking up, and by the time she was up and dressed, her mother was often already gone. She could not understand why her mother stormed out of the house as if she were always in a rush.

Lucy and her family lived just outside a small town in Oklahoma, and it would generally take her mother about an hour to get back from the store. Lucy's father molested her during that time. Lucy could never understand or justify why her mother would not wait for her an extra ten minutes. Left at the mercy of her abusive father on most Saturday mornings, Lucy thought that her mother would not protect her, and she felt abandoned.

The hurt and bitterness that affect the way many abused women view their mothers is frequently related to their mothers' inability to protect them. The clinical literature on incest has looked at the mother's culpability and the extent to which she was responsible for the occurrence of the abuse. It has been observed by many therapists that mothers often respond to their daughters' confessions of incest with disbelief or rejection. Sometimes the conclusion drawn is that the mother sacrificed her daughter or competed with her for the man's affection. Despite the current research that refutes such attitudes and beliefs, they remain a surprisingly powerful influence on some therapists and practitioners. Promoting such theories only enhances the alienation between daughters and mothers. When therapists influence their clients toward an explanation such as those mentioned above, it's not unusual for anger to greatly increase. Yet no competent studies have determined that mothers usually know of the abuse before disclosure on the part of their daughters, family members, or others. Also, it has been demonstrated that denial is a normal response to a profound crisis.

When I first met Lucy, she believed that her mother used her as a substitute so she would not be obliged to have sex with her husband. She had adopted this belief (that her mother had sacrificed her) many years after the abuse, during her first therapy session. Inclined to accept her therapist's theories and suggestions, she finally had an answer to the question that had plagued her for so long: Why wouldn't her mother wait for her? She had decided that her mother knew she was being molested and purposely did not wait for her so that she would be sexually abused. This is the belief that prompted Lucy's brutal breakup with her mother.

As I was asking Lucy questions, my first focus was to discern the beliefs she had at twelve years old versus the one she adopted later in life in order to complete the meaning of her experience. Interestingly, she was almost forgiving of her father, whom she described as a miserable human soul who suffered a terrible upbringing and felt neglected by his wife. Again, in Lucy's mind, her mother was mostly responsible for the weakness of her father. Continuing, I encouraged Lucy to describe to me the circumstances of her parents' lives and their most significant limitations.

Lucy explained that her parents married because they got pregnant with her. She felt it was not what either of them wanted. Her father became an accountant, and her mother worked as his secretary. Almost from the beginning, they did not get along. Both would get drunk at home on Friday nights after work. They would ultimately wind up fighting and were quite violent with each other. While Lucy was in bed, she could hear them yelling at each other and the sound of objects breaking. Lucy remembered the shocking language they used and the horrible things they would throw in each other's face—the brutal truth of how they felt and the disgust they had for each other. Lucy used to listen in the dark and wait until they stopped before she fell asleep, often very late at night. Sometimes her mother had bruises on her face, arms or legs the next day.

After gathering this information, I proposed that Lucy reiterate the story about the Saturday mornings, but this time without any assumptions, such as her mother intentionally setting her up for abuse, or even her father's reasons for molesting her. Lucy was uncomfortable with the process at first, and we had to pay close attention to her words when describing the story. She was, for the first time, going to explore using language without distortions, just stating the facts. Her emotional state went from anger to resistance, and later, from resistance to humility. She repeated the simplified, fact-based story a couple of times until she could be perfectly neutral with her words and emotionally unaffected. Then she wrote down the new story on paper. She replaced her assumptions with open-ended statements such as: "I don't know why my mother was leaving early and without me on most Saturday mornings" and "I don't know why my father abused me sexually."

This process helped Lucy access a state of internal congruency and prepare herself for an even more challenging exercise. I asked her if she would be willing to put herself in her mother's shoes and retrieve information about the situation from her position. Lucy bravely accepted.

From the point of view of her mother, Lucy could feel her struggle, namely waking up after a short night with a hangover and often with bruises. I asked Lucy if imagining a Saturday morning from her mother's perspective allowed her to access a constructive or positive intention for leaving early. What could her mother gain through this action? What was so important that it would prompt her to rush to the store?

Lucy realized that since her mother must have looked really bad after a hard night, she would want to arrive at the store right at opening time, before anyone she knew would be there. It was a small community, and quite a few of her husband's clients shopped there as well. Suddenly, Lucy broke into tears as she began to understand this important piece of the puzzle.

With this new awareness, other elements came to the surface to corroborate this possibility. She remembered a time when her mother's face was bruised and she did not go shopping at all on that particular Saturday morning. She did not even go to work the following week, waiting until her bruise was completely gone before resuming her normal routine. Lucy recalled how much her mother cared about what people in the town might think, and it became easy to imagine that she was hiding the truth about her relationship with her husband, which had been terrible since the beginning.

Lucy was starting to make an internal shift and, in a state of confusion, was not sure about anything anymore. I pointed out to her that I noticed something important when she was describing how her parents fought. Lucy said that they would pour out the most horrible words and say the meanest things to each other, led by their raw emotions and under the influence of alcohol. I asked her, "In all the times you heard them fight and lash out, did your mother ever mention anything about his behavior toward you?" Without a moment of hesitation, Lucy answered, "No." Then I asked again, "So, if I understand correctly, those two individuals were fighting to the core, tempers flaring under the influence of alcohol, and your mother—who knew he was abusing you—never threw that in his face? Never mentioned a thing?" Lucy simply answered with a question: "So was it possible that she did not know?"

Lucy was finally able to see and accept a new possibility: that her mother may have never willingly abandoned her to be molested. Lucy's belief system about her mother shifted that day. When I saw Lucy again three months after our session, she had lost twenty three pounds. She said that for the first time in her life, she felt at peace with her mother and even her father.

Lets us understand weight issues from an archaic point of view. Obesity is generally linked to a survival mechanism in relation to a conflict of abandonment.

Weight gain and water retention relates to the archaic conflict of the species when still living in the ocean. At this time of evolution, when accidently thrown out of water onto dry land, the living beings depended on the ebb and tide cycle, which would take them back to their element. The life of the species was threatened when being out of the water. The biological solution enabling their survival outside of their element (in this case the ocean) was for the kidney to retain water inside the organism. Figuratively if one feels out of one's element, like a "fish out of water", or being away from one's clan (i.e.: refugee or immigrant), the brain's solution is to retain water in the body until existence becomes possible again. Struggles for existence, having lost everything, and feeling abandoned or isolated from others can therefore be a trigger for water retention and weight gain. Obesity can also be linked to a fear of starvation. In nature, in order to survive, it is essential to eat. Being abandoned activates the sense of danger that one could die of hunger. A person who feels abandoned can tend to throw herself at food when it's available, in order to increase the chance of survival. The perfect program of the brain will command the organism to metabolize food into lipids, thus creating a greater reserve of fat. Oftentimes obese individuals gain weight even when they eat small amounts of food. This has to do with how their body is processing the little they eat, in a way that will permit them to survive for as long as possible. Metaphorically, being fat also allows one to appear physically imposing in front of potential predators and to better intimidate them.

In Lucy's case, consider how at twelve she felt abandoned by her mother, who was not there to prevent her father from molesting her. Lucy started putting on weight then, responding to a subconscious need to be big and protect herself from the predator her father represented. Weight gain and obesity, representing protection from the aggressor, often occur with people who have been sexually abused.

## MARC'S STORY

Marc was forty-nine years old when he came to see me. He had been diagnosed with cancer of the palate. The doctor he had consulted explained that he would have to go through invasive mouth surgery, and the severity of this procedure was the catalyst for seeking another solution.

As I worked with Marc to find the triggering event, a fascinating situation came to light. When he first came to see me, he was extremely angry with his father. He was living on the same property, a farm, as his father. As this was a large piece of land, Marc had his own separate house.

Earlier that year, his father had given him a windmill that would be his to renovate into an apartment. Once refurbished, it would become a valuable piece of property that Marc could rent out to tenants. But after just a few days into the renovations, his father said, "Let's put everything on hold. I don't think I can give the windmill to you after all." His father never explained why; he simply reneged on the deal.

Marc thought that his father was being completely irrational, unfair, and disrespectful. Feeling bitterly betrayed, he admitted to me that he had been dwelling on the situation for a few months. And as we looked together at each aspect of his life, it became clear that the conflict with his father had been the only peak event that year. At the time when Marc's tumor was found, he and his father hadn't spoken to each other in three months.

On the surface of things, it looked like his father had done something terrible. However, I knew there was no way I could truly help Marc if I didn't work with him to dig deeper and access a different perception. In other words, if I believed his story as he presented it, then I would only have the ability to help him discover the meaningful solution that his cancer represented, but not one that would fully help him resolve his issue.

The next step was to examine why cancer of the palate, in particular, would be triggered.

Marc's tumor was affecting the soft palate. The biological purpose of a proliferation of cells in the mouth is to increase the secretions permitting food to be assimilated and to allow for rapid swallowing action when necessary. Also, it is significant to note that at the most basic biological level, the mouth itself allows us to catch the morsels of food that we ingest.

When Marc was initially given the windmill, this valuable piece of property was quite a catch—a "morsel" he caught when his father "tossed" it to him. When his father informed him that he was going to take it back, Marc was already savoring the acquisition of the windmill, so, metaphorically speaking, it was already "caught in his mouth."

Another way to understand the metaphor of "assimilating the morsel" would be to imagine the following situation: A woman calls her husband at work, saying, "Oh my God, honey, we won the lottery! Meet me at home right away!" With that brief phone call, the husband just caught the "morsel"—the possibility of a whole new life. He leaves work immediately and starts dreaming of everything he wants: the things he will buy, the trips they will take together, and the debts they'll pay off. He is in heaven. When he gets home, his wife informs him that she was mistaken. The lottery ticket was from last week's drawing. The much-desired "morsel" is abruptly taken away.

The delectable "morsel" that Marc had caught—the windmill—was also abruptly taken away.

Exploring the palate cancer metaphorically, we began to investigate the underlying biological meaning. Symbolically, a tumor improves the function of the mouth, rapidly increasing cell proliferation so that one can produce more saliva to assimilate the "morsel" quickly, whether that "morsel" is a desired object, job, promotion, investment, or something else.

As Marc looked at his own situation in this way, he allowed himself to acknowledge how much he had wanted the windmill. He let himself feel how excited he was when he received this valuable asset, how shocked he was by the abrupt loss of it, and how angry he was that his father hadn't talked with him or offered an explanation.

Investigating further, I found out that Marc had two sisters. When I asked Marc if his father had given property to his sisters as well, he responded by saying, "No, he hasn't. One of my sisters lives outside the country, and I don't think she cares about this stuff. She's done well for herself. And my other sister lives nearby, and there will be some money set aside for her." He went on to tell me that his father had previously given him the house he was living in, as well as another piece of land. So the windmill would have been in addition to the real estate he had already been gifted.

The next step was to support Marc in standing in his father's shoes; again, this is not an easy task when anger and resentment are dominant emotions. I asked Marc to describe what he could see by looking through his father's eyes. He told me that his father came from a different generation of men. To that generation, it was a matter of honor: a man wouldn't have to explain his choices to his son. As Marc began to feel empathy toward his father—about the way he was raised to think and his limitations pertaining to communication—he began to understand his father's circumstances with greater clarity than ever before. He was a man with three children. If he gave everything to his son, there would be nothing left for his daughters. Through this exercise, Marc started to understand his father's motivations and that he just wanted to be fair to all of his children.

With this new awareness, Marc "got it." He realized that the money his father had set aside for his sisters had started to dwindle during the first few days of windmill renovations. If his father didn't make a difficult decision, and if he allowed the windmill project to continue, there would be nothing left to give to his daughters. Marc was flabbergasted that he hadn't realized this before.

As he saw and understood the positive intentions behind his father's actions, Marc was able to forgive him. A new reality and a different perception quickly took shape from that point forward. Marc no longer wanted the "morsel" and was more interested in being fair to his family. He became excited about giving the "morsel" back and making peace with his father. As the conflict disappeared, the biological solution of symbolically assimilating the "morsel" quickly was no longer needed.

Marc's palate cancer resolved within a few weeks after our session.

## PREPARING FOR A TRANSFORMATIVE SHIFT

Most clients I work with find it challenging to go directly to a place of empathy and forgiveness when it comes to painful relationships or incidents with parents, spouses, exes, and others. It's extremely difficult for them to step into others' shoes and be curious about their point of view when old hurts, resentment, and anger still operate beneath the surface. First, they need to express themselves fully, without suppressing their feelings. Then it is time to shift into neutral and simply look at the facts without making assumptions. Once those two essential steps happen, they are ready to go into reverse and explore the world of other possibilities.

When approached with willingness and a strong desire to heal, taking these steps sets the stage internally—in heart and mind—to be able to fully forgive. And that is when the "miracles" begin to materialize, because forgiveness of others and ourselves ignites one of the most healing and transformative shifts in consciousness imaginable.

Now it is your time, your opportunity, to make such a shift.

The following process will help you modify your perception of your own conflict, particularly if it involves a struggle with another person. Remember: most of our conflicts are based on a lack of awareness or a limited view of the reality that we, and others, have experienced. We create perceptions based on what our model of the world is and what the filters of our subconscious programs allow us to see. By exploring the reality of the other, you will be able to gather new and important information. This will widen your field of understanding and insight, re-creating an inner alignment and congruency that will allow you to let go of the struggle you are contending with.

Take action, and the following pages will reward you with new perceptions and new beliefs. Remind yourself that your main objective is to restore your health and that nothing else is nearly as important right now. It is time to challenge yourself and push beyond internal limits in order to change your current situation. It may be difficult to explore the perspective of someone you're still angry with. I also understand how hard it is to risk letting go of familiar beliefs, even if they're no longer serving you. However, the risk will prove itself to be worth taking.

The Notebook Shift process in the pages ahead will also provide you with added momentum in your movement toward resolution and healing.

## THE NOTEBOOK SHIFT PROCESS: CHANGING YOUR PERCEPTION OF A CONFLICT

In the previous chapter, you retrieved and retraced the event that is directly related to the triggering of your condition. You expressed how you felt without censoring yourself. You found the words to describe your deepest emotions. You described the personal values you felt were violated, and you said exactly what you believed this event meant. By doing so, you powerfully paved the way for the next set of steps.

The following process will allow you to explore possibilities regarding the meaning of this event—and potentially the true meaning that perhaps you never knew, until now.

**Step 1: Allow full self-expression**

Once again, write the story of the triggering event. It is possible at this stage that you may remember something pertinent that eluded you previously. Most important, describe what you saw, heard, and felt during the moment of the event that bothered you the most or had the greatest impact on you. You may include the emotions you described in the previous chapter. Go through each scene of the event precisely, as if you were looking at a movie. Write the story step by step, the way you perceived it as it was occurring.

**Step 2: Establish neutral statements**

Review your notes and locate each assumption. Write about the same event again, only this time simply stating facts. Let yourself be neutral. Release all judgments and assumptions about the other characters involved. Remember: we assume something when we accept it as true or certain without proof.

Replace each assumption with a new phrase that starts with "I don't know why" or "I don't know if." (See Lucy's and Marc's examples that follow.)

**Step 3: Explore a different reality (circumstances, limitations, positive intentions)**

Step into the shoes of the other characters in the story. This is your chance to explore a reality you may not have considered before. This process could be challenging, because your previous beliefs may have supported your reasoning for a long time. However, this reasoning no longer serves you; it has created stress and constraint. It is worth jumping into the realm of a new understanding.

Allow yourself to explore all characters in the story, this time focusing on their circumstances, limitations, and positive intentions. From the point of view of the other person (or people), connect with what they see and hear and how they feel during the event. Be honest when you enter into their character and see the world from their eyes. Call forth your courage as you delve into new realities, and allow yourself to examine the truth that others may have perceived.

**Step 4: Invite new perceptions; find a new meaning**

Based on your expanded awareness, allow for a new perception about the story to emerge. Refer back to the neutral statements you wrote in Step 2. For every time you wrote "I don't know why," ask yourself the following question: "What could this mean?" Look for possibilities that are positive, realistic, and based on your new observations and the information you gathered while standing in the shoes of the other(s). Make sure to take into consideration the model of the world of the other(s), upbringing, values and needs. Allow yourself to filter the experience in a new way and explore different meanings regarding the actions of others.

After each sentence starting with "I don't know why," now answer with "This could mean ..."

Freely express new possibilities, and write the new meanings you could assign to each sentence.

Lastly, what is the new meaning you could assign to the overall experience?

*Example—Lucy's case*

**Step 1: Allow full self-expression**

When I was twelve years old, my mother did not wait for me to go with her to the grocery store, because she wanted me to stay with my father, knowing he was going to abuse me sexually. I am so angry at my mother who did not wait for me. She did this on purpose. She wanted to use me so she would not have to have sex with him.

**Step 2: Establish neutral statements**

- I don't know why my mother did not wait for me when I wasn't ready to go to the grocery store.

- I don't know why my mother would take me with her only when I was ready on time.

- I don't know why she left me with my father. I don't know if she knew that my father was abusing me sexually while she was at the store.

**Step 3: Explore a different reality (circumstances, limitations, positive intentions)**

*Circumstances:* My mother got drunk with my father every Friday night. My father would hit her most Friday nights when they were arguing. My mother was bruised sometimes on Saturday mornings, and she looked like she was hung over. My mother knew many people in town because my father was the accountant for most of the small businesses, and she was his secretary.

*Limitations:* My mother could not stop the habit of drinking with my father most Friday nights after work. She did not have a good relationship with my father and felt ashamed about it. My mother did not know how to improve her relationship with my father. My mother often talked about leaving him but said she could not because of her child. She would lose her job and did not know where else she could work. My mother did not have friends or family support at the time. She was raised by parents who were violent with her, and memories of the abuse were part of her model of the world. My mother was isolated and did not talk about her problems to others.

*Positive intentions:* My mother wanted to take care of the family and go shopping even though she had a hangover and was sometimes bruised. My mother always took me with her if I was ready on time. My mother wanted herself and her husband to keep a good reputation in the town.

## Step 4: Invite new perceptions; find a new meaning

When I wasn't ready, my mother did not wait for me to go with her to the grocery store. She left me home alone with my father.

- This could mean that she wanted to be at the grocery store right at opening time, when no one had arrived yet. She was preventing being seen in bad shape by the clients she knew.

- This could mean that she welcomed my presence as long as I was not going to make her arrive late at the store, because she was afraid of losing her reputation if people knew she was in an abusive relationship.

- This could mean that she thought it was safe to leave me alone with my father for a couple of hours on Saturday mornings, and she had no clue that I was going to be sexually abused.

### *Example—Marc's case*
## Step 1: Allow full self-expression

My father gave me a windmill on his property and then betrayed me by taking it back without an explanation. My father is irrational, unfair, and disrespectful toward me. He never wanted to offer an explanation about his brutal change of mind.

## Step 2: Establish neutral statements

- I don't know why my father stopped the renovations of the windmill.

- I don't know why my father took back the windmill he gave me.

- I don't know why my father did not give me an explanation.

- I don't know why my father has not talked to me about it since then.

**Step 3: Explore a different reality (circumstances, limitations, positive intentions)**

*Circumstances:* My father owns a farm and has three children. He gave me the house I live in and also a piece of land. After he gave me the windmill, my father only had his savings left. The money he had set aside was being used to renovate the windmill he gave me.

*Limitations:* My father is old-fashioned and also does not communicate much. He was raised to never question the decisions of his own father. My father never expressed his feelings and would keep them inside. He had already given me most of what he owned besides his own house. The money my father had set aside was a relatively small amount, which started to be used up with the renovation of the windmill.

*Positive intentions:* My father wanted to keep some money set aside and not spend it all on the renovation of the windmill. My father wanted to continue owning the windmill for the time being.

**Step 4: Invite new perceptions; find a new meaning**

My father stopped paying for the renovation of the windmill, took it back from me, and did not want to tell me why he did that.

- This could mean that my father was afraid the renovation of the windmill was using up all the money he had left.

- This could mean my father wanted to keep enough assets so my two sisters could have an inheritance as well.

- This could mean he thought he was only generous with me and not fair with his daughters.

- This could mean he did not want to discuss it because he felt awkward, and maybe he would have liked for me to realize earlier the situation he was in.

After exploring new possibilities, take a moment to reflect on the event you worked on. As a result of this vantage point, what did you discover? Do you feel more neutral or more forgiving toward the other? Tune in to your body and mind, and notice any subtle or overt changes.

Know that you have taken an important step toward alleviating the stress that comes from unresolved conflicts from the past.

# 10

# Healing the Younger Self

What is the true origin of our emotions? We need to become aware of our automatic human processes, if we are to exert more control over them and if we are to attain mastery of the workings of our own mind. Our experiences, whether positive or negative, become part of our subconscious memory. Some of these experiences were once consciously perceived but may have been strongly suppressed or wholly forgotten by means of repression. Other experiences may have been barely perceptible enough to make an impression on the conscious mind in the first place.

We tend to believe that our conscious mind is in charge of our behaviors and choices. However, most of our limiting reactions are, in fact, governed by a whole set of imprints belonging to the past. When a traumatic experience, such as being abused in childhood, has not been processed and resolved, unconscious choices may lead an individual to re-create situations of abuse that will align with his or her internal maps.

As we have examined throughout the book, a specific coding and a set of beliefs are attached to each trauma. During a stressful or intense experience, the brain records everything you see, hear, feel, smell, and taste. Often we will reexperience a particular emotional state and respond based on the recurrence of such subconscious markers. For instance, a particular tone of voice may revive the memory of devaluation felt as a child while being reprimanded by a parent. After the occurrence of the original childhood experiences, we often hold onto the beliefs we adopted at the time of the unpleasant or disturbing event. As we go through life, we subconsciously reinforce such beliefs by filtering the world in ways that support them. Usually without conscious knowledge of doing so, we continue to reference limiting emotions and thoughts that may create unproductive or destructive patterns of behavior.

For the sake of health, healing, and happiness, it is important to re-code the past so that we can stop repeatedly accessing the negative emotional states that often produce stress and sometimes lead to illness.

The wounded younger self is awakened every time we are confronted by situations in the present time that have similar characteristics to painful past events. Because of past struggles, we most often develop an affinity for engaging specific kinds of situations. Such situations will inevitably violate important values and do so in ways that re-create the painful emotions that are familiar to our brain.

If you felt disrespected as a child, being respected as an adult might be one of your highest values, yet it may also be one of the most elusive. Your brain will filter the world around you so that it appears that your family, friends, or colleagues do not respect you. Then you will attract into your life the types of events that will confirm and give support to your internal map. In other words, your filtering mechanism will be perfectly designed to sort out information from events, only to demonstrate how others don't treat you well. Your subconscious expectation to "not be respected" becomes a magnet for circumstances that validate your model of the world and its distortions. But you are far from alone. Subconsciously, the majority of us learn to meet certain essential needs in a limited or wounded way. Every time we re-create our particular model, good or bad, we feel safe. It feels oddly like home to our subconscious.

Although it may seem irrational, a profound sense of security is subconsciously attained every time our brain can recognize a pattern of emotions. Have you noticed how often women who were beaten by their fathers as children will engage as adults in relationships with men who are violent toward them? Consciously, such a woman desires a loving and caring relationship, while her subconscious programming leads her to fall back into recognizable patterns and feelings. When the brain is confronted with an imprinted "known experience," whether positive or negative, a subconscious sense of safety is established. The subconscious memory of painful events, which one has lived through and "overcome," is stored as a winning experience for the autonomic brain. In other words, when we stay alive through any event, the brain—which does not judge experiences as either "good or bad"—will store the memory of that event as a useful imprint of survival.

Constantly present within our being, the younger self holds the memories that keep us on the same life "tracks." The younger self filters the world around us in a way that reconnects us with old recorded data when needed—or when we *believe* we need it. We are subjected to the logic of our subconscious, whose primary directive is to maintain the survival of the species. The brain does not make decisions based only on conscious desires. We can try hard to modify what attracts us, but the younger wounded self keeps us on a specific path that perpetuates the recurrence of familiar stories and conflicts. We move into the future with an affinity for attracting particular circumstances until we finally start reinterpreting the past through new lenses.

Fortunately, lives can change, and we hold the power to modify old imprints. We can learn how to become the mentor and protector of our inner child and provide it with the resources to cope during times of distress.

Remember that the brain does not differentiate past, present, or future. This characteristic of the subconscious allows us to modify the meaning of past stories, as well as create new programs to enhance our orientation toward the future.

Think about someone who may go through the same experience as you but who adapts to the situation with much less stress. Why is this? It is because he or she uses different criteria to evaluate the situation. Imagine, for instance, that someone pushes past you in the checkout line at a grocery store. When you assess the situation, you may feel rage because the criterion you use is "respect." At the same time, another customer who is also waiting in line may see the humor in the situation and feel amused by someone so unaware of his or her surroundings that he or she cuts in front of two people.

Emotions are a matter of perception, and our perception depends on the type of imprints we carry. Of course, our mood on a bad day will greatly provoke our limiting patterns of thinking to emerge. Any situation can be perceived in a myriad of ways. But, for as long as we blame the environment for our experience, we are deprived of power. When we draw upon our inner strength to change views and reinterpret what happened with a different awareness, we have the opportunity to release our emotional distress.

No matter what type of illness or imbalance you may be dealing with, it is essential to trace any subconscious distress related to it back to its origin and reframe the painful memories. There is no reason to carry around the hurt your younger self experienced, when it is possible to eliminate the pain and equip your mind with an empowering new awareness about past events.

Sometimes it is difficult for a person who has been abused, molested, or raped to access a state of understanding—let alone forgiveness—toward his or her aggressor. If this describes your experience, it is important to remember that others who have hurt you did not have access to another biological code from the one controlling their behavior. Their behavior was an expression of their subconscious blueprint and matched their level of consciousness.

## Evolutionary Recall—Expanding Your Perception

*"Consciousness sleeps in the stone, dreams in the plant, awakes in the animal and slowly becomes aware of itself in man."*

—Pythagoras

According to the French nuclear physicist Jean-Émile Charon (1920–1998), each electron in our body is an enclosed space, much like a micro-universe that contains a memory of all successively lived experiences since the beginning of time. We carry the memories of all stages of the evolution of the planet within us. We hold the memories of four specific "learnings" within our molecular database. Those four stages of our planetary evolution are mineral, vegetal, animal, and human.

During the mineral stage, stones were shaped by running water, earthquakes, and a multitude of geochemical processes, after which an estimated 1,500 different mineral species appeared. During this stage, *adaptation* was rampant and became inclusive in our biological make-up. During the vegetal stage, *flexibility* was acquired as plants, trees, and weeds adapted with movement; notice that rather than being resistant, the tree will always bend in the direction of the wind. During the animal stage came the time when marking and defending the *territory, sexual behaviors*, and protection of the offspring were assimilated. However, at this stage consciousness had yet to emerge. We can still observe this today in the way that wild animals mate and kill when needed, without remorse or regret.

In the fourth evolutionary stage—the human stage—the learned sequences just described remained while we acquired *consciousness*. Although we have evolved from the animal stage and have acquired values, not all human beings are at the same level of consciousness.

Sometimes we will encounter people who exhibit the behavior of the animal stage and have not yet mastered higher human values. Murderers, thieves, child molesters, rapists, and so on fall into this group. Knowing how to position ourselves with, or protect ourselves from, such individuals, especially if they are family members, is challenging. Every person's values are not of equal weight or understanding. This difference can be metaphorically illustrated by the way we go through the learning process at school. Some people make their way into college, while others are still in first grade. Important values, such as honesty, empathy, forgiveness, justice, honor, integrity, and respect, may not be available to a first grader, but they are available to a college student. We need to show patience with those who are still learning, because, in a sense, we have all been there.

This higher level of understanding about others, and the origin of their behaviors, will help you during your journey of reflection, resolution, and emotional healing.

## David's Story—Understanding the Roots of a Bio-Response

In 2007, a man named David, with advanced lymphoma, came to see me. During the course of our first session together, he shared the following story.

One memorable evening, surrounded by friends and family who had gathered at a posh restaurant to celebrate his thirty-second birthday, David's girl friend, Donna, informed David that she was leaving him. Earlier that evening, they had argued because he refused to wear a designer leather jacket she had just bought for him to wear at the party. It was a jacket that David felt was too tight on him, especially around his waist. They fought during the entire ride to the restaurant, and two hours into the party, before the cake was brought out, Donna announced in front of all the guests her decision to split up. She went on to explain that she could not stand her life with David for another day.

David was utterly shocked at the news, which was completely unexpected from his perspective. He also could not understand why Donna chose to end their relationship in public, and especially on his birthday! He felt attacked, humiliated, and devalued. Overwhelmed, caught off guard, isolated, and deprived of a solution, he did not know how to respond. He felt that something deeply rooted within him had been unmoored in that moment, and his emotional pain was unbearable. He was adrift in a sea of pain, and the party was over before the birthday cake arrived.

David never blew out his candles that night. For him, there was no thirty-second birthday.

Six months after this event, which led to a permanent separation from Donna, David was diagnosed with lymphoma.

When I first met David, he told me that it didn't matter whether he recovered or not. His life had been painful, and it felt to him like he was continuously in a state of conflict with other people. It was clear that our first priority together was to modify his belief that his life would continue to be hard.

As he began to understand some of the gestational imprints at the root of his turmoil, David realized that his subconscious programs were controlling his life. He started to put the pieces of the emotional puzzle together and understand how these programs predisposed him to certain types of difficulties.

During the time David was in the womb, his father, Edward, felt tremendous guilt for having left behind a young child from his first wife. And it was in this state of angst and shame that he married David's mother.

Edward often stated that he felt it wasn't fair for David to have an easy and happy childhood, considering how a struggling single mother raised his half brother. David felt that his father was very critical and harsh toward him and would systematically ruin his moments of joy. According to David's perception, his father was attempting to restore a form of fairness to his first son by preventing David from having a happy childhood.

During David's gestation, Edward was still fighting with his first wife about their past. Edward felt attacked by her because she was invading his privacy, sending cruel letters to his new wife and acting in aggressive ways. She was threatening and demanding financial support for their child, but at that time Edward was barely making enough to survive.

Within the toxic dynamic being played out, one of the elements that had the greatest impact on David was that he was conceived in a climate of attack. The ex-wife represented a threat to the family. She would sometimes show up in a rage and verbally attack David's parents, particularly his mom. Because of his parents' stressful situation during gestation, David "downloaded" an emotional distress related specifically to attack and powerlessness. Consequently, he was predisposed to experiencing a life of struggles with others in relation to attack and defense.

After addressing the triggering event related to the onset of his disease (being attacked and feeling powerless on his birthday) and working on gestational programs, David and I started to explore the past. We examined his childhood, looking for the possible programming experience that was directly linked to the stressful triggering event a few months before his cancer was diagnosed. We momentarily called forth the emotional states of feeling attacked, humiliated, and devalued, which David experienced at the time his girlfriend announced she would leave him. This would serve as David's anchor as he traveled back in time to recall potential events that felt similar to that traumatic event on his birthday.

Through this transderivational search, interestingly enough, a memory of his fifth birthday came to David's consciousness. It was an imprint that held a conflict of the same nature as the distress from his recent birthday; his felt experience was the same during both events. The past and recent experiences were linked by the same emotional state. David was able to reconnect with the original imprint, the source of the problem, which he had not revisited consciously in a very long time. Through this exploratory process, it is often possible for an individual to reconnect with several memories of the same nature. In David's case, this single event surfaced. His parents and family had gathered for his fifth birthday party. Being a shy child, David refused to blow his birthday candles out in front of the guests. His father got angry, slapped him, blew out the candles himself, and then pushed David's face in the cake. David had been humiliated in front of his family.

As you would imagine, David was shocked by his father's cruel reaction. He felt attacked, powerless, humiliated, and devalued in front of others. David imprinted a memory that was related to a fear of attack. He had been physically, emotionally, and psychologically violated by his father, and he had begun to perceive him as an enemy. He made the subconscious decision to protect himself at all costs.

At the age of five, David could not have accessed a perception that would allow him to understand the real cause or meaning of his father's outrageous reaction. And he didn't have the resources to alleviate his stress. All he knew was that he did not feel safe and no longer trusted his father.

After this event, the relationship with his father deteriorated. Now on high alert and protecting himself from attack, David began to develop a new behavior: defending himself any time someone imposed an idea on him or pushed him to do something he did not want to do. As a solution to ensure his own safety, his behavior became more and more aggressive toward others. As an adult, he instantly became angry when someone didn't agree with him, even on inconsequential subjects. He was also very sensitive to what people thought of him at work or at home. He kept looking for acceptance and recognition from others, but he didn't know how to get along with anyone. This orientation toward conflict, of course, carried right into his relationship. He and his girlfriend had a tumultuous relationship from the start.

When he recalled the event from his fifth birthday, David was very emotional and still deeply upset by the memory of his father slapping him and pushing his face in the cake. Interestingly, David's vision of the event was as vivid and palpable as if he were still five years old. His resentment toward his father was intense, and he still felt violated, devalued, humiliated, and overwhelmed by rage.

I asked David to look at the scene from his fifth birthday on an imaginary screen. This would give him some emotional distance, enabling him to review it like a spectator versus being part of the experience. From that point of reference, he could observe the event more objectively and from the vantage point of his adult self.

David's first challenge was to understand his father's circumstances and limitations, so that he could start accessing a state of empathy toward him. David accepted the challenge of looking at his father from a neutral point of view, in order to access more accurate information. For the first time in his life, he was open to discovering the positive intentions hidden behind his father's behavior at that time.

David started by recounting that his father, Edward, had grown up very poor. Edward's father had died before he was born, and his mother and grandmother raised him. From the age of fourteen, Edward provided for both of them. As we continued to look at his father's formative years, David realized that Edward had no imprint of a father-son relationship. While growing up, Edward never experienced the influence of a man as an educator, mentor, or protector.

I asked David if he thought that his father ever had a birthday cake. David started to feel quite emotional as his awareness began to grow. He thought about the possibility that his father may never have celebrated a birthday of his own, let alone had a birthday cake. He could see why Edward would feel disappointed and then irritated by what must have appeared as a stubborn attitude during the birthday party. From Edward's point of view, David was acting like a spoiled child.

This process helped David understand that his father never really had the chance to just be a child; therefore, he could not relate to his son's behavior. Edward had no reference points for understanding David's reaction as that of a kid who felt shy and uncomfortable being the center of attention.

As I worked with David, he was shifting his perception, and his psyche began to modify the meaning of that early event. At this stage of the intervention (based on NLP), I asked David to define what resources were most needed at the time of the traumatic event when he was five. What would have helped him process this experience in a less stressful way? David expressed that his younger self needed new resources such as security, acceptance, resilience, and understanding. He said he also needed to access a state of empathy and awareness, so that he could understand his father's limiting behavior. His father's behavior—his poor judgment and lack of understanding of his son—was related to his own wounds.

David was able to retrieve feelings of security, acceptance, resilience, and understanding that he had felt at other times in his life. Consequently, he had the power to offer those emotional states as resources to the younger David during the moment of stress. I asked David to step inside the "movie" of this childhood experience and imagine himself standing next to his five-year-old self, symbolically playing the role of a mentor. David approached this vulnerable boy with care and saw himself offer the new resources to him. Then he whispered to him, telling his younger self about his father's upbringing.

Still inside the movie within his mind, David also met with his father, gifting him with the resources of communication, patience, comprehension, and empathy toward the young David's behavior. By stepping into this scene from the past, which he now had the power to heal, David was mentoring his father as well as himself.

As a result of connecting with his father and his younger self, a new emotional state started to emerge in relation to this event. The young David was provided with enough resources to experience his circumstances in a very different way. After realizing the lessons he had learned and the wisdom he had gained from his childhood trauma, David was more at peace. His personal history had changed.

Once David was done mentoring his younger self and his father, he could let them go back into the past and allow himself to return to present time. I then asked David to visualize these new resources on an imaginary time line, making his new beliefs, knowledge, and resources available to all the moments of his life where they would have been useful.

We made several connections between his old trauma and the recent situation with his wife. David realized that Donna had subconsciously played a role in reactivating an old emotional stress. Somehow, Donna's programs suitably matched David's program. Her story interacted with David's story in a way that met the expectations of his subconscious mind. She played a role in retriggering the memories of his fifth birthday —the feeling of being attacked and devalued in front of others.

Although Donna had her own responsibility in relation to this current event, David had come too far in our work together to tolerate any barriers to his transformation. He allowed himself to explore her personal limitations and circumstances with an open heart. He felt a depth of empathy for her that he hadn't been able to access before going through this process. It was emotionally freeing for David to observe the interactions between his wife's and his own psyche and the merging of programs that led both of them to such an odd and destructive breakup. He was empowered by his new perception—he could see the situation with his girlfriend as a reflection of their personal programs instead of being emotionally blinded by the painful content of their story.

David felt more at peace with the story of his thirty-second birthday. After a brief pause, I asked him to think about his fifth birthday again and tell me how he felt about it. He said that he no longer felt rage or anger. His memory had shifted, and he felt a sense of compassion for his father. He now thought of this past event as the story of a father and son who had to learn about each other. He felt as though he had forgiven his dad, and he noticed a warm sensation in his stomach. A few tears ran down his cheeks and a smile gently appeared on his face.

The wounding that was experienced by his five-year-old self had played a major role in the programming phase of David's illness. Because his father attacked him, David perceived him as an enemy before whom he felt powerless. As a consequence of his father's violent reactions, David instinctively developed a behavior of defending himself against the environment. David's felt experience during the shocking moment at five years old created an imprint that would later be awakened during the traumatic event with his girlfriend. At thirty-two years old, in order to adapt to a shock of the same nature he'd experienced in childhood, David subconsciously activated his lymph system, which represents the defense system in the body.

During the active phase of a conflict related to feeling devalued and powerless, the biological solution involves a microscopic necrosis of the lymph nodes to allow more lymphocytes and monocytes to pass through.

During the resolution phase of such conflict, cellular mitosis (duplication) will repair the necrosis, thus resulting in tumor growth. For as long as the conflict is not fully resolved, an individual may oscillate between active and healing phases of the conflict.

I want to clarify that David's lymphoma was not triggered when he was five; only a memory and its imprint remained present and unresolved in the depths of his subconscious mind. Years after the original impact, a stressful event on his birthday—the perceived attack and devaluation by his girlfriend—awakened the old imprint and triggered a biological response.

During a moment of unmanageable stress, the autonomic brain receives the message that one or more of our vital needs are not being satisfied. Subsequently, the subconscious takes over in order to express a satisfactory program of its own. The only programs available to the subconscious are archaic. Of course, the logic of the subconscious is not to our liking when illness becomes the response. The only way to make peace with the phenomenon of a *bio-response* is to understand that it holds an important message, like a spiritual calling for transformation and ultimately personal growth. As Carl Jung said, "Illness contains the gold you will find nowhere else."

After working on a few other events related to his father, David was a different man. His level of consciousness had increased and the wounds from the past were well on their way to healing. He experienced a sense of freedom he hadn't known was possible and reported feeling like a more powerful version of himself had emerged.

After David found a way out of his emotional struggles, and after only three months of medical treatments, his cancer vanished. His doctors were surprised at how quickly he improved.

## HEALING THE YOUNGER SELF—A SELF-HELP PROCESS

The following nine-step technique, which is based on NLP, will empower you to tend to your own healing from the deepest place in your mind and heart. It will provide you with the structure to revisit past events and change your perception at the time of conflict. Moreover, it will help you to recall the emotional struggle you experienced right before your illness and use it as an anchor to reconnect with a related memory.

You can also use this process to directly address and resolve any stressful event that still feels unresolved within you.

**Note:** Regarding certain conditions, such as fibromyalgia, obesity, MS, paralysis, and other chronic ailments, it may be more challenging to locate the time of the triggering event, since early symptoms are often unnoticeable. In this case, I suggest that you work directly on stressful memories that you feel relate to the nature of your condition. In other words, you don't need to use the triggering event as a thread to go into the past and retrieve a memory. Instead, you can directly address a memory that you feel is related to your illness. The instructions below will guide you in either case. Before starting the following process, I suggest that you review Chapter 4, page 67 and refresh your memory regarding the differences between triggering and programming events.

**Step 1: Connect to the Emotional Trigger**

Call forth the stressful event that you associate with the trigger of your condition, so that you can use it as an anchor to go back to past events of the same nature. Although your perception has changed, allow yourself to reaccess the unpleasant feelings related to this experience. Let yourself recall the moment of distress. Allow the emotions to emerge for a brief moment, and let yourself connect with your primal brain.

Write down everything that comes to your awareness.

- What did you go through emotionally during the triggering event?

- What was the moment that bothered you the most?

- What did that moment mean to you?

- What did you feel in that moment?

- What did you think or what did you say to yourself when it was happening?

If you are unclear about your triggering event, think about your health disorder and use it as an anchor to connect with the emotions you feel are associated with that disorder. Apply the bio-syntax process you previously learned on page 122. Then continue to step 2.

## Step 2: Awaken Your History

Ask your subconscious mind to cooperate with you and guide you back in time to a moment of your life directly related to your present emotions. If you so desire, you can close your eyes and repeat to yourself the emotions you felt during your triggering event and/or the emotions you are experiencing right now about your condition.

Next, allow your subconscious to take you back along your time line to moments where you recall having the same kind of emotions.

Keep going back in time until you recall the earliest experience in your life that made you feel that way. To facilitate this process, ask yourself the following questions:

- What is the memory behind those feelings?

- What do those feelings remind me of?

- When did I feel this way in the past?

- When did I feel this way for the first time in my life?

As you travel back through time, you may recall a few events of the same nature, during which you experienced the same negative state. Make note of your age at each related sequence you recall.

After you connect with the earliest memory, take a moment for yourself. As emotions resurface, be gentle with yourself and take your time before continuing to step 3.

## Step 3: Become a Neutral Observer

You may now decide to analyze the earliest event you have found that relates to the feelings you've identified. From a neutral perspective, begin to observe the scene on an imaginary screen, as if you were watching a movie of your younger self.

Take note of your perceptions at that time, as well as your beliefs and emotional responses.

- What did you believe was happening?

- What behavior(s) did you adopt at the time of stress in order to cope?

- What conclusions did you come to, based on this experience? Did you come to conclusions about yourself, others, or life?

- What decision did you make, based on these conclusions?

Continue to look at that early memory from a neutral state, through the eyes of your adult self. See the other characters, if any, in the scene. Applying the process you learned in the Notebook Shift, and referring back to that section if necessary, observe the other character(s) from the point of view of a neutral witness.

- Define their circumstances, background, limitations and obstacles.

- Identify any positive intentions they may have had, whether conscious or subconscious.

- Observe how they were trying to attain their vital needs without having the resources to act differently.

- Observe how they may have been a prisoner of certain subconscious programs. Maybe they were repeating a pattern of behavior they had learned from their own parents, or maybe they were not exposed to enough knowledge to make better choices.

Remember: although their behaviors may seem unacceptable from the point of view of your younger self, look for elements or clues you could not have been aware of, because of the limitation of your age and lack of information, when the problem occurred.

### Step 4: Contact Your Inner Wisdom

Quiet your mind now and listen to your inner wisdom. Allow it to reveal the following information about that earliest event:

- What *inner resources* did you (and others) need at the time of the event? For example, identify the emotional states that would have been useful, such as communication, understanding, empathy, love, compassion, patience, discernment, courage, awareness, calmness, confidence, centeredness, and so on.

- What knowledge did each character in the story need so that he or she could act differently? What resources would you like to offer so that he or she can benefit from a new awareness through you?

In this step, remember to allow your deepest inner wisdom—the still, small voice within—to provide you with the answers to these questions.

### Step 5: Mentor Your Younger Self

You may already realize that most of the resources that you and the characters in your story needed are available to you today. You have probably mastered some of these traits, qualities, and states of being.

Now you have the opportunity to draw on these resources and call forth your strengths to mentor your younger self. You can also mentor other characters involved.

- First, jump onto the imaginary screen, which is playing your moment of struggle.

- See yourself as standing next to your younger self, and begin to whisper your new understanding and insights to this precious part of you.

- Provide the younger you with the resources you feel are most needed, symbolically transferring them to your younger self.

- Do the same with the other characters in the story.

Notice how it feels to offer your clarity, perspective, and assurance to your younger self and others. As you help your younger self and other characters in your past, you are influencing and healing your present.

## Step 6: Access a New Emotional State

Allow for the positive resources to balance the negative emotional state you were experiencing in the past. And now, from this balanced state, write down your answers to the following questions:

- How would it have felt to own these resources at that earlier time? Would you have had a different behavior? Made a different decision?

- How does having access to these resources make your past memory feel different in the present?

- How is the new awareness of your story changing your perception?

Now, thank your younger self and all the characters in the scene for allowing you to do this intervention. You may feel that you no longer need to hold on to this negative imprint and may choose to let go of the distress. You may have access to feelings such as clarity and safety. You may also feel that a sense of freedom is available to you after these new realizations. Welcome the new feelings within yourself.

## Step 7: Transform Your Time Line

Step out of the imaginary screen and create a picture of your time line in your mind.

As you travel back to the present, ask your subconscious mind to review your history and to apply the new resources and knowledge to each moment of your life when it would have been useful.

Stop briefly at each past experience and bear witness to your history being modified in a positive way.

**Step 8: Revisit the Past**

Take a moment to relax before revisiting your past memory.

Now, trusting yourself and the process you have guided yourself through, look to see how your once-negative feelings have changed.

**Step 9: Step into the Future**

Imagine the future and how your new perception would serve you if an event of the same nature were to occur. How would it allow you to filter the world differently? Do you feel better equipped to handle the situation? More powerful? More resilient? More confident?

Write down the specific qualities, feelings, behaviors, and states of being that you now know you can access at any time, in any given situation.

# 11

# The Secondary Gain of Illness

Depending on the needs and values we want to satisfy, we develop many different facets or "parts" of ourselves that serve to accomplish specific outcomes. These facets take shape outside our conscious awareness, and they serve a useful function in helping us survive. The anthropologist Gregory Bateson (1904–1980) referred to these processes as the "ecologies of the mind." Each of our parts has a purpose and assists in attaining certain needs and fulfilling certain values, according to our model of the world. For example, a child may scream in order to be heard by a parent who would otherwise not pay attention to his or her demands. Initially, the screaming behavior may have been useful in gaining the attention the child needed. Years later, this aspect of the younger self may still be in place and, unfortunately, used in contexts where it is no longer necessary and where proper adult communication would be sufficient to get results, namely, being heard.

Sometimes such programs continue to operate subconsciously, even though they are outdated. A behavior is merely a tool to attain your needs in the quickest way possible. Neuro-pathways are created through repetition, as limiting behaviors become strongly linked to attaining certain results. This is how a limiting behavior can become unyielding to change and turn into a habit or an addiction. Whether it be smoking, nail biting, or drinking, the symptomatic behavior remains useful for as long as the underlying benefit is not otherwise fulfilled in a satisfying way. If a smoker feels that he can calm down, focus, and quell his fears with cigarettes, the strategy to help him change his habit should be primarily directed toward finding ways to satisfy those particular needs before attempting to stop smoking. The behavior of smoking is only present because of the needs and values it allows him to fulfill.

Attempting to define a human being by his or her behaviors is not useful because ultimately, as the saying goes, "we are not our behaviors." Behaviors do, however, provide important information that tells a story about our inner conflicts, conditioning, beliefs, and more. As for habits and addictions, you become attached to what is satisfied through a behavior, not the behavior itself.

Similarly, an illness can be looked at as a biological behavior. In addition, it is possible to observe that the position an individual maintains of being sick and holding on to a particular illness may have some incidental secondary gain for him or her. The secondary gain of illness is defined as the advantage that often occurs simultaneously with the illness. One may choose to stay ill and remain in that role for subconscious "useful" reasons. A subconscious resistance to healing may occur and sabotage the objective of getting well, because vital needs are being fulfilled through the existence of the illness.

So there may be *two* distinct benefits to illness.

One benefit is entirely connected to what triggered the illness in the first place. Originally, illness is triggered by a mechanism that actually enables us to lower stress by allowing the biological expression of an emotional struggle. The other benefit can be connected to external gains: for instance, social, financial, or those related to getting love or exerting our will. At a deep level, the needs and values that are momentarily fulfilled through having an illness are related to avoiding the return of the original stress. For example, a woman who has triggered breast cancer based on her perception and an unmanageable conflict with her husband who is having an affair may be able to reestablish a satisfying relationship with him through the presence of her illness. Her husband is now completely focused on her well-being and entirely devoted to her. He comes home right after work, spends a lot of quality time with her on weekends, and tells her that he loves her and that she is the most important person in his life. Now the woman is having her vital needs met (mainly security, significance, and love) through being ill. She is not aware that subconsciously the illness has been her best ally to satisfy those needs.

Anything that works to create pleasure and remove stress is recorded in our nervous system. In the above hypothetical example, illness has a strong connection with healing the woman's relationship and appears to have "fixed" the environment in a way that eliminates the stress of a potential affair or breakup. The trade-off remains in the subconscious realm because consciously the woman really wants to heal. However, somewhere in her subconscious is the memory of when she *did not have cancer*. This was a time when she also *did not have a solution* to fix the issue with her husband and suffered tremendous stress in her relationship. Now an association in her mind indicates that illness offers a way to gain something positive, which is the relationship she wants to preserve. There is no assurance that without the illness she would be able to achieve the same results. While holding on to the illness allows her to gloss over a lack of resources for resolving her partner conflict, it obviously does not eliminate the problem.

Once the triggering event of an illness as well as the programming events have been uncovered, it becomes important to check the role the illness is playing in someone's psyche in supporting one to meet one's needs and values. It is sometimes astonishing to discover how one has subconsciously learned to receive important advantages through one's illness and has come to believe that without the illness, life would become even more challenging.

At this point, a distinction should be made between "needs" and "values." Human needs are, of course, vital and directly related to adaptation during our evolution. Maslow's hierarchy of needs (see page 44) gives us a clear view of the essential human needs to be attained gradually on the way to experiencing fulfillment. To briefly recap, the foundation of our life is supported by the satisfaction of four types of needs called *D-needs* (Deficiency needs), so named due to the lack and deprivation that are commonly experienced in relation to not satisfying those needs. They include our basic *physiological* needs, the need for *protection and se-*

*curity*, the need for *relationships, love, and belonging*, and the need related to *self-esteem and importance in relation to others*.

Stress can become unmanageable when one or more of our *D-needs* are not met. The subconscious can instigate a biological response, i.e., illness, corresponding to the high stress related to such deficiencies. An emotional conflict is the result of one or more unsatisfied needs. An illness is the consequence of the stress associated with not meeting these vital needs. Once the illness has occurred, a secondary gain can emerge from holding on to the illness. Such gain is in turn connected to satisfying one or more of these vital needs.

In a situation in which they are urgently required, our human needs will draw us in a stronger way than our values. Our values correspond to what we build our life around after our needs are met. Core values, which are adopted based on life experience, represent what is important and meaningful to us and what we move toward.

The following case is a clear illustration of the complexity behind illness and behaviors. It poignantly demonstrates how core values and meeting vital needs subconsciously drive us. At each moment, we are motivated to fulfill them according to our primal and personal programs.

## LAURA'S STORY

I once consulted with a woman named Laura, who was afflicted with multiple sclerosis (MS). I went to her apartment for our session together, because she couldn't move her legs and was in a wheelchair.

Very quickly after delving into her situation, we got to the triggering event, which was the big stress prior to manifesting MS. Laura was a teacher at a high school, and she decided to go on a ski trip arranged by some of her colleagues. It would be eight of her fellow teachers together for a long holiday weekend, and it would be the first time she accepted an invitation to do anything with them collectively. Laura's recollection was that it was the first time she had been *invited* to do anything with her colleagues outside work. She never felt like she was part of the "clique," as she saw it. She wanted to feel like a valuable part of the group, but more often than not, she felt like she didn't fit in.

Even though Laura wasn't a good skier and knew it, she was determined to look good. This would be her chance to fit in with the group, to find her place among them. However, when it came time to get fitted with her ski equipment, she made hasty decisions. In her state of gnawing anxiety about how the weekend was going to unfold, she didn't really pay attention to whether the skis, boots, and poles fit her well and were comfortable. There was far too much on her mind. She and the other teachers took a long tram ride to reach their cabins up at the top of the mountain. This is where they would be for the better part of three days, and Laura would have no escape from the pressure of trying hard to be liked, accepted, and approved of by everyone.

As soon the group started skiing on their first day, Laura immediately felt horrible; her gear didn't fit her properly. Her boots were too tight and her skis were too long. She was frightened to ski to begin with, so the ill-fitting equipment only exacerbated her distress.

Feeling unsafe and fearful that she might plunge down a ravine, Laura felt mortified. She was embarrassed about picking the wrong equipment and feeling so afraid. Her low self-esteem wouldn't allow her to say anything or ask for help. For her, the bottom line was that if she complained, she would be seen as a nuisance and wouldn't be accepted.

To state the obvious, downhill skiing is a vertical movement from up to down. Fear of falling is fear of a vertical downward movement, and Laura's stress was increasing each and every minute during the descent, as she felt so fearful of going down the slope. She wasn't socializing, laughing, or enjoying the experience with the group at all. In contrast, she was certain that the others were laughing at her. She wasn't connecting with anyone. Instead, she felt totally devalued in comparison to them and observed how comfortable they seemed to be while skiing.

In Laura's case, there was tremendous stress related to movement *every minute of the ski trip*. As she exerted a considerable effort to follow her skiing mates down the steep slope, her stress level was climbing, and her mind recorded the metaphor "descent equals danger." When the terrain became flatter and smoother at the end of the descent, Laura's fear diminished. But, instead of relief, a strong emotional state of self-devaluation overwhelmed her, and her mind also recorded this secondary stress. As she continued to compare herself to her fellow skiers, she could only see herself as a failure. At this point she was experiencing a double conflict, one connected with *movement* (in this case, a *vertical movement* when going down the slope), and the other with *self-devaluation* (as she was progressively coming out of the descent, thinking of herself as a failure in comparison to the others).

Laura endured the conflict of *self-devaluation in a vertical movement* for three days as she constantly anticipated the next skiing descent. She even thought about it at night. At a primal level of thought, she needed an immediate solution, as she was continuously overstressed and could suffer exhaustion or even die due to the danger related to *inadvertence* (being distracted by the conflict and losing awareness of environmental dangers). The solution to the fear of movement (the fear that movement is dangerous and may lead to death) is for the brain to prevent future movements that cause stress. Multiple sclerosis does exactly that by stopping the communication from the brain to the limbs. So if Laura could no longer move her arms and legs, she would no longer suffer the high stress of going down the slope. The perfect solution of the brain is always to provide a biological modification that will resolve the emotional struggle. Laura could not consciously access a satisfying solution to her struggle. Based on her limiting beliefs and perceptions, Laura remained in the same situation for three days, struggling with unmanageable stress without expressing her problem.

There are always several solutions to a conflict, but if the individual finds no satisfying solution, whether a practical way out or one that permits him or her to detach from the problem altogether, the subconscious mind, whose purpose is to prolong survival, will come up with an alternate solution—one that can only be biological.

In this case, the ultimate subconscious solution was to *block a function* by triggering a paralysis so that Laura did not have to move anymore. The brain activated a program to stop the production of myelin, which plays an essential role in the proper functioning of the nervous system. Myelin protects and insulates neurons. It also facilitates the quick and accurate transmission of electrical current down the body of the nerve, thus enabling locomotion. In Laura's case, demyelization began to occur and was later diagnosed as multiple sclerosis. Prompted by a precise felt experience during the ski trip, MS gradually allowed Laura to stop future movements. Being unable to move became the perfect solution to never again feeling devalued and fearful about vertical movement.

Many times, when we observe others, we find ourselves thinking that we would know exactly what to do in their circumstances. However, in the subjective and very personal experience of a conflicted individual, the only viable solution during an emotional crisis is the one that matches one's immediate needs according to deeply ingrained programs. In this case, Laura believed that she did not have a way out of her situation.

Halfway through our session together, Laura began to understand the root cause of her illness; it made perfect sense to her. As we started to tackle the phase in which she was going to work on shifting her perception, Laura made a startlingly honest admission. "Isabelle, don't work with me," she said. "If I heal from MS, I'll have to go back to being a teacher. I hated my job, and I am much happier right now." Laura also admitted that she was receiving a disability check, which paid her bills.

It was clear that Laura's MS provided her with a strong secondary gain, allowing her to fulfill her needs. Because of MS, she felt financially safe, did not have to deal with devaluation at work, and did not have to look for another job at the age of fifty-six. She was also receiving a lot of care and attention from her family and was surrounded by a small group of friends and neighbors. She had always lived alone without a partner, but now she had visitors and did not feel as lonely. Her life was full of variety, between the visits of her physical therapist, her massage therapist, and family members who were closer to her than ever. Her new life situation made her feel safe, and MS seemed to her like an acceptable price to pay in order to meet her needs and live a joyful life. Her illness was evolving slowly, and she felt that her life was much better since her paralysis. Laura asked me to respect her wishes for the time being. Honoring her free will, I only worked with her that one time.

This encounter with Laura reminded me of a simple yet poignant thought that someone once shared with me: "We can't help an elderly person cross the street when they want to stay on the same sidewalk."

## ELIMINATING THE SECONDARY GAIN OF ILLNESS

Unlike the previous example, you may be interested in eliminating what is possibly causing you to subconsciously hold on to your illness. To help yourself heal, allow yourself to investigate and discover whether there is a struggle between the two internal parts of you that may be in conflict. As one part of you may want to reestablish proper functioning of your organs, another may be subconsciously motivated to hold on to your condition at this time.

It is important to be willing to look closely and honestly at the part of you that may be creating an obstacle to healing. It is essential to do so without judgment, but instead with an attitude of interest and curiosity. This part holds a positive intention and contains a wealth of information about you and your subconscious strategies. The part of you that has emerged to create an obstacle to your healing is designed to help you fulfill particular needs and avoid certain stresses. Each part of you has a valid purpose and function, and if your illness remains, you may have put in place a subconscious strategy that interferes with your objective of complete healing. Above all, you can always find ways to connect the illness to a positive function in your life, primarily the growth that will come from it. But it seems it is only when the benefit is fundamental at a primal level that the subconscious doesn't "unplug" from a health disorder and allow our natural healing capacity to engage.

The first step is to identify both parts and to connect with them individually. Once you have accessed them, you will discover the roles, purposes, and positive intentions they fulfill. You may call one part the *objective*—the part of you that wants a healthy body. The other part may be referred to as the *objection*—the part of you that creates interference in attaining your objective for complete health and wellness.

A client of mine named Stephanie had a hard time freeing herself from a leg tumor. Her first symptom had started shortly after experiencing a big fight with her boss. Although her tumor was benign, it kept her from walking, forcing her to be in and out of her job as a sales representative. She had spent fourteen years on the road selling organic supplements to her clients, but the past two years had been difficult in her company. Stephanie discovered that the quality of the products she was selling had changed, and not for the better. Although the word "organic" was written on all the packaging, she learned that some of the products were not. When I asked her what having the leg tumor gave her or how it benefited her, she knew immediately. Right away she answered, "It allows me to not work." When I asked her what she thought may be the positive aspect of not working, Stephanie uttered the word "relief." She then explained that her fundamental values were violated every time she felt that she was lying to her long-term customers about the products she was selling.

Stephanie's secondary gain was obvious, as the leg tumor gave her a way to stay in alignment with some of her most profound values, such as trust, integrity, honesty, loyalty, and respect. Although a part of her wanted to have a healthy leg and walk with ease, another part created an obstacle so that she would not endure the pain of lying to her customers. The conflict between those two parts needed to be resolved.

Both of Stephanie's facets had validity. The positive intention of the objective is to recover and have a healthy leg so that she can walk, work, and enjoy life. The positive intention of the objection is to stop the struggle she has every time she deals with her customers in ways that violate some of her most important values.

I asked Stephanie if she thought that the objective could, in the future, provide the objection with the values it is attached to, so that the illness would no longer be useful. She understood that she was experiencing an internal fight between two parts. It was as if the *objection* did not trust the *objective*—the part of her that had continued working in an environment where important values such as trust, integrity, honesty, loyalty, and respect were frequently violated.

Stephanie expressed that she would be happy to find a solution, so she would never again be forced to lie to her customers. She decided that she would either get permission from her boss to be truthful about the supplements or leave the company and find another job. Now it was time for negotiations to begin, for an emotional alignment and integration permitting the internal conflict to cease. The objective made a promise to the objection to work right away on a solution, so that Stephanie's cherished values would no longer be violated. After she made this powerful decision, the leg tumor would no longer have a meaningful role to play in helping her to satisfy her values.

Stephanie made sure that the promise the *objective* made to the *objection* was honored, and within a few weeks she was working for another company. Stephanie kept her promise by finding a new way to honor her most important values. As she reestablished alignment within herself and respected her work ethics, the three-inch tumor in her leg quickly regressed to the size of a small pea. Stephanie soon found her stride again, walking with ease and confidence.

## SECONDARY GAIN INTROSPECTION

You can also uncover the hidden reason (or reasons) that may be leading you to hold on to an undesirable condition. Whether you want to address a limiting behavior, a weight problem, or a serious illness, the following exercise will help you access precious information and allow you to make a shift at a subconscious level. Thereafter, you will be able to tap into your creativity and design resourceful strategies to satisfy your needs without the "help" of your condition.

**Step 1: The Objective**

Take a moment to look closely at your objective part, which you defined in the beginning of this section, part II. Allow yourself to connect with the outcome you are seeking to produce and start defining the needs and values that will be fulfilled once you attain your objective. Use the following questions to help with this process.

◆ *What is the positive intention of the part of me that wants to attain a state of health?* Make sure to keep in mind a positive representation of the organ(s) you are working on and state your objective precisely: for example, "I desire to have a perfect, functioning colon." Or, "I desire to be fit and thin."

Example: Stephanie wanted to have a perfect leg with healthy muscles and tendons.

◆ *What is important for me in this outcome?* (Refer to your answer as "A.")

Example: What is important to Stephanie is to feel good, walk, work, and go where she wants.

◆ *Once I obtain A, what will I get that is even more important?* (Here you will identify a set of values.)

Example: What is even more important is that Stephanie will have health, freedom, and happiness.

Take notes as you access this information; they will prove to be useful as you move forward.

**Step 2: The Objection**

Quiet yourself and inquire within. Is there a part of you that objects to attaining your objective? Trust that your subconscious has a well-intentioned purpose. If the part of you that plays the role of the obstacle is reluctant to let go of your health disorder, know that there is a reason behind the behavior of holding on to your condition. Allow yourself to access and feel the facet of you that is creating an obstacle to your healing. Maybe this part of you has something to say. You may ask it to communicate with you consciously. Notice any internal responses, such as feelings, images, or sounds, as you ask yourself the following questions.

◆ *What is the positive intention of the part of me that is holding on to this health disorder?*

Example: Stephanie no longer has to suffer at her job.

◆ *What is my condition permitting me to gain or accomplish that is important to me?* (Refer to your answer as "B.")

Example: Stephanie no longer has to lie to her clients.

177

♦ *When I get B, what do I get that is even more important?* (Here you will identify another set of values.)

Example: Stephanie is able to satisfy values such as trust, integrity, honesty, loyalty, and respect.

♦ *What important needs am I fulfilling while my condition persists?*

Example: Stephanie no longer feels devalued by her actions and feels safe because she is not lying (satisfying her needs for significance and security).

♦ *What do I fear might happen in the future if I were to become perfectly healthy?*

Example: Stephanie fears that if she heals, she would be tempted to go back to a job where she would suffer from having to be dishonest with her clients.

Again, take notes as you access this important information.

**Step 3: New Solutions**

Now, look at the objective and the objection as two distinct facets of yourself, with different needs and values. (Interestingly enough, they sometimes share common values.) Notice that both parts have a positive intention and that the function of the obstacle is useful at this moment, since the objective part has not yet created a strategy that will allow the objection to disappear. Realize that once the part of you holding on to the objection is fulfilled, the objection should no longer persist. The values you have referred to as "B" in this exercise are meant to be fulfilled by the objective part through new strategies. By employing these new strategies, the objection's agenda for subconsciously maintaining the health disorder will become obsolete. The health disorder is only a tool for a secondary gain, not a necessity. You need to make a strong commitment in order to provide yourself with the values necessary for your well-being. In doing so, the part of you that created the illness will no longer need to exist to satisfy them. You must put in place alternative ways to fulfill your needs and values so that your physical integrity can be reestablished. For instance, a woman learns to love and respect herself, first and foremost, rather than continuing to get her husband's love and attention by being sick.

Take a moment to ask yourself if you would be willing to come up with new solutions in your life so that you would not need the help of an illness to meet values such as safety, security, love, trust, money, significance, respect, and so on. Allow your creativity to surface and start shaking up the system you once had in place. Ask yourself the following questions in order to challenge your present strategy, which you can replace later with a more resourceful one.

- *What price am I going to pay if I hold on to my condition because of the secondary gain I have identified?*

- *Is my health important enough for me to change the way my life is organized right now? (If needed, I can make changes in small steps.)*

- *How could I fulfill the needs and values associated with the obstacle while being healthy?*

- *What new skills do I need to learn in order to become independent of my condition and to attain my needs and values without its help?*

- *What new choices can I make in my life to free myself from being dependent on the love, importance, security, safety, or any other benefit that I may have received from the environment while being ill or out of balance?*

- *What new beliefs could I adopt to support the new life strategies I am creating?*

- *Am I important enough to do everything I can to attain my objective of being perfectly healthy?*

Take a moment to write down your innermost thoughts, feelings, desires, and visions, and create a new plan of action.

## Step 4: New Commitments

The objection, the part of you that ran the limiting behavior or health disorder, may now be willing to stop interfering with your healing process, providing the objective part can commit to fulfilling the needs and values that are so important to the other part.

Sometimes, just being aware of the existence of your two parts and their struggle may be powerful enough to automatically prompt a new response, which will replace the role the objection has played until now. However, it is most likely that you will have to do the deep work of observing and evaluating your life and making the necessary changes. In Laura's case, attaining her needs without MS seemed insurmountable to her. From a position of being really sick, it can feel quite daunting to examine each aspect of your life that you may need to address. Making new and vigorous decisions can be a challenge at times. It's important to keep in mind how overwhelming an illness can be.

But just imagine what could have happened if Laura had decided otherwise. One option is that she could have promised herself to never again work in a profession she did not like. Maybe Laura could have opened up to learning another skill and becoming financially independent without having to teach high school students. She could have decided that she was young enough to work another ten years and be willing to not depend on government help. She could have explored new ways to invite the attention of her friends and family that included emotional openness and vulnerability. It seems that decisions other than the ones she adopted would have opened possibilities for her to recover.

Take a moment to connect with your subconscious and your internal wisdom, and ask yourself the following questions.

- *Do I prefer to keep my condition at this moment, and is it the path I prefer to stay on? Or am I ready to let go of it?*

- *Do I feel that it is possible for me to let go of the old strategy I used to satisfy important needs and values?*

- *Am I willing to commit to new ways to meet my needs and values, other than through illness?*

- *Can I promise myself to respect my needs and honor my values in the future, while taking responsibility for fulfilling them on my own?*

◆ *Am I in complete agreement with eliminating any secondary gain related to my condition?*

Write down the answers that come to you from deep within.

## Step 5: Healing Declarations

The following statements hold the powerful resonance of understanding, self-responsibility, and optimism. Repeat each sentence to yourself, in order to strengthen your commitment to satisfying your needs in healthy ways.

◆ *I understand the positive intention of the illness (or limiting behavior).*

◆ *The illness has served an important purpose, and I recognize its importance.*

◆ *I am aware of the needs and values I must fulfill on my own, and I no longer need to be ill to satisfy those needs and values.*

◆ *I am now willing to eliminate the secondary gain related to my condition.*

◆ *I trust that subconscious inspiration will help me find new healthy solutions.*

◆ *I will now reassure the part of me that created the objection, by committing to finding new ways to satisfy the needs and values that I previously satisfied through the illness.*

◆ *Since the purpose of the illness is to help me evolve, I accept the opportunity to transform and overcome this condition.*

◆ *I will be creative in finding ways to fulfill my needs while staying healthy.*

◆ *I am in alignment with myself as I now depend on me to meet my needs.*

◆ *The objection (illness or behavior) no longer serves a purpose.*

# 12

## Freedom from the Parental Project—Claiming Your True Path

As we look around us, we can see that many people have given up trying to live a purposeful life because they believe it's too difficult. Many give up on the possibility of regaining their health, energy, and vitality as well. What are the subconscious factors that influence our attitudes and beliefs? And what factors influence our destiny?

When we observe the challenges and constraints of life, they may seem external to us, but they are in fact the result of our own subconscious activity. We engage in certain behaviors and accept certain circumstances quite automatically, and most often based on programs of which we are not aware.

Despite our own independence as individuals, we are predisposed to the events we attract into our life and the choices we make.

In this chapter, you will see that your life is related to a much greater purpose than the one you may currently perceive. Knowing that your subconscious brain is strictly programmed in terms of survival may lead you to adopt a new philosophy on life, one in which the notion of "right or wrong" gets replaced with a growing understanding of the laws of biology and meaningful survival strategies.

## THE SUBCONSCIOUS PARENTAL PROJECT OF THE CHILD

According to Marc Fréchet, human beings fulfill a purpose in their lives that corresponds to their parents' conscious and subconscious plan (or "project") during the gestational phase and up to one year after birth. The emotions and stresses parents experience during that time define the type of trajectory the child will experience in his or her life.

The climate during conception and gestation, and especially the parents' struggles, needs, and desires, will ultimately act as programs the child will express later on in life. They represent the unconscious projection of the parents onto the child, which predetermines, to a large degree, the behaviors, jobs, friends, careers, and overall destiny an individual will fulfill, including the accidents and illnesses they may experience.

The *project purpose* (see page 60) is the name used to represent the subconscious "assignment," handed down from the parents to the child, that acts as a law for all human beings. It illustrates how the psychological conflicts of the parents become part of the biology of the child.

Some parental projects are limiting and can be released, if needed, by bringing to consciousness their meanings and realizing they are programs that are no longer necessary for survival. However, this universal principle also extends far beyond limitation, applying to every innovation and creation. For instance, before Thomas Edison invented the lightbulb, he had the project of creating light through electricity. The lightbulb is the object that both expresses Edison's project according to his vision and *fulfills a purpose* that perfectly matches the project.

During the course of one's life, the inherited project sometimes manifests in the form of an illness, which represents the materialization of an emotional conflict that one parent (or both) endured during their child's gestation. As already explained, the psychological conflicts of the parents are downloaded to the fetus for survival purposes. This download is an important internal mechanism of adaptation that helped living beings survive and populate the world.

The circumstances, events, emotions, struggles, and conflicts of the parents are transmitted and imprinted to the subconscious hard drive of the offspring, resulting in the acquired project. The child will express the meaning of the subconscious parental project by fulfilling the purpose related to it.

Ultimately one will attract all circumstances in one's life in order to give sense to the project that has been written into the subconscious script.

As you explore the *project purpose* programming that may be affecting your life, it is important to remember that this transmission is unconscious; therefore, no one is guilty. There is no one to blame, including yourself. As always, examining this layer of influence with compassion for your parents and yourself will help you gain a greater sense of well-being, without the weight of judgment or regret.

## SYMBOLIC SOLUTIONS FOR SURVIVAL

The dualistic nature of the mind enables us to want something consciously while being opposed by the subconscious brain. This type of internal split creates a life struggle. Imagine a woman whose mother had difficulties with her spouse during her pregnancy. Her project was to get a divorce and leave her violent husband, but she never had the courage to do it. It is possible that the offspring (the daughter) will attract a violent husband (or partners) from whom she will separate, thus liberating the subconscious stress of her mother. So, in order to make this survival scenario possible, she attracts violent men who manifest the role needed in the story. Consciously, of course, the daughter wants to create the opposite of such painful relationships. However, subconsciously she alleviates her mother's stress every time she gets away from such a man. Symbolically, it is a solution for survival that would have been useful to the mother and is now expressed repeatedly by her daughter.

Etched into our psyche is the story of what was happening around the time we were conceived and up to a year after birth—and that story is attached to our survival. We could say, "I am alive because of that!" As a result, the subconscious has stored that information as a program that will be repeated.

Fortunately, once we become aware of certain patterns, we can evaluate whether we want to be governed by them or not. To understand this concept, imagine buying a computer that comes loaded with several programs. You might use these programs until they no longer satisfy you. For example, if you no longer want to use an outdated program for your accounting needs, you could choose to replace it with an alternate program of your own choice. The old program was part of the built-in package that came with the computer you bought, and one day you can decide to replace that program with one that will serve you better.

In the same way, your brain is a powerful computer that contains programs that were downloaded during gestation. In order to change the course of your life and reclaim your true path, it is necessary to realize that the projects you downloaded from your parents do not belong to you. Unconscious parental projects are part of the "package" you carry, until self-knowledge and growing awareness allow you to let go of outdated programs. In BioReprogramming® this is known as "unwanted imprints." While it's true that some programs are very useful and positive in our life, others can be brought to consciousness in order to be eliminated.

## DISCOVERING A NEW SENSE OF MEANING AND PURPOSE

In the process of uncovering and working on your parental subconscious project, you will likely come to a greater understanding of the reasons behind all events and decisions that have occurred in your life. Again, since these programs are transmitted subconsciously, please keep in mind that no one is the perpetrator or the victim of such transmissions. As I stated earlier, it is helpful to view this dynamic as an aspect of the laws of biology. Within the complex arena of the subconscious brain, there are stored programs that we still have the opportunity to eliminate in order to claim the power to walk our own path, to live life by our own conscious design.

Ultimately, we are each seeking wholeness in our life. We want to create a life that makes sense to us. And some of us want to know that there is a reason behind both the pain and the grace that we have experienced.

By uncovering the subconscious memories you carry, you will understand the purpose of your path and why you have attracted certain people and circumstances thus far. Studying the climate surrounding your parents during your gestation, and up to a year after your birth, will give you clues about the programs you may be expressing. By undergoing this exploration, not only can you regain your physical well-being, but you can also give new meaning to your life, your relationships, and the world itself.

*"Nothing has a stronger influence psychologically on their environment and especially on their children than the unlived life of the parent."*

—C. G. Jung

As we reflect on our parents' life circumstances and limitations, it is essential to recognize that we now have greater access to resources than they did at the time surrounding the inception of our *project purpose*. We have evolved away from certain rules, traditions, beliefs, and life constraints. And in so doing, we have choices today that they did not have then. Once it is understood that we don't need to endlessly reproduce and follow old maps, the opportunity before us is to become very clear about our goals and to embrace a new purpose. If we seize the opportunity, we find that we have the inner resources and courage to let go of familiar problems and stop re-creating struggles by resolving old conflicts through a higher level of consciousness.

Let's explore what this might look like.

If your father lost all his money abruptly while you were in the womb, your subconscious solution to his financial loss might be your inability to make money. Or, even if you do make money, you might be unable to save it. You might have the habit of spending it right away, so that you will never lose it all like your father did. This is a clever and somewhat radical way of avoiding the stress of abrupt, substantial financial loss, isn't it?

In another example, it is possible that your parents worked hard and dreamed of professional success with such fervor that you are expressing the result of that project by owning a successful company and loving what you do. Again, some projects can lead to wonderful results and achievements.

The bottom line is this: What do you want to repair in order to proceed happily with your life today, unaffected by the pain of the past? Is it a memory of abandonment, the loss of a child, a partner conflict, or a financial crisis? Is there a type of accident that keeps recurring in your life—one that is directly related to either or both of your parents during your gestation? Was there a conflicted relationship between one of your parents and his or her sibling at that time, which you are now desperately trying to resolve through the tumultuous relationship you have with your own sister or brother? What is the climate surrounding you right now? Is it an ambiance of fear, poverty, isolation, or lack? What aspects of this climate are similar to those surrounding your family when your *project purpose* was formed?

This is where the work starts: by investigating the past. You don't need to have a lot of information to start making interesting deductions. Much like a detective, you will start putting pieces together by looking at your life and searching for clues in the past that can be linked to your present challenges.

Sometimes parental projects are not directly related to painful events; nevertheless, you may not be fully satisfied with what you are experiencing and expressing in your life. For instance, it could be that your parents traveled from city to city, working as musicians. As a result of the subconscious download related to this lifestyle, you find yourself unable to settle anywhere. In that case, you could eliminate such influence by simply bringing the program to your awareness, acknowledging it, and deciding to let go of it. At the end of this chapter, you will find a special meditation that you can use to take you through these three powerful steps toward freedom.

## NEW LIFE STRATEGIES—TOOLS FOR REPAIRING THE PAST

After accessing a new awareness of the parental programs you are carrying, the next step is to reflect on the types of resources you could symbolically offer to your parents. At the level of consciousness, how might you be able to symbolically help your parents through a specific stress or the difficult overall circumstances they were enduring at the time of your gestation and birth? You can find answers by embarking upon a brief inner journey through time. Imagine going back in time as you are right now, as your adult self, to provide new ideas, tools, beliefs, and perceptions— resources that could have helped your parents handle their situation differently. Needless to say, what happened in the past won't change. But interestingly, what can change is the memory in your subconscious brain. You can repair the past internally through your own psyche.

If one or both of your parents went through a specific stress during your gestational period, such as the loss of one of their parents, loss of a job, divorce, or another type of separation, the impact of such an imprint can be lifted off your psyche by making certain resources available to your parents at the time of their struggle.

Remember that the subconscious does not differentiate between past, present, and future. For instance, if you place your full attention on recalling an old memory right now (whether pleasant or unpleasant), you may be engulfed by emotions, and chances are your emotional state will be processed by your subconscious as if the event were occurring in present time. The emotions associated with the memory will be true to your subconscious, which will react to them accordingly.

While the conscious mind has the capacity to recall the past, be in the present time, and imagine the future, the subconscious only stays connected to the present, alert to the environment and insuring survival. Because of this phenomenon, we can recall certain events of the past and bring them forward in our consciousness, allowing our subconscious to process them as if they were occurring in the present.

We can therefore modify the impact of certain subconscious memories, even if they originated with and belong to our parents. As we transform what "could have been" by imagining solutions, we no longer need to carry our parents' burden. New resources that could have been useful during certain struggles can be provided symbolically to minimize or eliminate the stress encountered. What "could have been" becomes "what is" for the subconscious, which records a new version of the story. Changing mental maps by symbolically giving resources to our parents during the period of the *project purpose* can allow for a change of path *today*. We become active in healing the past and are no longer assigned to the same subconscious projects.

The same way we can find information in the past to explain the present (cause and effect), we can also send information from the present to the past to repair a problem.

We may ask ourselves: *What resources did my mother and father need at the time of their struggle?* In the process of inquiry, we might come up with resources such as acceptance, faith, flexibility, trust, determination, patience, discernment, knowledge, creativity, and resilience. We can then imagine a scenario in which our parents would have benefited from modern resources that would be available to them if they were here today in the same situation. This exercise should be done without judgment and with love and empathy toward them.

It is also useful to look at our own responsibility in the parental project and from the perspective of "effect requiring and perpetuating the existence of a cause." We can ask ourselves specific questions that unleash great powers of healing and transformation, such as the following:

> *What am I doing today that is still symbolically feeding and keeping alive the projects of my parents? For instance, am I divorcing so that my mother can be liberated from my father? Am I experiencing breast cancer so that my mother can nurture her dying child? Am I unable to find work, and therefore have no boss, so that my father is no longer a victim of verbal abuse at his job?*

Once we let go of the inherited limiting programs, we will adopt new behaviors, and our brain will eventually "cast" new actors to play out the scenarios of our life. Our environment will change and new opportunities will manifest.

We may only stay passive—tolerating limiting beliefs and patterns—for as long as we are unaware of the principles of the *project purpose*. Now that we possess this important knowledge, we can efficiently redesign our future. Once we go into action to repair the past and figuratively "deliver" this information to our parents, we create a new dynamic that liberates everyone involved. Once this crucial aspect of parental transmission is understood and we take responsibility for freeing ourselves from the past, we become the master of our destiny.

It is also essential to learn how to create new programs that are not part of our hard drive. For instance, an individual may have a program of financial abundance, but not one related to creating a successful relationship. Once you let go of certain aspects of your parental project, clarity about what you want to create in your life is essential.

To illustrate this point, I would like to share with you a few of my client's stories.

- Geraldine was unable to get pregnant. She had tried for nine years. From the moment her parents knew that they were pregnant with her, they regretted having another child, as there were already three at home. Her parental project was summarized in the statement "I wish I was not pregnant." To alleviate her parents' stress, Geraldine could not conceive. At the age of thirty-eight, just three months after working on her parental project, Geraldine was able to conceive, and she gave birth to a little girl.

- Louis could not keep a job for more than a few months and struggled with this dynamic over seventeen years of his active adult life. After working on his parental project and discovering that his father had lost his job twice while his mother was pregnant with him, Louis was able to get hired again, and he still works for the same company.

- From the time she was twenty-four years old, Helena would wake up in a state of panic every night at 3:00 am. When Helena's mother had been pregnant with her, also at the age of twenty-four, she almost lost her two-year-old son. She woke at 3 am to find him suffocating and turning blue. If she had not woken up at the sound of her child struggling, he would have died while she slept. Helena was able to let go of this fear that belonged to her mother and which resulted in subconsciously waking up at 3 am to symbolically save the child. After our first session, she slept through the night for the first time in six years.

◆ Christian hated water. He was afraid of it and never wanted to learn how to swim. While Christian was in the womb, his father's brother had drowned while on vacation in Hawaii. Upon understanding the impact of this event on his family during his gestation, Christian became open to learning how to swim.

◆ Melanie was diagnosed with glandular breast cancer when she was forty-two years old. Her mother, Dorothy, was twenty-one years old when she was pregnant with Melanie. During that time, Dorothy's mother was in a car accident and died. At six months pregnant, Dorothy endured the unexpected shock of the death of her mother—a maternal conflict. During our session, Melanie remembered that a few months before her cancer diagnosis, her mother, Dorothy, had been diagnosed with lymphoma. Melanie understood that the maternal conflict she was expressing was matching the one Dorothy experienced with her own mother. Interestingly, Melanie triggered her cancer at twice the age corresponding to her mother's shock when pregnant. When Melanie experienced a subconscious stress related to worrying about her own mother, she subconsciously awakened a stored memory *and its biological solution*. Melanie worked on her *project purpose* and maternal conflict, and she recovered her health in the process. (In the next chapter, we will delve further into the significance that age, dates, and numbers can have in the process of BioReprogramming®.)

## TRAVELING BACK TO THE PARENTAL PROJECT

In this section, you can begin to put this layer of the BioReprogramming® Method to work. In order to accomplish this, you will need to describe your parents' lives during the time between your conception and turning one year old. Ask yourself the questions provided below in order to investigate your *project purpose*.

**Note:** Since there are no rules in this process, you can enlarge the spectrum of your search and observe your parents' lives from the moment they decided to conceive (if that was a conscious decision). If you were adopted, you have been influenced by the projects, life conditions, and emotional conflicts related to your biological parents during your gestation. But as soon as your adopted parents were emotionally connected to you, even if you were still in the womb, you started to be influenced by their emotions and thoughts as well, the result being a combined project purpose.

## Your Project Purpose

How old were my parents when they got pregnant with me?

Were they already married?

What job were they doing?

What was their financial situation?

What was the climate surrounding them? For instance, was it a climate of poverty or abundance? Security or fear? Peace or conflict?

What were the relationships like between my parents and their families at the time?

Did anything in particular happen in the family at that time?

What were my parents' desires?

What were their struggles or conflicts?

Did they go through a shock or traumatic event?

*Note: You may answer the questions for each parent independently, as well as describing their common desires, projects, or struggles, if any.*

## Your Realizations

Upon reviewing your answers to the above questions, observe your own life. Investigate your parents' lives to find clues related to your life. What were your parents' unfulfilled dreams? What were their struggles or conflicts? Think about and sense the atmosphere surrounding them at that time. Write a description of their emotional stresses, if any. Observe the structure of the story and make deductions.

## The Connections with Your Life Story

Start to connect the dots, noticing the connections between your parents' circumstances during gestation and your own circumstances. Establish the link between your life path and your parents' projects, which were derived from their emotional conflicts during your conception. What are you struggling with today? What would you like to change in your life? Is there a health disorder that may be linked to the emotional struggle of one or both of your parents?

What are you expressing that actually belongs to them? What solutions are you providing for their struggles? What is happening in your life today that you sense is directly connected to your parents' wishes or emotional distress during the time between your conception and one year old?

### *Ryan's Example*
My Project Purpose

> *My parents married at a fairly young age and were not sure they wanted children. My mother was twenty-one years old and had started a singing career in opera when she found out she was pregnant with me. She was pursuing an exciting opportunity and did not wish to have a child at that time. She felt her life was interrupted by her pregnancy. She struggled emotionally with being pregnant before fulfilling her artistic goals. She stopped singing completely and was sad, frustrated, and angry about having missed her chance for a career as an artist. As long as she was going to have a child, she absolutely wanted to have a girl and was extremely disappointed at having a boy. My father was twenty-five years old and did not want a child yet. While my mother was pregnant, he was working as an architect's assistant. He was employed in a field he liked while he continued to study to become an architect, as this was his dream.*

My Realizations

> *My parents both wanted a big career, and having children was not their first priority. They had to sacrifice and adapt in order to*

*have me. My mother never went back to singing after my birth and then had my brother two years after me. My father was working toward success. There were no specific traumas or shocks during that time period, but my mother suffered from not being an opera singer.*

The Connections with My Life Story

*Today, I am a stage manager for musicals in New York City. Although I wished to become an actor, I did not succeed. I am happily engaged in a gay relationship. I realize that I work in the artistic field (my mother's project) but not in the spotlight (my mother's conflict). I design and build stages like an architect, and I am successful in this field (my father's project). I am proudly gay and would not want to be any other way. However, I feel that my biology may be an expression of a subconscious loyalty to my mother, who absolutely wanted a girl and never had one. I don't have children (both of my parents had a conflict with having a child at that time). I am enjoying my life overall, but I am struggling with not being a father. It is my big sadness.*

### Alexandra's Example

My Project Purpose

*My parents were not married when I was conceived. My mother had an affair with a man who was twenty-one years older than her and married with two children. She was twenty-four and he was forty-five. He had promised my mother that he would marry her one day, after his kids were raised, but as soon as he knew she was pregnant, he broke up with her. She was devastated. My mother never wanted me to know my father. She gave me to my grandmother, who raised me until I was twelve years old. My mother remained involved in my life all along, and once she was financially secure, I moved in with her. We lived together until I was twenty-one years old.*

My Realizations

*My mother did not have a husband or a partner. She had to hide my father's identity. She never wanted me to know who he was. She was in love with him when he left her and struggled with having to separate from him. My father did not want to have me. My father chose to separate from my mother. My father did not want to ever know me.*

The Connections with My Life Story

*Since my Project Purpose is "You will never know your father," I remained separated from my father all my life, giving sense to my mother's project that I should never know him. I was raised by two single mothers, first my grandmother and then my mother. I was never able to get married, since the conflict of my mother during gestation related to "an impossible relationship." Most of my boyfriends left me, including the last one, with whom I was very much in love. I have often felt abandoned and separated, which was part of the climate around my gestation and birth. My breast cancer was triggered a few months after the separation from my boyfriend last year, when I was fifty-one years old. This resonates with the "partner conflict" my mother had with my father, whom she loved. He left her and asked that she never contact him again. She felt separated from the one she wanted to love and be loved by, which corresponds to an emotional conflict linked to the breast. I could never create a successful relationship with a man. I had breast cancer after a breakup, as a biological expression of my mother's "partner conflict" during gestation.*

**Note:** Children who have the project of not knowing their father will often experience difficulties with algebra at school. (This was true for Alexandra.) They cannot solve the equation as it relates to X. In other words, they cannot find the answer: X. Symbolically, finding the unknown (X) would be betraying the subconscious project of the parents: "You will not know your father."

## LETTING GO OF THE SUBCONSCIOUS
## PARENTAL PROJECT—A FIVE-STEP PROCESS

**Step 1: Empathize**

Understand the circumstances and limitations of your mother and father. Investigate certain life events you are aware they went through. Imagine what life felt like for them during that period of time. What were they experiencing from their point of view? What were their wishes, conflicts, and emotional struggles? Put yourself in their shoes (one parent at a time), and allow emotions to surface.

**Step 2: Detach**

Disengage from your parents' projects and conflicts by realizing they do not belong to you. The following metaphor illustrates this point:

> *One day a woman carried a very heavy suitcase onto the train. As she struggled to move through the narrow train with the suitcase, she kept trying to push it toward the door. Her niece asked, "Aunt Susan, what are you doing with this suitcase?"*
>
> *She answered, "I am pushing it toward the door so that when the train stops, we can get out with it!"*
>
> *Her niece told her, "But can't you see that this is not your suitcase? Why are you carrying someone else's heavy bag? You can put it down—it's not yours!"*
>
> *The aunt put down the suitcase that was not hers and immediately felt lighter and free to move forward.*

**Step 3: Identify New Resources**

After you recognize your parental project and the programs you are expressing, think of the resources you could symbolically provide to your parents. This exercise will help you effectively deprogram the old stresses you may otherwise continue to express through certain behaviors or health disorders. Once again thinking of the period of time from conception to one year of age, ask yourself the following questions:

What resources could I give to my mother and father to help them navigate through that time period? What did they need to know, understand, or believe that would have helped them alleviate their stress? What new philosophy of life could they adopt? How could they overcome their conflicts?

As you observe your parents with compassion, you may access the kind of resources they would have needed. Remember, this is not about changing the past, nor is it about judging their actions. It is about changing your parents' perceptions and reframing the meaning of events, so that they feel differently about their circumstances.

**Note:** The resources you choose to symbolically give to your parents should provide them with the power of self-responsibility versus depending on changes accomplished by others in the environment.

For instance, in Ryan's case, it seems his mother would have benefited from the resource of *flexibility* so that she could accept having a boy. Maybe she also needed the resource of *creativity*. Could she change her decision to stop singing and still continue enjoying it while being a mother? If she stayed open to future possibilities and still worked on her craft, would her sadness be alleviated? Today Ryan knows female artists who were able to manage their careers while raising their families. Could his mother adopt the belief that this is a possibility, so that another chance to sing professionally could present itself in her future? How would this new decision affect her emotional state at that time? Would she be less frustrated? More hopeful?

## Step 4: Heal the Past

Imagine that your parents are equipped with the resources you provided. How different would they feel? To what degree would their struggles be alleviated? How much wisdom would they gain through this new knowledge? While you imagine your parents accessing the resources you provided, feel how their perception is changed and how their emotions become more manageable. Feel how different your life could have been if your parents had access to the resources you offered them today—not as a way to feel regret about what "wasn't," but to expand your imagination around what "can be" in the timeless realm of the subconscious mind.

## Step 5: Create a New Life Project

In the light of your new understanding—about your parents' lives and the project purpose you have been expressing—it is time to create your own project, so you can express your own purpose.

Now you can design the ideal project for your life. This could be as simple as claiming a project which is the opposite of the one you no longer want to express.

Let's look at Alexandra's example:

After giving new resources to both of her parents during the inception phase of the *project purpose*, Alexandra created a new life project. The original projects were "You will not know your father" and the memory of "an impossible relationship" in a climate of abandonment and separation.

Alexandra decided to change those projects and claim the following:

"I have a biological father, and I recognize him!"

"I will create a successful relationship with a partner!"

"I will be surrounded by and stay connected with the ones I love."

In letting go of her old project and programming her new one, Alexandra reprogrammed herself to attract a father figure into her life for the first time (even though it was not her biological father). Not only did she meet a new love partner and created a successful relationship, but her partner's father accepted her immediately into the family. Alexandra jokes about it, saying, "He was the first to fall in love with me, even before my partner, John, did!"

As Alexandra worked on her subconscious conflicts, she was able to overcome her illness. She has been healthy and happy for the past six years.

## Creating Opposite Projects

In addition to Alexandra's story, explore the following examples to gain familiarity with the technique of creating a project that is the opposite of the one you are struggling with:

**Example 1:**

Project: Not having a child, so I don't have to commit to a relationship and can remain free.

Creators: The biological parents.

Purpose: Being unable to get pregnant and not creating a family.

As a result of the project, the offspring won't have a child and will stay free, not committing to a relationship.

Opposite project: Having children and creating a family with a partner I chose to have a relationship with.

**Example 2:**

Project: Separating from my spouse.

Creator: The mother.

Purpose: Not having contact with my spouse.

As a result of the project, the offspring may go through separations and divorces. The illnesses that resonate with issues of separation concern the skin.

Opposite project: I connect with the ideal partner. I stay connected with the one I love. I am connected to myself and to others.

**Example 3:**

Project: I can't forgive my brother for the "dirt" he did to me.

Creator: The father.

Purpose: Holding on to a story of the past and being unable to let go.

As a result, the offspring may encounter situations involving others that are difficult to let go of and will likely hold on to old stories with anger. Such an individual may have problems with his or her sigmoid colon as a result.

Opposite project: I forgive others and let go of the past. I evacuate all anger and free myself.

**Note:** We usually desire the opposite of what we were programmed to experience. This notion offers important clues about what occurred in our parents' minds during the project purpose period. If you dream about having a good relationship, it's probable that your parents did not have one. If you wish to have a child but can't, it's likely that one or both of your parents did not want a child at the time they had you. (Remember: this does not mean they didn't love you, only that they were coping with their own life challenges, beliefs, and programs.).

## CREATING A NEW IMPRINT—AN ACTIVE MEDITATION

First, write your new project on a piece of paper and read it out loud several times, using a powerful and determined tone of voice.

Next, incorporate your personal content into the following meditation, and repeat it as often as you feel is needed.

> *Today I decide to create a new project for my future. I acknowledge all biological programs that have permitted me to stay alive so far, and I thank my parents for the gift of life, no matter what their intentions were during the time I was conceived and until I was one year of age. I fully realize that the emotional conflicts, life struggles, and subconscious projects of my parents do not belong to me. I ask my subconscious brain to eliminate all of the limiting programs that are not mine and in particular (insert the unwanted parental project or conflict) _____*

> *_____.*

> *I have learned from my old program, and I am now ready to let it go. I free myself from this limiting imprint, so that I can claim my own path—my true path. I symbolically give my parents the resources they needed at the time to alleviate their stresses and struggles, which include (name the resources)_____*

> *_____*

> *I let go, once and for all, of that which does not belong to me. My decision is to create a new project for myself here and now (name new project):_____*

> *_____*

> *I will express this new project, which is in alignment with my new path. I am programming my future here and now, and I am free. I am in alignment with my true self. I thank my subconscious brain for letting go of the old program and accepting a new one. I do not need to know exactly how this process is going to take place. I trust the power of my subconscious mind.*

*Note: you may use this meditation to let go of one unwanted program at a time.*

Once you fully let go of the parental project, healing can manifest and your life can really change.

# 13

# Healing Ancestral Loyalties

One of the main threads woven throughout this book is that we are subconsciously programmed to ensure the survival of the species. Each generation of human beings carries millions of bits of past information. We all inherit ancestral memories and express the programs associated with them. As the pioneering psychologist Anne Ancelin Schützenberger described, each one of us is a link in the chain of generations, and we sometimes repeat—whether we want to or not—certain situations, events, behaviors, or illnesses as an act of loyalty to our ancestors. In part, we pay the debts of our ancestors by attracting certain circumstances into our life that awaken archived emotional imprints.

Nothing so far allows us to fully prove such transmissions at a psychological, physiological, or neurological level. However, based on empirical studies, the presence of such subconscious transmissions is undeniable. The legacy of our forebears haunts our psyche and shapes our life. Traumatic legacies are transmitted across multiple generations and define our relationships with ourselves, our loved ones, and the larger culture.

The subconscious brain's only mission is to support our survival, so it does not have any interest in our complaints. Whether or not we are happy about what we attract does not concern our subconscious, which simply follows its intrinsic programs. That being said, we can cleverly influence our path by undoing the limiting aspects of our ancestral downloads and reconfiguring certain neuro-pathways for the desired results.

In this chapter, we will walk back further along the time line explored in Chapter 12 with the *project purpose*.

By their very nature, the roots of plants and trees are usually invisible. Similarly, so are the root causes of some of our most challenging problems. While we tend to dig into our childhoods for assumed causes of our adult struggles, sometimes the cause originates from a much earlier time and place. As discussed in previous chapters, the subconscious is greatly connected to our ancestral imprints. We trigger biological expressions of old conflicts that have not been expressed or resolved by our predecessors, and now it is your role to unravel and understand those issues. We can repair old stories and unlock deep-rooted stresses in order to stop carrying burdens belonging to other members of the clan. As we do this, we liberate our ancestors as well as ourselves.

Toward this goal, the following pages offer a perspective on dates, ages, and numbers.

## THE CODING OF NUMBERS

Anne Ancelin Schützenberger observed that depending on their birth order, individuals are uniquely connected with certain members of their clan. For instance, the numbers one, four, seven, and ten are intimately connected, as are the numbers two, five, eight, and eleven and the numbers three, six, nine, and twelve. These sequences can be prolonged according to the number of offspring. Since, biologically, life starts at the moment of conception, the order in which the offspring are positioned takes into consideration all pregnancies, including abortions, stillbirths, and miscarriages from the same biological parents. (Half siblings are not part of the same equation.)

The order in which family members are connected can be easily determined and remembered when you refer to the Generational Matrix diagram on page 208. You will get the opportunity to create your family tree and start your investigation in the next few pages. In the meantime, let's add a few more elements to inspire your observation and expand your ability to make connections.

When we observe our life and what we choose to do as a job or hobby, there is sometimes within that choice the expression of a family secret or struggle. One of my clients, Marie, was working as an artist, creating iron sculptures. She always felt an internal sense of struggle doing this work and was disappointed with her creations most of the time. She suffered emotionally with each project, but nevertheless felt that there was nothing else she wanted to do in her life. While investigating her family tree, she discovered that her great-grandfather had struggled in a very demanding job all his life and died early because of it. He worked in an iron mine in Minnesota from the age of fourteen until his death at forty-three. Was Marie expressing a subconscious loyalty to her great-grandfather by doing her iron sculptures? Her struggles stopped once she realized that she was working with iron by choice, not by necessity like her ancestor. In the wake of understanding that she no longer needed to carry the memory of her great-grandfather's struggle with iron, she started to enjoy her work. Prior to this type of analysis, before making the connection between her work and her great-grandfather's struggle, it had proven difficult for Marie to enjoy herself when making her art. But now she was free.

Another phenomenon that can occur within the family tree is called the Anniversary Syndrome. It relates to events or symptoms that occur repeatedly in direct connection with an anniversary, such as the death of an ancestor, an accident, or any type of significant event experienced by a predecessor. For instance, my client Vincent crashed his car into a tree the day of the anniversary of his father's death. When Vincent was fourteen years old, his father was coming home from work one night when he drove off the road, hit a tree, and died. Vincent was twenty-eight years old when he had the same type of accident. Interestingly, not only did his accident take place on the anniversary of his father's death, but he was also double the age he had been (fourteen years old) when his father died.

It is also more common than one might imagine that individuals express illnesses that are the biological expressions of shocks belonging to ancestors. The following story precisely illustrates this type of occurrence.

## MAXIME'S STORY

Maxime was twenty-four years old when he came to work with René, one of my students. He was otherwise healthy and fit, but a tumor had developed close to his Achilles tendon. René started his investigation by looking with Maxime to see if there was any significant shock or emotional struggle that could have triggered this health issue, and they found no notable stress factors prior to the appearance of the tumor. René then explored potential childhood emotional conflicts, searching to see if Maxime was dealing with a sense of devaluation—the emotional backlash of believing that he wasn't good enough in some way. And in this case, René looked most specifically at emotional conflicts related to movement or performance. None of these types of conflicts could be found in his past or present. The next layer to consider, then, was the gestational period and whether any events or story lines happening with one or both of Maxime's parents at that important developmental stage could be linked to the occurrence of the tumor in present time. Looking at each possibility methodically, they found nothing along these lines either.

The tumor was proving to be a big mystery that led them on a fascinating journey further into the story of Maxime's ancestors. Together they laid out the family tree with names and dates. They looked at the type of life Maxime's ancestors had led, their stresses and challenges, and who died at what age and from what cause. When they came to the story of Maxime's maternal grandfather, the mystery turned into a *revelation*.

Like Maxime, his grandfather was a number one in the clan, meaning that both were the firstborn children, followed by brothers and sisters. The historic invasion of Normandy started on June 6, 1944, along the fifty-mile stretch of the Normandy coast where American, British, and other allied forces fought the Germans. During that time, Maxime's grandfather was involved with the Resistance movement in Paris. As the news spread that the invasion had begun, the Resistance fighters created barricades in the streets of Paris to fight the Germans. During a battle, Maxime's grandfather and his comrades were taking cover behind a barricade. At some point, the shooting ceased. Thinking that the German soldiers were dead and the battle was over, Maxime's grandfather slowly rose up on his toes to look over the barricade, when a bullet struck him in the head. He died instantly. He was twenty-four years old. A fellow fighter who witnessed the event recounted the story to Maxime's grandmother, who was twenty-three at the time.

René asked Maxime, "What does this tumor stop you from doing?" "It stops me from going up on my toes," Maxime reported. In the clan that Maxime had been born into, rising up on your toes at the age of twenty-four meant danger. Maxime at that age developed a tumor in his ankle as a solution to ensure the survival of the clan. At the time of his grandfather's death, Maxime's mother was three months old. The ancestral download to Maxime's subconscious took place when he was conceived years later.

As you know now, we inherit the programs that are useful for survival when we are born, and most often these programs are related to big shocks and traumas within the clan. As solutions to the big stresses, these types of programs have been observed to skip a generation or more, although there are no real "rules" in this regard.

Maxime's story illustrates that we are not born as blank slates but with evolutionary downloads comprising millions of years of evolution, the memories of our clan, and memories stemming from our gestational period.

In addition to what we inherit, we also carry our personal self-created histories. In essence, we write our personal programs as well. We go through our own experiences and imprint more programs, which subsequent generations will eventually inherit.

Enmeshed with the programs that were downloaded to the hard drive known as the brain, these influences come together to produce our patterns. In Maxime's case, what triggered the manifestation of his tumor was marked on the calendar of his biological programming. At the crossroads of a specific date and being in his twenty-fourth year, Maxime developed a tumor that was the biological solution to prevent him from rising up on his toes. Written into the downloaded program was the imprinted memory that doing so meant certain death.

In Maxime's case, there was no other emotional resolution work that he needed to engage in. Nothing in his own life connected to the tumor, and the conflict belonged entirely to his ancestor. As the cellular memory of the conflict was liberated, Maxime's body responded immediately and the tumor dissolved within two weeks with no medical intervention. In this instance, the awareness of his grandfather's download was enough to resolve the decades-old program. Not only was Maxime freed from the impact of the ancestral program, but future generations would be freed from it as well.

## INVESTIGATING YOUR FAMILY TREE

In order to gather more information about your ancestors and their potential influence on your life, I suggest that you draw up your family tree. You may need to interview certain elder family members for this process, paying special attention to birth orders and gathering information about the most significant aspects and events of your ancestors' lives.

## ANCESTRAL TREE

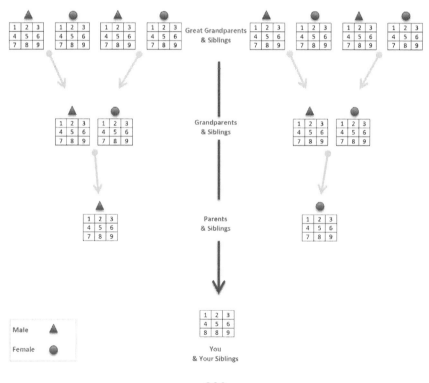

However, please be cautious in your approach so as not to insinuate any fault, blame, or guilt regarding their actions. In addition to your detective work, having the intention to let go of ancestral memories is an essential step, and your subconscious will fully comprehend it. Your desire to work at the ancestral level has power in and of itself.

As you draw up your family tree, organize it with your mother on the right side and your father on the left. Do the same for their parents, their grandparents, and so on (see diagram).

As you write the names of your clan members, recall significant events related to each of them—both those you personally remember and those you discovered with the help of other family members. Remembering the social context (historical, cultural, economic) and personal context (travels, education, expatriation) of their lives, write down as much as you can about their loves, losses, successes, and struggles. The following checklist of significant event types or family characteristics can aid you in filling out the picture:

– Births
– Illegitimate births
– Adoptions
– Loss of children
– Difficult intimate relationships (with a spouse or other)
– Marriages
– Love affairs
– Separations
– Divorces
– Physical abuses
– Sexual abuses
– Immigrations
– Expatriations
– Incarcerations
– Illnesses
– Inheritances

– Bankruptcies
– Deaths
– Poverty
– Betrayals
– Abandonments
– Territorial conflicts
– Job losses
– House or property losses
– Struggles with a sibling(s) or other member(s) of the clan
– Accidents
– Shocks (of any type)
  Personal traits or qualities
– Professions
– Acquisitions
– Personal achievements
– Financial successes

**Note:** If you are an adopted child, you inherited programs from your biological family tree as well as from your adopted family. You are part of the subconscious collective of your present family and your biological ancestors and are influenced by both. Also, your parents were both programmed to adopt you according to their own imprints and the circumstances arising from them.

Go as far back as three or four generations. If you feel that you didn't acquire enough information, trust the process and work with what you have. It might just be enough to help you eliminate some of your present challenges. And it will still be possible for you to utilize the meditation process at the end of this chapter to release unwanted programs.

If you know your exact birth order and those of your clan members, you may be able to see who is primarily connected with you (referring again to the Generational Matrix diagram). Identify the birth order of your parents and grandparents as well as uncles and aunts, and connect numbers that are on the same vertical lines in the square.

As you proceed, please be aware that while you may carry a number that corresponds to someone in the clan, it does not automatically mean that you will carry their programs. Again, there are no rules, and perhaps the most important aspect of your investigation is the need to conduct it with an open mind.

After you create your family tree and include the pertinent information about your family members, take a few moments to think about your life as it relates to your clan.

The following three-step process will help you free yourself from subconscious ties and realign your loyalties, so that you can move forward in your life with greater ease, peace, happiness, and health.

**Step 1: Self-Inquiry**

Ask yourself the following questions, writing your answers in your journal or on blank sheets of paper:

- *What have I been struggling with that is not yet resolved in my life?*

- *What behavior do I want to eliminate?*

- *What health issue do I want to eliminate?*

- *What direction have I taken in life that doesn't feel like my own?*

- *What circumstances am I repeatedly attracting that create stress in my life?*

- *What problem is recurring that I would like to eliminate?*

**Step 2: Identify the Ancestral Cascade Effect**

Observe your family tree and identify the family member connected to you by birth order, as it relates to your most significant challenge(s). Ask yourself the following question:

- *What ancestral memory am I expressing through an illness, a behavior, or a particular life challenge?*

*An example of an illness:*

Linda's great-aunt Verna lost her daughter, who died at eighteen years old during a ski trip. Verna never recovered emotionally after her daughter's death. Linda and her great-aunt Verna are both number two in birth order. Linda triggered breast cancer shortly after her own daughter moved away from her at the age of eighteen to find work in another city. Linda worried constantly about her daughter not being safe and subconsciously expressed a biological solution to her conflict through a breast issue. Linda's exacerbated concern (fear) resonated with the story of Verna, who could not protect her child when she went away from the nest.

*An example of a behavior issue:*

Steven is a fourteen-year-old who lies to his parents most of the time, about most things—even when it seems unnecessary. In birth order, he is a number four. Steven's great-grandfather (number one), who was Jewish, was captured by the Nazis during World War II. They promised not to kill him if he told the truth and gave information about where two Jewish families were hiding. After the great-grandfather revealed the truth, he was killed and the two families were sent to a concentration camp. Four generations later, Steven lies as a survival solution for his great-grandfather who chose to tell the truth and was killed. This statement could summarize the program that Steven inherited: "Telling the truth equals death."

*An example of a life challenge:*

George lost his bakery at forty-six when his rent became unafford-able. His grandfather lost his factory during World War II in Italy, also at the age of forty-six. George and his grandfather are linked by the same birth order, both being number three in their family.

As you continue your investigation, write down the names and stories of family members whom you feel are directly related to your emotional, behavioral, or physical state. The following question will help focus your attention in a powerful way:

◆ *What patterns am I repeating in my life that resemble those of one or more of my forebears and do not belong to me?*

Below you will find the same checklist of examples of significant event types and characteristics mentioned above. You can now use it to identify what conflicts, patterns, or situations you may be expressing or repeating as a descendant.

- Births
- Illegitimate births
- Adoptions
- Loss of children
- Difficult intimate relationships (with a spouse or other)
- Marriages
- Love affairs
- Separations
- Divorces
- Physical abuses
- Sexual abuses
- Immigrations
- Expatriations
- Incarcerations
- Illnesses
- Inheritances

- Bankruptcies
- Deaths
- Poverty
- Betrayals
- Abandonments
- Territorial conflicts
- Job losses
- House or property losses
- Struggles with a sibling(s) or other member(s) of the clan
- Accidents
- Shocks (of any type)
- Personal traits or qualities
- Professions
- Acquisitions
- Personal achievements
- Financial successes

## Step 3: Heal Invisible Patterns of Loyalty

Once you have gathered and contemplated this important information, take a moment to affirm that the conflicts or patterns originating with your ancestors do not belong to you. Always keep in mind that they were transmitted to you subconsciously because of the biological laws of survival of the species. These conflicts and patterns are no longer necessary in your life, and you have a divine right to claim your freedom from them.

Similar to the process at the end of the previous chapter, here you can work on each program or pattern you desire to eliminate, inserting your story in the meditation that follows:

*Today I recognize and acknowledge that I am expressing a program that does not belong to me but, in fact, belongs to (name the person)_____ . I desire to eliminate this program from my subconscious and free myself from this ancestral memory. I am asking my subconscious to give back this conflict to (name the person) _____. (Note: If you don't know to whom the program you want to eliminate belongs, you can give it back symbolically: write "To whom it may concern" and trust that your subconscious will do the work.)*

*I thank my ancestor for his/her existence and courage, and I understand that he/she did the best he/she could, considering his/her circumstances and limitations at the time. I symbolically offer my ancestor the following knowledge, advice, and resources so that I no longer have to express a struggle belonging to him/her or provide a solution to his/her emotional distress today. (Name the ideas and resources you would like to offer your ancestor that could have helped him or her at the time. This could be as simple as providing a strategy or encouraging an emotional state, such as independence, detachment, flexibility, or faith.)*

_____

_____

_____

_____

*I now claim my independence from old programs, all of which are no longer useful to me. I free myself from all burdens, conflicts, afflictions, struggles, and emotional stresses belonging to other members of the clan. All parts of me are in agreement with this statement.*

*I am free from ancestral programs. I am free to create my own life! I create my future here and now, on my terms and with power. I thank my subconscious for allowing this change to happen.*

*Now that I have freed myself from these programs, I can create the opposite programs of the ones that were a challenge to me until now. The opposite programs are (describe the opposite programs; see examples below): _____*

*_____*

*In doing so, I claim the right to new programs, which will lead me along a whole new path: one that matches my vision and supports the fulfillment of my destiny.*

*Examples of opposite programs:*

- The opposite of a program of poverty = claiming a program of financial security and abundance.

- The opposite of a program related to a difficult marriage = claiming that you are creating a loving, respectful, and successful relationship.

- The opposite of a program related to the loss of a child = claiming a program of healthy reproduction, safe parenthood, protection, and life.

- The opposite of a program of devaluation = claiming a program of significance and recognition.

As you move through each of the above steps, design your new path in vivid detail. Remember to use only positive terms to free yourself from the past as you create your new destiny.

# 14

# The Circle of Health

Through the power of your own determination, courage, and most of all your willingness to grow, you can now continue to expand your knowledge using the Bio-Breakthrough Dictionary that immediately follows. It is a reference guide that you can turn to again and again in your process of healing and evolving.

It is likely that when you began your journey through these pages, you had already sought understanding and healing through various methods—remedies, treatments, guided meditations, and, of course, books. And whether this is your first self-help book or your fiftieth, my wish is that you acknowledge yourself for your commitment to your well-being. By utilizing the information and steps in this book, you have learned the noble craft of self-healing and emotional mastery.

Now it's time to review the self-analysis masterpiece you have created, revel in the discoveries you have made, and reflect on the healing journey you have experienced.

Let's briefly revisit where you have been and what you have done.

You first stated your health issue and then defined your exact healing objective. You learned how to connect with the meaning of your health disorder, tracing it back to the triggering event related to it. You then altered the emotional state related to the triggering event by changing your perception at the time it occurred. You traveled back in time and helped your younger self access powerful resources to deprogram past imprints.

Later, you investigated your parents' lives during your gestation and uncovered your subconscious parental projects. Internally, you offered resources to your parents so that you no longer have to express solutions to their struggles through your own existence, and you are free to create your own life project.

Finally, you pieced together your family tree and looked at the lives of your ancestors. You made connections between certain aspects of your life and theirs by observing behavior patterns, illnesses, significant choices, and mystifying challenges. You explored the ways in which some of your struggles may be expressions of loyalty toward them. After thanking them and symbolically giving their conflicts back to them, you internally provided them with new resources as well, so that they, too, can be freed from their stresses and limitations.

Upon discovering your *parental project* and investigating invisible ancestral loyalties, you began to reclaim your *own* path—one that you personally designed, independent of unwanted influences.

After traveling so far back in time to do your inner work, you are closer than ever to the purpose of your soul. With every step you take to remember your innate and profound desires for health and happiness, and as you claim your right to full self-expression, you are realigning with your true self.

## THE PATH TO THE CENTER OF YOUR TRUE SELF

The truth is, we never know what is going to happen next. This is particularly important to keep in mind if you are afflicted with a health disorder that has been given a bad prognosis. Yet the internal resources and power to change do exist. As the stories of Jeanne, Lucy, Marc, and the others show, a health disorder can be a chance to grow in consciousness, away from limiting beliefs and unwanted programs. It is an invitation to finally forgive—both yourself and those who have hurt you—and to be changed by the love that comes rushing in on the heels of that forgiveness.

The road you have traveled, from the moment of your conception—when you downloaded your subconscious parental projects and became the loyal holder of ancestral blueprints—up to this very day, is an unfathomable and beautiful mystery. You are alive today because of all that took place before you were even conceived and everything that has happened in your life until now.

*Ultimately, you can expect a miracle, because you are one.*

If you have a serious or chronic health issue, you may have traveled farther away from your center, the home of your true self. Your soul is waiting for a shift within your psyche so that you can regain your core equilibrium. An emotional conflict, whether ancestral, gestational, or personal, threw you off balance. But as you now realize, the more you release limiting programs, the closer you get to your center.

This is also true even if you aren't afflicted with a particular health condition. You may still sense that you are far from your center because of the strong influences of gestational or ancestral programs that you are expressing. Ultimately, the Circle of Health that I am about to describe can greatly serve you as a map to support your unique process of self-empowerment.

## CREATING YOUR CIRCLE OF HEALTH

Imagine yourself connected to your center and vibrating in alignment with all parts of the universe. In this state, how do you feel? What doors open for you? What possibilities are within reach? In sync with the forces of the universe, what can you do? What do you want to do? We could say that your center represents a perfect *residence* of vibration in the universe. As spiritual beings who are evolving in consciousness, we each feel the pull of this resonance, this radiance. And it is only when we are biologically, emotionally, and spiritually healthy that we vibrate the closest to our center. The higher our level of consciousness, the closer we get to our true self.

Now that you are vibrationally attuned to your center, imagine four concentric circles with you in the center. All combined, this is your overall Circle of Health, a metaphorical map of the layers of your programs. By helping you investigate and resolve your issues, it is meant to help guide you back to your center.

Referring to the Circle of Health diagram, review the four main steps you have worked on in the previous chapters and reflect on them as parts of the larger picture. Each of the steps can be seen as a layer within your Circle of Health. As you explore the set of circles, start with the outermost one, and then survey the next circle as you gradually move toward the center. Allow yourself to be creative in your review of this material. You can imagine walking along the circles in your mind, draw the circles on a piece of paper, sketch them out on a large white board, or create imaginary circles on the floor.

Essentially, you can use the Circle of Health as a tool to symbolically access different aspects and phases of your programming. As you do this exercise, you are allowing your mind to comprehend the totality of your discoveries and your journey as a whole.

Outlined here in a distilled way, the four main steps you have worked on in the previous chapters are integrated within the Circle of Health as follows:

**Circle 1—*Triggering Event:*** Define the meaning of your illness and uncover the event directly related to the emotional distress that triggered the health disorder that you want to eliminate (see page 122). Access an alternate perception regarding the triggering event related to your condition and let go of the conflict (see page 143).

**Circle 2—*Programming Events:*** Travel back into your past and access the personal experiences that programmed you at a subconscious level to have this particular health challenge. Provide your younger self with resources in order to heal old wounds (see page 161). You may uncover particular dates and events corresponding to bio-memorized cycles, which are part of your time line of personal programs, and these should be integrated as well (see page 73).

**Circle 3—*Project Purpose:*** Uncover your *project purpose* and offer resources to your parents. Create your own life project (see page 182).

**Circle 4—*Ancestral Programs:*** Investigate your family tree and unlock ancestral loyalties that became programs that do not belong to you (see page 208).

## CIRCLE OF HEALTH

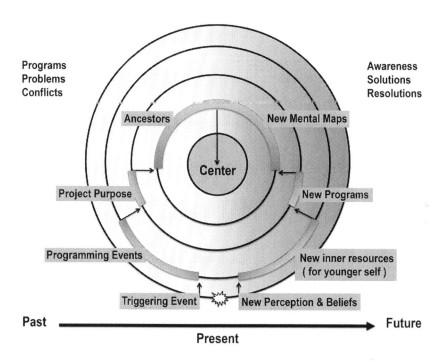

Imagine yourself traveling from one level to the next, and work your way to your center. As you traverse each layer, you may feel the freedom of a newly available path at each level. For instance, you may feel the freedom of having changed your perception of the triggering event. Then you may enter the circle corresponding to your life story and feel the lightness of your younger self, which no longer carries limiting perceptions from the past. You may feel free from painful beliefs and decisions that arose from that perception. You may access the freedom of a new path as you enter the level corresponding to gestational programs. And finally, you may sense what it feels like to be liberated from ancestral imprints, which are no longer yours to carry.

As you look over your Circle of Health, allow yourself to appreciate the work you have already accomplished and to integrate the metaphor it represents. It is also possible that other relevant memories and dates of events will come to you later. The Circle of Health will be forever available to you, any time you wish to reenter it to map out and clear up any aspects of your programming.

As you use this map, you will uncover the meaning of your life story—*which your mind will strongly recognize*—and solutions beyond your expectations will manifest.

## YOUR IDEAL VIBRATIONAL POINT—A MEDITATION OF DEEP HEALING

Now that you have integrated the Circle of Health, you can reach your center along a new path and be well on your way toward your future.

As you observe the road you have traveled, place your focus once again on your center, your ideal vibrational point. Having resolved so many aspects of your life, test your emotional state from this position. Do you feel more centered and in alignment with your true self? Are there layers of your psyche that are inviting further investigation? Give yourself time to gradually continue with this transformational work. Have faith and patience. You now have the tools you need, and you can trust the Circle of Health, as you will always be welcome to enter and explore it again.

In closing, I invite you to read and repeat the following meditation as often as needed. You might also write it down longhand and place it on your desk or night table. In this way, you will stimulate your subconscious to assist you in the healing process on an ongoing basis.

Simply begin by imagining yourself in the middle of your healing circle, connected to your soul, which is always your ideal vibrational point.

> *I am aware that I subconsciously allowed a health disorder (or limiting behavior) to manifest as a result of an experience of emotional distress. I realize that my perception at the time did not allow me to meet one or more of my vital needs. Today, I have repaired the stress of the past because I revisited it with a new perception—a perception that empowers me to meet my needs and inspires me to forgive myself and others. I am free from old beliefs. I am free from my past and the wounds of my childhood. I have brought resources*

*to my younger self, and I will take care of my inner child for the rest of my life. I am free from parental subconscious programs. I forgive my parents for their limitations, and I thank them for giving me life, no matter what their circumstances and limitations were. I am now responsible for my life. I owe it to myself to make my life a masterpiece, with my own projects and purpose in alignment with my most profound desires. I am free from all limiting ancestral programs. I am ready to live life on my terms. I thank all my ancestors for the gift of life. I offer them my discoveries so that they can heal as well. I thank all human beings who have played a role, good or bad, in the theater of my life up until now. I am in resonance with my true self and attract all life-affirming circumstances that correspond to who I am today. I am free from the past. I thank my subconscious mind for assisting me in my new journey toward health independence, freedom, and happiness. I am now in full alignment with my purpose in life, and I am connected to my soul.*

*It is time for me to embrace my future and welcome the powerful liberation of walking a new path.*

# Part III: The Bio-Breakthrough Dictionary

# The Bio-Breakthrough Dictionary:
## Introduction

The information provided in the *Bio-Breakthrough Dictionary* will help you make connections among various organs or imbalances and the nature of the emotional conflicts associated with them. You will discover that each health disorder is far too precise to be a random incident resulting from a mere cellular coding error. As you gain clarity about the nature of your emotional conflict, you will be able to make great progress in your quest for health. A new and growing awareness will allow you to see what you need to address in your life. As you come to understand the true origin of your condition, your ability to manage your issue can dramatically shift and allow, perhaps for the first time, an opportunity for your subconscious mind to let go of the archaic program of survival that was put in place to support you during times of stress.

## THE POWER OF SELF-RESPONSIBILITY

In preparation for getting the greatest benefit from using the dictionary as a reference guide for health disorders, there are a few key points to keep in mind as you proceed.

We arrive at a crucial turning point in the healing journey when we remember something that perhaps we knew all along in our heart: the environment is not responsible for our emotional struggles. Rather, it is our perceptions and subconscious programs that are at the root of our distress.

225

With the newfound knowledge that we unconsciously attract situations, circumstances, and people that are a match to our conflicts, we can start freeing ourselves from unwanted programs. Rather than blaming others for our problems and challenges, we can recover our power by honestly taking responsibility for our programs and, therefore, the life we created—including the illnesses, heartaches, failures, and other setbacks we have endured.

## A WORD ABOUT IDENTIFYING THE TRIGGER OF AN ILLNESS

A tremendous shock will not necessarily trigger an illness. It depends on many factors, such as your perceptions during the shock, the duration and level of your stress, and your capacity to cope.

If you have a health issue, it is possible that you don't recall a specific shock that you experienced in the few days, weeks, or months prior to your symptoms. Sometimes an illness can be triggered by something other than a shock. The mechanisms of the subconscious mind are extremely complex and not yet entirely understood. However, the reminder of a shock or the return of the date of an event that the autonomic brain recognizes can sometimes trigger a biological response. Also, illnesses can be triggered after a long period of chronic stress.

It does not appear that certain illnesses, such as cancer, take years to develop on the physiological level. Often the recurrence of an old emotional conflict can be the source of the onset of illness in present time. By investigating your historical background, you can be your own detective, gathering information and looking for clues that will help you to understand the nature and roots of your emotional conflicts. Whether you are dealing with cancer or any other illness, you need to examine how you may have been predisposed to it and investigate your personal story and inherited programs.

While understanding the exact nature of the emotional conflict is important, actually *resolving and getting past* the problem are essential. That way, if challenges arise in the future that are similar to those that triggered your physical condition, you won't be impacted in the same way.

## A WORD ABOUT THE PHASES OF ILLNESS

Dr. Hamer discovered that there are two phases to an illness—the active and healing phases (see page 53). Additionally, depending on the organ and tissue affected, certain health disorders manifest themselves primarily during the recovery phase—the resolution of the emotional conflict—of an illness. This particular occurrence depends on the origin of the embryonic tissue solicited to express the biological response and involves organs related to the new brain mesoderm and ectoderm layers. Understandably, it is somewhat surprising, and perhaps unsettling, to discover this new notion. The healing phase of an emotional conflict can cause serious symptoms. One should not stop medical supervision because one thinks, or was told by someone else, that one is experiencing the resolution phase of one's disease.

While the findings described in this book make remarkable scientific sense, they also need to be further explored. Since it appears that illness is directly related to our subconscious programs and our levels of stress, it can be difficult to predict with certainty the course that an illness or symptom might take. The way the subconscious mind functions is complex, and the body's responses that are triggered cannot always be anticipated.

## THE LINK BETWEEN OUR HUMAN NEEDS AND OUR PHYSIOLOGY—A FINAL WORD

If you approach your exploration of the body as an opportunity to bring you to a deeper understanding of your vital needs, you will be well on your way to accessing the power to heal. Finding a solution to any emotional conflict involves a process of introspection, letting go of certain limiting perceptions, and the realization that meeting our needs is always possible, no matter the circumstances. Each moment is a new opportunity to perceive the experiences we are going through with a more empowering and self-loving perspective and attitude. As conscious human beings, we have the freedom to break away from our basic animal programs and the correlated fears that limit us. Through new perceptions about how to meet our needs, and a change in our philosophy of life, we can rise above our old programs. This is our challenge, but it is also our chance to heal at the deepest level.

# The Bio-Breakthrough Dictionary: Organs and Conditions

It is essential to read this book before you start using the dictionary. As you peruse the pages of the dictionary, reading about the many astonishing organs and systems of the human body, you will essentially be looking into a mirror that reflects the important needs we explored throughout the book. At first our needs are physiological; thereafter, they relate to security and protection, then significance and belonging, and finally boundaries.

The dictionary entries focus on the emotional conflicts associated with the primary organs of the human body, as well as specific health disorders and common ailments. In some cases, there will be more than one emotional conflict that might apply to a particular organ or condition.

The vital organs (such as the lung alveoli, stomach, liver, and colon) are intimately connected to our physiological needs (like catching the "morsel" of food and oxygen). The enveloping organs (such as the dermis, pericardium, and pleura) are related to the need for security, shelter, and protection. And our muscles and bones, which allow us movement in order to stay together, mirror our needs for belonging and significance in relationship with others. Our coronary arteries, bronchi, and bladder are related to our need for boundaries. (The embryonic origin is only included when the discussion pertains to an organ. See the Embryonic Layers section, page 45, for details.)

While examples are frequently offered to demonstrate how emotional conflicts may be expressed, in certain instances, descriptions of conflicts are purposely defined within a wider scope or in few words. This allows plenty of space in your thought process to make connections with your own unique circumstances. In any case, as you read and investigate the different themes and meanings, notice what resonates most for you, and trust your instincts.

The information provided in this dictionary is not a substitute for medical diagnoses or consultations with your professional health-care provider.

## Accident

An unpredictable and potentially dangerous event.

**Emotional conflict(s):** Often an accident occurs when one is subconsciously in disagreement with the path one is on or the direction one is taking. It can also represent the recurrence of a cycle that corresponds to the memory of a distress of the same nature (see bio-memorized cellular cycles on page 73).

## Achilles Tendon

A tendon of the posterior leg, serving to attach the calf to the heel. It is one of the most powerful tendons of the leg.

*Embryonic origin: new brain mesoderm.*

**Emotional conflict(s):** Often is affected when an individual feels devalued in a context of sports or fitness. It may also symbolize one's need to perform within one's business at a higher level, wanting to go beyond one's limits.

## Acid Reflux (GERD)

*See Hiatal Hernia.*

## Acne

A skin condition that causes inflamed red growths, blackheads, and cysts to form.

**Emotional conflict(s):** A feeling of being soiled from an aesthetic point of view. Emotional stress related to not feeling confident about one's sex appeal. One feels the need to protect oneself from being damaged by the scrutiny of others and fears losing face.

*Example:* A young adult feels devalued about his or her appearance because of criticisms from the environment or being compared to others during puberty. He or she develops acne as a result.

*Note: Acne rosacea* often resonates with a notion of separation from the clan.

## Acromegaly

Hypertrophy of bone tissue (increase in size) caused by overproduction of growth hormone by the pituitary gland

**Emotional conflict(s):** An issue related to a need to be bigger and stronger.

*Example:* One feels the need to create a stronger bone structure in order to impress the enemy and defend oneself.

## Addison's Disease

An autoimmune disease related to the underfunctioning of the adrenal cortex.

**Emotional conflict(s):** Pertains specifically to a conflict of self-devaluation for not moving in the right direction.

*Also see Adrenal Glands.*

## Adhesions

The sticking together of different tissues, resulting in an abnormal union of membranous surfaces.

**Emotional conflict(s):** Being attached in an excessive way to negative thoughts or old stories. May symbolize the need to heal a scar quickly after surgery. One may metaphorically want to reconnect pieces of oneself, when feeling fragmented by an emotional wound.

## Adrenal Glands

Located on top of each kidney, adrenal glands produce steroid hormones such as norepinephrine and cortisol, which play important roles in monitoring the body's stress response.

*Embryonic origin: new brain mesoderm.*

**Emotional conflict(s):** Pertains to feelings of having gone in the wrong direction or having made the wrong decision. As a result, the brain's perfect solution is to reduce the secretion of cortisol. A state of fatigue will then force the individual to stop proceeding along the "wrong path." In nature, adrenal exhaustion is related to a mechanism of survival. It provides a solution for animals when they get lost from their herd, which symbolizes being "off track." For instance, the sheep that has moved away from its flock (and is heading dangerously in the wrong direction) will be subjected to a temporary necrosis (tissue death) of the adrenal gland, which causes the animal to stop from straying farther off. As soon as the animal is back on the right track, the resolution phase of the direction conflict occurs and cortisol levels go back to normal. Although this does not imply that we must "follow the pack" (which could be family, close friends, coworkers, a certain group, etc.), we may feel that we have taken the wrong path (literally or figuratively), and we may struggle with our choice.

*Example:* A man is in a relationship with a woman for three years when she expresses her desire to get married. He goes along with the idea only to please her, although he feels that he does not want to get married. As the weeks pass during the wedding preparations, he feels increasingly tired, until he reaches

232

a state of complete exhaustion. As a result, he asks her if they can postpone the wedding. She gives him an ultimatum and threatens to break up with him if he makes her wait any longer. They end up calling the wedding off. A few days after they separate, the man's cortisol levels increase and his energy comes back—all because he feels in alignment with his choice.

*Also see Addison's Disease.*

## Agnosia

Inability to recognize sensations because of a cerebral deficit (often after a brain injury).

**Emotional conflict(s):** Distress related to a conflict involving the senses. An event can prompt the need for the loss of one or more of the senses in alignment with a specific conflict.

Sometimes the subconscious may prompt an accident causing the impairment of one of the sensory functions, such as seeing, hearing, feeling, smelling, or tasting.

*Example:* One feels metaphorically that one's situation at work "stinks" and winds up having an accident, resulting in a brain injury that stops one from being able to smell one's surroundings.

## Algodystrophy

A shoulder/hand condition that involves a combination of symptoms, such as painful muscle aches, edema, and sometimes wasting of the muscles.

**Emotional conflict(s):** Involves two conflicts of devaluation, one followed by the other. The first conflict is of devaluation related to movement, which may lead to a sprain or fracture. If, during the healing phase of the fracture, the person has a second conflict of devaluation, then algodystrophy may occur. For instance, one may feel devaluated in relation to the "bad timing" of the injury, or about not healing fast enough, thus stopping the healing phase from occurring.

*Example:* A man falls down the stairs in his house and breaks his arm. While his arm is in a cast, he feels devalued because he is unable to use his right hand to do important work. The fracture happens exactly at the time when he thought he needed to be the most efficient at work. Algodystrophy occurs because he is continuously thinking that he is not healing well or fast enough.

## Allergies

A hyperreaction of the immune system. An allergic reaction occurs when an individual's immune system reacts abnormally to a harmless substance in the environment.

**Emotional conflict(s):** An allergy occurs based on the memory of a stress due to a separation. An allergic reaction is unrelated to the toxicity of the allergen. The part of the body that has recorded the stress will be triggered every time a particular allergen is present in the environment. An allergic reaction often involves the squamous epithelium of the skin and may also affect the sinuses and the throat. When the trauma of separation is strongly associated with fear, the allergic reaction will affect the trachea and bronchi.

Allergies give us important clues about memories of a separation that have not been fully processed. Allergies solicit the ectodermic tissues, causing instant reactions that are prompted by memories of disconnection and are linked to the first time the separation occurred. By identifying the memory of separation linked to the allergen, one may be able to eliminate the allergy. It is important to remember that the brain makes metaphorical associations (see the examples below).

*Example:* A child may be eating strawberries when his father tells him that he will be sent to a boarding school. At that moment the strawberries become subconsciously associated with the stress of being abruptly separated from the family. This shock will create a feeling of separation in the context of strawberries; subsequently, every time this child smells or eats something that contains strawberries, he will have an allergic reaction.

- An allergy to milk products may be related to an abrupt separation from the mother as an infant.
- Allergies to gluten may be linked to a memory of separation while wheat or bread was present in the immediate environment.
- An allergy to the sun may be directly related to a separation from the father, since subconsciously the symbol of the father is the sun.

Different ectodermic tissues of the body can be affected by an allergy, based on the nature of the conflict:

- Skin: conflict of simple separation
- Sinuses: conflict of separation associated with a felt experience of "this stinks!"
- Trachea and bronchi: conflict of separation associated with fear
- Eyes: conflict of separation associated with vision
- Digestive system: conflict of separation associated with a felt experience of "this is indigestible!"

**Note:** Also consider the separations the parents went through in their respective lives during gestation, to understand the allergies that their child may express.

## Alopecia

Partial or complete loss of hair from areas of the body where it normally grows.

**Emotional conflict(s):** Generally related to a combination of three conflicts, including a feeling of separation, devaluation, and loss of protection (fear).

Alopecia pertains to feelings of self-devaluation in a context of separation, with an underlying sense of injustice. When the head is affected, it can relate to feeling disconnected—either intellectually or spiritually—and unable to grasp subtleties, especially those related to spirituality or God.

## Alzheimer's Disease

Mental deterioration that occurs progressively, due to a generalized degeneration of the brain, thus resulting in episodes of memory loss, disorientation, and dementia.

**Emotional conflict(s):** Subconscious need to forget terrible memories in order to escape the reality of the past. This condition allows one to erase painful memories, such as abuse, rape, war, or concentration-camp atrocities. It can also pertain to being unable to understand certain problems well enough to find solutions for them. It can express a struggle between having to face the truth and a need to deny the evidence.

**Note:** This condition can also be the expression of the nonresolution of a multitude of emotional conflicts that have occurred throughout one's lifetime. Chronic conflicts that alternate between active and healing phases may have created scars in many areas of the brain (control centers of the biological expression of our organs), causing memory impairment.

## Amenorrhea

An abnormal absence of menstruation.

**Emotional conflict(s):** Can be the expression of one's feelings of opposition toward one's mother during puberty. It can also relate to a conflict with one's sexuality and a subconscious desire to remain a virgin.

## Amnesia

Loss of memory (partial or total).

**Emotional conflict(s):** Can be associated with an emotional distress linked to separation and being unable to grieve the loss of a loved one. The condition is related to a profound desire to forget painful memories. Also, one may feel the need to fade out and disappear from the world as if one were not authorized to live.

### Amyotrophic Lateral Sclerosis (ALS) (also called Lou Gehrig's disease)

A disease of the nerve cells in the brain and spinal cord that control voluntary muscle movement.

**Emotional conflict(s):** Distress related to self-devaluation connected to movement, especially in terms of regretting a gesture.

*Example:* A man slapped his brother in the face and regrets having used the "wrong gesture" with his sibling. Subconsciously he destroys the muscles in his body to ensure that they cannot be used in an unsuitable or undesired manner in the future.

### Anemia

A condition related to having an insufficient number of healthy red blood cells to carry adequate oxygen to the tissues, resulting in pallor and weariness.

**Emotional conflict(s):** Deep self-devaluation, combined with the absence of interest in life. Anemia involving a lack of iron in the organism is the expression of a conflict of devaluation related to the act of "doing," specifically due to an inability to go into action.

*Example:* A woman feels constantly criticized and mistreated by her only daughter and, at the same time, feels that she has nothing to live for. She develops anemia as a result.

**Note:** Refractory anemia (also called aplastic anemia), a blood disorder in which the bone marrow produces insufficient new blood cells, is related to a resistance to being helped. It is often a symptom of powerlessness in the elderly person who feels that there is no point in doing more in order to continue living.

### Aneurysm

An enlargement or ballooning of a portion of an artery. With the potential to rupture, an aneurysm can be situated on any artery of the body, and its seriousness will depend upon its size and location.

**Emotional conflict(s):** Related to wanting to prove something and going against others in the process. When the aorta is concerned, an aneurysm can pertain to territorial issues within the clan (blood) or with a member of the clan. One is being pushed to do something one doesn't want to do and feels under pressure.

*Example:* A man feels pushed by his father and brother to leave the family business, and he struggles with being rejected from the clan. As a result of this conflict he develops an aneurysm.

## Angioma

Benign growth derived from the vascular or lymphatic vessel walls.

*Embryonic origin: ectoderm.*

**Emotional conflict(s):** Distress associated with having too much or not enough contact (skin) with the clan (blood). Territorial conflict related to the clan, experienced in a tonality of separation with a lack of self-worth.

## Ankle

The ankle is the joint where the foot and leg meet. It is an intricate network of bones, ligaments, tendons, and muscles.

*Embryonic origin: new brain mesoderm.*

**Emotional conflict(s):** Related to self-devaluation in movement (often sports). May be linked to a conflict related to direction at a specific moment or during a prolonged period of time.

*Example:* One may be torn between leaving or staying at one's job—doubting the direction one should take—and sprain one's ankle as a result.

## Anorexia

A condition characterized by self-starvation or a loss of appetite. One is obsessed with the fear of becoming overweight. Individuals with anorexia are often disconnected from the reality of how they look. They see themselves as fat, even when they are extremely thin.

**Emotional conflict(s):** Due to the combination of two active conflicts involving the cerebral cortex. One is linked to a painful and indigestible territorial conflict, and the other is related to another type of territorial issue, such as "losing" territory or being unable to "mark" the territory. Quite often, an issue with the mother will be linked to anorexia. For instance, the problem may pertain to having a difficult relationship with a mother who is perceived as cold or indifferent. Or an early memory of being weaned abruptly can be part of the issue. Anorexia can also be related to rejecting the mother (or mother figure) and not wanting to become like her.

*Example:* A young woman endures a situation that is indigestible, involving someone within the clan, such as sexual abuse or incest (territorial anger). If this conflict occurs simultaneously with another type of territorial issue, such as seeing her mother as a rival and competing with her in the territory, the young woman may become anorexic.

## Anus

Situated at the lower end of the anal canal, the anus is the external opening of the rectum through which the solid wastes (stool) of the body are eliminated.

*Embryonic origin: ectoderm.*

**Emotional conflict(s):** Conditions of the anus relate to an identity conflict. One feels that one's place has been taken by someone else and experiences a sense of separation from one's territory. Figuratively, a problem with the anus can also be the expression of one's distress due to the violation of an important alliance with another. The absence of an anus in a newborn (imperforated anus) can represent a biological solution to the fear of being sodomized, which would have been originally experienced by either a parent or an ancestor.

## Anxiety

A state of apprehension, ranging from mild uneasiness to intense dread, that is typically accompanied by compulsive behavior.

**Emotional conflict(s):** Staying on high alert and obsessively looking for clues ("proof") about being either guilty or innocent in a given situation. Intensively mobilizing energy to be prepared in case of a need to protect oneself. Living in survival mode as if danger is imminent.

## Aorta

The main artery of the body. Its role is to supply oxygenated blood to the entire body through the circulatory system. It originates from the left ventricle of the heart, passes over the heart, and runs down in front of the backbone to the abdomen, where it splits into two smaller arteries.

*Embryonic origin: ectoderm.*

**Emotional conflict(s):** Problem stemming from a loss of distal territory (at a distance) or related to the content within the territory. Issues with the aorta can also relate to difficulties with having many territories at once and being unable to manage them (such as many houses or several businesses).

## Appendix

The appendix is a pouch attached to the first portion of the large intestine. It is believed to have been part of the digestive system in our primitive ancestors. It is a vestigial remnant, indicative of our ancestors' predominantly herbivorous diet, which can also be observed in some animals. For instance, the horse stores food in the appendix, which operates as a first stomach.

*Embryonic origin: endoderm.*

**Emotional conflict(s):** Concerns related to a situation perceived as awful and indigestible. A conflict related to an ugly situation that stays on hold, from which no exit is possible. There can also be a need to keep something aside for later use, such as food or other essential resources, and not being able to do so.

## Armpit

The hollow space situated under the arm at the shoulder level.

**Note:** The embryonic origin will depend on the area affected.

**Emotional conflict(s):** A feeling of self-devaluation related to being unable to symbolically put the offspring "under the wing" and protect them. In an opposite fashion, problems with the armpit can also refer to feeling overly protected by one's parents and devalued for not being independent as a human being.

## Arrhythmia

A condition that occurs when the electrical impulses in the heart that coordinate the heartbeat don't work properly.

**Emotional conflict(s):** Conflict of loss of territory or its contents, felt in a masculine way (often a conflict of a sexual nature). Feeling pressured by an authority. This conflict can also pertain to feeling out of balance with time and not finding the right rhythm.

*Also see Heart.*

## Arteriosclerosis

Hardening and thickening of the walls of the arteries.

**Emotional conflict(s):** An issue related to being unable to get out of the house and feeling bound by one's surroundings. For instance, being obligated to stay home to take care of a sick parent or child. It can also be linked to having difficulties expressing love to others.

## Arteritis

An inflammatory condition of the inner layers or the outer coat of one or more arteries.

**Emotional conflict(s):** Distress related to a sense of separation and devaluation within the clan. During the active phase of such a conflict, a portion of the arterial walls necrotizes, thus allowing more blood to flow through the arteries. During the healing phase, the arterial walls are repaired and strengthened by calcification of the fats.

*Example:* A man is experiencing a self-devaluation conflict related to his mother, who threatens to disinherit him every time they argue. He develops arteritis as a result.

## Arthritis

An inflammation within one or more joints. Symptoms of arthritis include pain and limited function of the joints.

**Emotional conflict(s):** Linked to a conflict of self-devaluation that relates to combat or a situation of opposition. When the upper limbs are affected, it indicates a situation where one is holding back. When the lower limbs are concerned, it indicates a lack of flexibility or a resistance to following others.

Arthritis often reflects a person's lack of confidence in being able to support others. It can also be the expression of one's fear that a loved one who represents support may break down or fail (in that case, the fear of failure related to the other is integrated as if it was happening to oneself). Juvenile arthritis may be linked to self-devaluation about one's gesture or movement in a context of familial oppression.

## Ascites

An accumulation of fluid (usually serous fluid) in the abdominal (peritoneal) cavity. Conditions such as abdominal cancer, congestive heart failure, liver disease, or kidney failure can cause ascites.

**Emotional conflict(s):** The role of ascites in the case of abdominal cancer is to prevent adhesions within the intestinal walls when a tumor grows, which may cause a blockage. In general, the accumulation of liquid prevents the sticking of internal tissues, creating space within the organs so that they can continue to function. If the quantity of ascites is too abundant, a certain quantity can be removed in order to decompress the diaphragm and relieve pain.

**Note:** Existing ascites can increase due to water retention related to a conflict of annihilation (total defeat) and feelings of isolation and/or abandonment (kidney conflict) while having to face an illness or a bad prognosis.

## Asthma

*See Lungs.*

## Astigmatism

A vision condition that causes blurriness, due either to the irregular shape of the cornea or, sometimes, the curvature of the lens inside the eye.

**Emotional conflict(s):** Linked to separation in the context of vision, often related to loving and hating someone at the same time. The biological solution is to contort (or deform) the view of the part that is problematic and causes stress. It can also pertain to one's desire to hide one's suffering by creating a blur around it.

*Example:* A man who loves his wife and at the same time no longer likes the way she looks develops astigmatism as a subconscious solution to contort what he does not like to see.

## Ataxia

A lack of muscle coordination during voluntary movements, such as walking or picking up objects.

**Emotional conflict(s):** Distress related to movement and the fear that becoming highly competent in a certain context (moving up) could become a disadvantage. Being pushed down during a moment of ascension (for instance, during sports or when being reviewed for a job promotion). Physical distress associated with having to push beyond limits, when help should be available.

*Example:* A woman walks home from work every day while knowing that her husband could easily pick her up and alleviate her burden. She develops ataxia as a result.

*Note:* The condition known as Friedrich's ataxia pertains to a conflict related to a social fall and a lack of protection from the father.

## Atheroma

A condition affecting artery walls in which plaques (cholesterol) form beneath the intima (innermost layer of endothelial cells).

**Emotional conflict(s):** Loss of love and feelings of disempowerment within one's territory. Distress related to injustice and loss of pride.

## Atrophy (Muscular)

Muscle atrophy is the wasting away of muscle mass. Body parts or tissues become smaller or degenerate.

**Emotional conflict(s):** Feelings of devaluation related to movement. Conflict related to having had the wrong gesture (literally or figuratively) or not being able to effectively take action. The atrophy appears in the area of the body related to the devaluation.

## Attention Deficit Hyperactivity Disorder (ADHD)

Difficulty paying attention, focusing, and concentrating, especially in children. Condition characterized by the inability to be still and a tendency to act on impulse.

**Emotional conflict(s):** Memory of emotional stress of one or both parents during gestation. Most often, a conflict associated with the mother's fear about her child not moving and searching for proof that her child is alive inside her. After birth, as the child grows, he or she may symbolically express a solution to the mother's fear by being overly active.

## Autism

Condition comprised of a range of complex neurodevelopment disorders, characterized by communication difficulties; social interaction impairments; and restricted, repetitive patterns of behavior.

**Emotional conflict(s):** Problem related to the presence of two active conflicts, which create what is called a schizophrenic constellation in the brain (a hemispheric stalemate). One of the conflicts is associated with an intense fear (larynx); the other relates to territorial anger (lesser curvature of stomach, and the biliary and pancreatic network). The panic-fear conflict is often related to being caught off guard by the presence of a predator. A child may subconsciously escape reality in relation to a danger that is too great. Autism represents a solution that allows one to plunge into another dimension where life is safe. Symbolically, autism can be related to having to keep a secret. It may also be linked to communication issues in the family or to the memory of the exile of a clan member.

Important reminder regarding children with autism: The life of the parents during gestation, and up until the child is one year old, needs to be investigated, as do the stories of the ancestors.

## Autoimmune Disease

An autoimmune response is the result of the body attacking normal cells with autoantibodies. At the core of the immune system is the body's ability to tell the difference between the self and nonself—what is us and what is foreign.

**Emotional conflict(s):** A struggle related to self-destruction and self-intolerance. An autoimmune disease can also occur as an expression of feeling unwanted and rejected by parents. One may also feel that one doesn't have the right to defend oneself, or one may have a tendency to take the blame for others.

# B

## Bad Breath (Also: Halitosis)

May be the result of poor dental-health habits, or may be a sign of a gastric problem.

**Emotional conflict(s):** An issue pertaining to territorial anger that is repressed. Bad breath comes from the secretion of hydrochloric acid in the stomach or duodenal bulb, which is produced to symbolically increase one's territory. The stomach's lesser curvature will ulcerate, thus creating more space (symbolically) to contain the anger. Certain types of individuals can be considered "stomach types" because they often react with territorial anger.

*Example:* A man works for his father but continuously fights with him because he cannot do what he wants to within the company. As a consequence, he develops a gastric ulcer as well as bad breath.

## Baldness

Partial or complete lack of hair.

**Emotional conflict(s):** Distress related to a separation linked to feelings of self-devaluation. The area affected with the hair loss corresponds to the area that symbolizes the separation. Baldness can also be associated with a conflict of a spiritual nature or feeling separated from the universe and higher levels of consciousness. It can also correspond to a period of self-doubt and a feeling of being disconnected from God.

*Example:* A woman loses her hair in a certain area after the death of her mother, who had the habit of affectionately putting her hand on her head on that specific spot.

## Bartholin's Glands

Two glands located slightly posterior to the left and right of the opening of the vagina, which secrete mucus that lubricates it.

*Embryonic origin: endoderm.*

**Emotional conflict(s):** An issue related to separation with a sexual tonality. Problems with Bartholin's glands can also pertain to being disgusted by sex, experiencing pain during intercourse, or feeling that sex is imposed.

*Example:* A woman feels neglected by her husband and develops a tumor of the Bartholin's glands. Subconsciously, she allows the production of more secretions in order to attract her husband sexually through the sensation of lubrication, as well as the odor that is produced.

243

## Basedow's Disease

*See Thyroid (Graves' disease).*

## Belching

The releasing of built-up air within the upper stomach.

**Emotional conflict(s):** An issue related to communication and being unable to freely exchange words. One has difficulties staying relaxed and open during a conversation.

## Bell's Palsy

A unilateral facial-muscle paralysis of sudden onset, characterized by muscle weakness and a distorted facial expression.

**Emotional conflict(s):** Emotional issue related to motor skills with a tonality of "losing face." Conflict linked to feeling humiliated in front of others.

*Example:* A man makes fun of his wife, who is not finding her words while trying to express herself in front of a group of friends. She feels ashamed in front of others and triggers Bell's palsy.

## Black Stools

Can indicate the presence of digested blood. Black stools can also be a sign of bleeding in the gastrointestinal tract.

**Emotional conflict(s):** An issue related to territorial anger. The stomach's lesser curvature will ulcerate to expand the territory and create more space to contain the anger.

## Bladder

The urinary bladder is a muscular sac in the pelvis that collects urine excreted by the kidneys before it exits through the urethra. It is located just above and behind the pubic bone.

**Emotional conflict(s)—*two distinct types:***

**Ectodermic bladder:** Corresponds to the mucosa of the bladder and is linked to a territorial conflict in which one feels unable to mark boundaries. During the active phase of such a conflict, an ulceration of the mucosa will allow the widening of the bladder in order to improve its capacity to contain more urine to mark borders.

*Example:* A man feels like he can't create boundaries at work when he is asked to make room for a new coworker in his office. Suddenly he has to share the territory, which he feels belongs to him. In another example, a woman may trigger a bladder symptom when she is unable to organize her territory or feels invaded.

**Endodermic bladder:** Involves the submucosa of the bladder and pertains to an ugly situation within the territory.

*Example:* An elderly man's children treat him in a disrespectful and nasty manner, after he invites them to move into his house so that they could live rent free and save money. The man feels that he is treated badly in his most precious territory (his home) and triggers polyps of the bladder.

# Blepharitis

Inflammation of the eyelash follicles along the edge of the eyelid, which creates itching and irritation.

**Emotional conflict(s):** Linked to separation, specifically to the fear of losing sight of someone.

*Example:* One witnesses the drowning of a person before one's eyes, without being able to help the person. This can cause a feeling of visual separation, thus prompting the ulceration of the conjunctiva for the purpose of seeing farther away and reestablishing visual contact.

# Blindness

*See Macula (Macular Degeneration).*

# Blood

*See Spleen.*

# Bone

Rigid organ made of dense connective tissue that constitutes the skeleton. The role of bones is to support and protect the organs of the body, produce red and white blood cells, and store minerals.

*Embryonic origin: new brain mesoderm.*

**Emotional conflict(s):** Deep self-devaluation, feelings of unworthiness and unimportance. Depending on the tonality of the conflict, a specific part of the skeleton will be affected. The biological purpose of decalcification, loss of bone density, or bone osteolysis is to eliminate the structure, which corresponds to the area of devaluation. If one is able to overcome one's issue of self-devaluation, the bone can restore itself through a bone-building process (during the recovery phase).

*Example:* A woman who has had a mastectomy feels that she has lost her femininity. If she perceives herself as worthless sexually, she may develop a problem of the hip bone (organ associated with femininity and sexuality), thus symbolizing the reduction of her self-worth.

## Bradycardia

Slower-than-normal heart rate. The heart usually beats between sixty and a hundred times a minute in an adult at rest. If a person's heart beats fewer than sixty times per minute, he or she may have bradycardia.

**Emotional conflict(s):** Related to a territorial-loss conflict. It may also be associated with a lack of affection from the father. Metaphorically, bradycardia can express a need to slow down feelings of love (i.e., putting the brakes on emotionally).

## Brain

The center of our nervous system that controls the other organ systems of the body. Our brain is mainly comprised of:

**Neurons:** highly specialized nerve cells that transmit information throughout the body in both chemical and electrical forms.

**Glia cells:** nonneuronal cells that maintain homeostasis and provide protection and support for the brain's neurons. They also form myelin. There are different types of glia cells, such as microglia cells, macroglia cells, and Schwann cells.

*Embryonic origin: Most glia cells are derived from ectodermal tissue. The exception is microglia, which are derived from hematopoietic stem cells.*

**Emotional conflict(s):** See the following possibilities regarding brain tumors, which should be investigated with caution due to the complex nature of the brain. Please be aware that these findings are in a state of constant evolution.

- When a stress syndrome (unmanageable stress) occurs, part of the brain modifies itself in order to trigger a program that will target a specific organ. The area of modification is directly related to the organ associated with the emotional conflict. Glia cells proliferate when the brain relay is repairing itself during the resolution phase of a disease. Such a phenomenon is accompanied by an edema within the same localized neuronal network. (See pages 59–60 for a specific example regarding brain relays, according to the theory of Dr. Hamer.)

- A shock may not always express itself in organs of the body (aside from the brain), but rather, the brain itself can be the target organ when the conflict is of an intellectual nature. It is a conflict that pertains to having to surpass a problem or achieve an unattainable mission. The biological symptoms of a conflict of devaluation related to intellectual capacities may appear in different ways, such as bringing more blood to the neurons (vascular disease) or hyperactivity of the glia cells in order to function with more power (tension headaches). Glia cell proliferation (brain tumor) corresponds to a felt experience of having to find a solution that is beyond normal intellectual capacities. The biological purpose of glia proliferation is to increase the amount of oxygen and sugar available to the neurons to improve their performance.

**Note:** A brain tumor can be understood as the conjunction of two conflicts. One of them pertains to a particular struggle, and the other is of an intellectual nature: one has to extend oneself beyond one's intellectual limits in order to find a solution to that struggle. The localization of a brain tumor depends on the area of the brain that monitors the organ that correlates with the conflict. The nature of the conflict underlying the intellectual devaluation can be revealed once the location of the brain relay affected by the tumor is identified.

*Example:* A single mother goes beyond her usual capacities at work in order to meet a deadline, agreeing to do demanding and stressful computer work until late at night. She feels overwhelmed as she tries to take care of her child and be a good mother at the same time. One morning, she can't feel the fingers of her right hand. She is diagnosed with a brain tumor, thus expressing a motor conflict directly related to pushing beyond her limits while having to type on the computer.

## Breast

In a right-handed woman, symptoms of the left breast reflect a conflict related to the nest and a desire to nurture that corresponds to a mother/child or daughter/mother concern. The right breast reflects a conflict with the extended nest, which is someone or something that one mothers secondarily and without any sexual coloration (partner, family member, friend, house). In a left-handed woman, the content of the above conflicts is reversed: the right breast reflects a conflict with her offspring, and the left breast reflects a conflict with the extended nest.

**Special note:** The following discussion pertains to the four main types of breast cancers.

### Milk gland:
An exocrine gland organ in mammals that produces milk for the sustenance of young offspring. Mammary tumors originate from glandular tissue and present as a solid mass.

*Embryonic origin: old brain mesoderm.*

**Emotional conflict(s):** Cancer of the milk gland originates in the cells that produce milk and is related to a "nest-worry conflict." This conflict is linked to a mothering incapacity, when a woman has a strong concern about her child or anyone she mothers secondarily, such as a spouse, an ill friend, or a dying parent.

**Milk ducts:**
Also referred to as galactophores or lactiferous ducts. They are the pathways that carry milk from the lobules of the mammary gland (where milk is made) to the tip of the nipple. Cancer of the milk ducts (intraductal carcinoma) forms in the lining of a milk duct within the breast. The ducts in the breast are made of the same tissue as the epidermis.

*Embryonic origin: ectoderm.*

**Emotional conflict(s):** Conflict of separation in the nest and a yearning to nurture (a need for mothering, contact, and communication). If a woman can't nurse (literally or figuratively) because she lost contact with her child, the breast may "burst" because of the accumulation of milk she produces. The milk duct ulcerations will permit to contain an increased flow of milk so the breast does not get congested. After the resolution of such conflict has been initiated, a ductal tumor and swelling will appear in the ulcerated area.

*Example:* A woman might have a nest conflict because she unexpectedly lost contact with her son who was thrown in jail. She feels separated from her son, as if he had been figuratively pulled away from her breast. She wants to "nurture" him and protect him but cannot. A few months after her son is released from jail, she feels a lump in her breast.

**Breast skin cancer (melanoma):**
Melanoma is a cutaneous lesion that affects the skin and can appear in the breast.

*Embryonic origin: old brain mesoderm.*

**Emotional conflict(s):** Related to one's integrity and feeling stained, which affects the dermis. It can also be linked to an actual physical assault against one's integrity in connection with the breast.

*Example:* A woman may have a subconscious need for creating a shield within her skin to protect her breast from being touched. She may feel dirty or stained after finding out that her husband has deceived her. Her condition allows her to metaphorically safeguard her breast.

**Breast neurofibromatosis (von Recklinghausen's disease):**
A disorder that affects the nerves of the breast through the growth of multiple, often soft sessile peripheral tumors on the nerve endings.

*Embryonic origin: ectoderm.*

Emotional conflict(s): Related to a desire to separate, to cease contact. This type of conflict can prompt the growth of thousands of little tumors on the nerves in order to prevent sensory information from circulating and telling the brain that contact is being made. This biological response acts in the opposite fashion to a conflict of separation in the nest, such as in intraductal cancer, where contact is wanted. In the case of von Recklinghausen's disease, the conflict pertains to contact that is imposed, unwanted, and needs to stop (i.e., "I don't want to be touched right now").

## Broca's Area

Region of the brain related to speech, located in the cortex of the dominant frontal lobe. Damage to Broca's Area causes aphasia, characterized by hesitant and fragmented speech with little grammatical structure.

*Embryonic origin: ectoderm.*

Emotional conflict(s): Emotional distress related to speech. Conflict of the personality in which one feels that one is not being heard, along with a sense that there is no point in speaking. Conflict related to being unable to explain something. Fear of talking or of saying the wrong thing.

*Example:* A man corrects his elderly mother in a harsh way when she speaks. Feeling as if every sentence is a mistake, she experiences increasing difficulty pronouncing words and slowly loses her speech.

## Bronchi

*See Lung.*

## Bruxism

A condition in which the individual grinds or clenches his or her teeth.

Emotional conflict(s): Related to having to stay silent. Conflict about having to keep a secret and not releasing the unspeakable, such as memories of molestation, rape, incest, and so on. Feeling powerless and unable to discuss problems pertaining to the clan. Having to "shut up" about the truth.

## Bulimia

An eating disorder characterized by consuming a large amount of food in a short amount of time and purposely expelling the food by vomiting. This behavior is commonly referred to as "bingeing and purging."

Emotional conflict(s): Bulimia occurs when there is the combination of two conflicts: one being related to fear and disgust and the other pertaining to digestion (with a territorial tonality). Bulimia can also be related to memories of starvation and lack of nourishment that is essential in order to remain alive.

## Bunion (hallux valgus)

A deformity characterized by a prominence on the inner border of the foot, which affects the big toe.

*Embryonic origin: new brain mesoderm.*

**Emotional conflict(s):** Related to self-devaluation in the context of direction. One feels obligated to follow a direction that one did not choose on one's own.

*Example:* A woman feels forced by her husband to stay home with her children when she would like to go back to work and develops bunions as a result.

## Bursitis

An inflammation of the bursa (the fluid-filled sac which functions to reduce friction between a tendon and skin, or between a tendon and bone). This condition often affects a shoulder, knee, elbow, hip, and sometimes foot or Achilles tendon.

**Emotional conflict(s):** Profound self-devaluation in the tonality of the part of the body affected; often related to not feeling "capable" in a certain situation.

*Example:* A woman does not feel like she is a good daughter because she does not visit her mother enough, and she develops bursitis in her left shoulder (devaluation in the context of a mother-daughter conflict).

## Calcaneum

A large bone forming the heel.

*Embryonic origin: new brain mesoderm.*

**Emotional conflict(s):** Profound self-devaluation in the tonality of movement. When stepping forward, the heel is the bone involved at the very beginning of this movement. When one has regrets and feelings of devaluation regarding the step one took, literally or figuratively, they can affect the calcaneus. It can also relate to an identity conflict that expresses one's doubt about who one is and what stops one from finding oneself.

**Note:** The heel can also represent the movement toward another realm, such as death, or the need to go somewhere other than earth. It resonates with a need to know the origins of things.

## Calcium

*See Hypercalcemia.*

## Calvarium

The domelike upper part of the cranium, comprising the superior portions of the frontal, parietal, and occipital bones.

*Embryonic origin: new brain mesoderm.*

**Emotional conflict(s):** Emotional distress related to self-devaluation of an intellectual or spiritual nature. Since intelligence is intimately connected with the brain, problems with the calvarium can indicate one's struggle with intelligence, morality, or spirituality.

*Example:* A woman blames herself after the suicide of her sister because she did not find a solution to help her. She feels that she did not act in a "smart enough" way, and therefore experiences intellectual self-devaluation. As a result of such distress she develops a condition of the calvarium.

## Canker sore

A small ulcer of the mouth, tongue, or lips.

**Emotional conflict(s):** A struggle related to symbolically having a mouthful of words that can't be contained. One can't verbalize what one thinks. Ulcerations of the mouth and tongue during the active phase of the conflict allow one to make room to contain the surplus.

*Example:* A man does not verbalize to his wife how he feels, until one day he explodes and pours his heart out (he develops canker sores).

## Candida Albicans

Candida albicans is a fungus related to genital and oral infections, often manifesting as an overgrowth of yeast.

**Emotional conflict(s):** Distress related to the death of a person or of a relationship. A genital infection can be linked to the ending of a love affair. An oral infection may be linked to an old memory of separation from the mother, associated with a subconscious fear of not being fed.

**Note:** For an infant, the absence of contact represents the danger of death, and the larynx is the organ that allows a child to scream and get the attention of the mother in order to reconnect. This can explain symptoms of candida in the back of the throat.

*Also see Fungus.*

## Cardiomyopathy

A condition in which the heart muscle becomes enlarged or thickened. Cardiomyopathy makes it harder for the heart to pump blood and deliver it to the rest of the body.

**Emotional conflict(s):** An issue related to forgiveness, in terms of not having the power to forgive or let go. Conflict of powerlessness in the context of love. One can't forgive oneself, someone else, life, or God. Or one feels that one cannot be forgiven by others.

## Carotid Arteries

Two large arteries, one on each side of the head, that carry blood away from the heart and supply the head and neck with oxygenated blood.

*Embryonic origin: ectoderm.*

**Emotional conflict(s):** Loss of intellectual territory. One is struggling to defend an idea or an opinion. Symbolically, issues of the carotid arteries are linked to a need for an increase of the blood supply to the brain so that one can defend one' intellectual territory.

## Carpal Tunnel Syndrome

A condition in which there is pressure on the median nerve of the wrist. The median nerve supplies feeling and movement to parts of the hand.

**Emotional conflict(s):** Conflict of self-devaluation regarding the wrong gesture. This condition may also stem from feeling no longer capable of repeating the same gesture in the context of work, or feeling pressured by an authority and unable to perform what is asked. It may also reflect a struggle of not being able to let go of something or someone.

*Example:* A woman can't let go of her daughter, who is about to go to college, and triggers carpal tunnel syndrome.

## Cartilage

Firm, fibrous connective tissue found in various parts of the body, such as the joints, larynx, and respiratory tract.

*Embryonic origin: new brain mesoderm.*

**Emotional conflict(s):** Self-devaluation in the context of movement. A conflict related to being forced to stay in a certain position while lacking the strength to sustain it. An issue linked to feeling inadequate or unskilled to perform a movement properly.

## Catalepsy

A condition characterized by rigidity of the body or a lack of response to external stimuli, and sometimes seizures accompanied with a loss of consciousness.

**Emotional conflict(s):** Distress related to having to contain aggressiveness. Also, conflict associated with a need to disconnect from oneself when "transgressing"—going against a rule and experiencing what has been forbidden.

## Cataract

A clouding of the lens of the eye. The lens is a transparent and clear structure within the eye that helps to focus light on the retina, as well as focusing the eye on objects at various distances. The retina is the light-sensitive tissue at the back of the eye.

**Emotional conflict(s):** Distress related to not wanting to see a certain situation. For instance, older people often have cataracts because they don't want to see the fact that their children don't come to visit them. This condition can also be related to not wanting to see clearly during a painful experience, such as aging or the deterioration of a once-close relationship: a conflict related to wanting to put a veil over something to avoid seeing reality. It can also be related to feeling as if something was ripped away right in front of one's eyes.

*Example:* A woman has an abortion and imagines how her child has been abruptly stripped from her body. She develops cataract of the left eye as a result.

## Catatonia

A state of apparent unresponsiveness to external stimuli in a person who is apparently awake. It is a state of neurogenic motor immobility where the behavioral abnormality manifests as a stupor.

**Emotional conflict(s):** This condition is a sign of the combination of two conflicts. One conflict relates to a frontal fear, and the other is connected to a fear of what is coming from behind (felt at the neck level). It allows one to stay immobile and symbolically as far away as possible from two predators at once—one in front and one behind.

## Celiac Disease

An autoimmune disorder of the small intestine that interferes with the absorption of nutrients from food, resulting in vitamin deficiencies. Individuals who have celiac disease cannot tolerate gluten, which is a protein found in wheat, rye, and barley. Among other symptoms, gluten intolerance commonly results in diarrhea, abdominal pain, and bloating.

**Emotional conflict(s):** Gluten intolerance is often related to the distress of having been weaned too abruptly from something that contains gluten. This condition can also be associated with stressful experiences or traumatic stories within the clan, where flour, bread, or cereals were present in one's environment.

## Cellulite

A condition in which the skin appears to have areas with underlying fat deposits.

**Emotional conflict(s):** This condition can pertain to a fear of abandonment originating during the period of breast-feeding, or to memories of rejection during childhood. It can be the result of unexpressed resentment toward others or self-rejection. Cellulite can also be associated with a "silhouette conflict" (conflict about one's shape), which can manifest secondarily to weight gain.

## Cervix

*See Uterus.*

## Chicken Pox

A skin disorder associated with the varicella zoster virus. It causes a skin rash that is itchy and manifests as red, raw pockmarks.

**Emotional conflict(s):** A problem related to an abrupt loss of contact in a context of change.

*Example:* A mother leaves her child at a day-care facility for the first time. The child experiences a conflict of separation from the mother. Since other children at the day-care facility are most likely experiencing a similar conflict of separation with their parents, they may also be affected with the virus.

## Cholesterol

An essential structural component of cell membranes, required to build and maintain proper membrane function. Cholesterol is formed predominantly in the liver.

**Emotional conflict(s):** An issue related to having to do everything alone. One believes that one can only count on oneself to achieve or do anything. Symbolically, cholesterol represents the material that allows one to "construct" and, therefore, may increase when one feels a lack of support and resources. There can be an experience perceived as a territorial loss when others don't play the role they are expected to play in terms of support.

## Chondrosarcoma

A form of tumor composed of cells that produce cartilage.

*Embryonic origin: new brain mesoderm.*

**Emotional conflict(s):** Related to self-devaluation in correspondence to the part of the body affected.

*Example:* A woman repeatedly falls on her staircase and experiences a devaluation related to her legs and her perceived lack of capacity in using them. She develops a chondrosarcoma in one of her legs, symbolically strengthening it.

## Coccyx

The small triangular bone at the base of the final portion of the vertebral column. In humans, it is commonly known as the tailbone.

*Embryonic origin: new brain mesoderm.*

**Emotional conflict(s):** An issue related to sexuality and forced access to the rectum. See memories of anal relations, sexual touch, sodomy, and the use of an anal thermometer. Problems with the coccyx can also pertain to sexual devaluation regarding homosexual relations.

## Colitis

An inflammation of the mucosal layer of the large intestine (colon).

**Emotional conflict(s):** Recurrent conflict related to the inability to digest something. An individual is periodically irritated while feeling disempowered.

*Example:* A woman endures verbal mistreatment from her boss and can't process it. She develops colitis as a result.

## Colon

The last part of the digestive system that forms a great reservoir along which the contents are passed very slowly. The function of the colon is to extract water and salt from solid wastes. In the cecum and ascending colon, liquid is absorbed before residue reaches the transverse colon and takes on the consistence of feces. The wastes are moved through the descending colon and transferred to the sigmoid colon before being eliminated from the body through the rectum.

*Embryonic origin: endoderm.*

**Emotional conflict(s):** An issue related to something that is ugly and indigestible. Anger about a situation perceived as disgusting, gross, and vile. Subconsciously, the "morsel" is too filthy to be expelled. The uglier the conflict, the farther down a condition will manifest in the colon.

*Example:* An individual cannot digest the fact that he is accused of stealing and is fired from his job, even though he is innocent. He develops colon cancer as a result.

## Conjunctivitis

An inflammation or infection of the membrane lining the eyelids (conjunctiva).

**Emotional conflict(s):** Fear of visual separation, related to losing sight of someone.

*Example:* A woman sees her dog drown before her eyes without being able to save him, and she develops conjunctivitis.

## Connective Tissue

Tissue that provides structure and support to organs and other tissues by connecting or separating them.

*Embryonic origin: new brain mesoderm.*

**Emotional conflict(s):** Minor conflict of self-depreciation, often related to movement. The tonality of the conflict is directly related with the part of the body affected.

*Example:* A swimmer feels devalued and worried about an upcoming competition. He develops a necrosis of the connective tissue related to the deltoid muscle. During the reparation phase after the emotional conflict is resolved, he will experience excessive buildup of new connective tissue.

## Constipation

The condition of infrequent or strained bowel movement.

**Emotional conflict(s):** An issue pertaining to not being able to "let go" of something or someone. Fear of not being able to move things along. One feels a need for progress and the movement of the "morsel" toward the outside. For instance, one has a conflict about one's project being stuck. Also, another type of conflict may be symbolically related to movement, in terms of "not wanting to go" but "having to go" (for example, to work, to school, or on a particular trip).

## Coronary Arteries

Vessels that encircle the heart in the manner of a crown and supply the heart muscle with blood rich in oxygen.

*Embryonic origin: ectoderm.*

**Emotional conflict(s):** Fear of territorial loss (house, job, spouse, children, friend, belongings, etc.), triggering the need to fight to preserve the territory.

The biological solution is to trigger ulcerations enlarging the lining of the coronary arteries, allowing increased blood and oxygen flow to improve muscle power during combat. After combat, the lining of the arteries is restored (replenishment through cholesterol). A heart attack usually manifests during the peak of the restoration phase. This phenomenon is partially related to the size of the cerebral edema, which appears during the resolution phase of the conflict. (See page 58 for the illustrative story of the bull elk.)

## Coronary Veins

The veins that run parallel to corresponding arteries. Their function is to drain blood from the muscular tissue of the heart to the coronary sinus (a collection of veins joined together to form a large vessel).

*Embryonic origin: ectoderm.*

**Emotional conflict(s):** An issue of the heart, such as being heartbroken, that is often associated with a territorial loss of a sexual nature. Feeling insignificant in a relationship in terms of decision making, or feeling unimportant as a partner.

## Cortisol

*See Adrenal glands*

## Crohn's Disease

An inflammatory disease of the lining of the digestive tract that can lead to abdominal pain and severe diarrhea.

**Emotional conflict(s):** An issue related to a combination of conflicts, such as not being able to digest a "morsel" that represents indigestible "dirt" (often related to the clan) and a fear of lacking something vital (often accompanied with a feeling of powerlessness). One feels unable to assimilate something vile that is going on within the clan.

*Example*: A mother refuses to loan money to her daughter who lost her job and is struggling to survive, although she gave money to her son so that he could go on a vacation. The daughter feels deprived and cannot digest the mother's behavior, perceiving the situation as foul and wicked. She develops Crohn's disease as a result.

## Cystalgia

Chronic inflammation of the lining of the bladder wall, which results in chronic bladder pain, painful bladder spasms, and often frequent urination.

**Emotional conflict(s):** A struggle related to not being able to organize the territory. One feels that one can't recognize one's limits within the territory and fears that one's surroundings will become disorganized.

## Cystitis

*See Bladder.*

## Dandruff

*See Hair Loss.*

## Depression

A mood disorder characterized by episodes of sadness, apathy, frustration, or emotional isolation, to an extent that interferes with daily life. Depression is often accompanied by low self-esteem and a loss of interest and pleasure in most activities.

**Emotional conflict(s):** Depression is related to emotions of guilt and low self-esteem. It originates with a territorial issue in which one feels that if one were to fight for one's territory, one could only lose. There are three main territorial conflicts at the root of depression:

- Biological conflict of loss of territory or its contents (coronary arteries)
- Fear of the imminent attack by the adversary in the territory (aerial territory conflict); more generally, human conflict (dispute) within the territory (bronchi)
- Incapacity to mark the territory to create boundaries (ectodermic bladder)

Any of the above conflicts, combined with a feeling of defeat and self-devaluation in comparison to the other, will result in a hormonal deadlock (state of desexualization at a functional level) and lead to depression.

*Example(s):*

- A man loses his wife to another man and devalues himself in comparison to him. He will trigger a depression with an undertonality of territorial-loss conflict.
- A man fears the criticisms of his wife and sees her as an adversary. At the same time, he feels she argues much better than he does and that he can't win fights with her. He will trigger a depression with an undertonality of a human conflict (dispute) within the territory.
- A woman is sick and needs the help of her mother-in-law for a few weeks. At the same time, she compares herself to her mother-in-law, who appears to be more talented than her in everything she does around the house (cooking, cleaning, organizing, etc.). She feels that her territory is

invaded and boundaries are crossed. She will trigger a depression with an undertonality of territorial-marking conflict.

## Detached Retina

A sight-threatening event, occurring when the retina becomes separated from its underlying supportive tissue. The retina converts light rays into impulses that travel through the optic nerve to the brain, where they are interpreted as the images we see.

**Emotional conflict(s):** A struggle related to a visual stress, such as being faced with a horrific image. One may trigger a problem with the retina later in life during a situation that awakens an old stress related to seeing. The detached retina is a protective mechanism that allows one to avoid seeing something horrible and traumatizing.

## Diabetes

A condition related to the functional impairment of the beta cells of the pancreas (located in the islets of Langerhans). The role of insulin is to remove glucose from the blood. Diabetes is characterized by insulin insufficiency, thus resulting in high blood sugar (aka "hyperglycemia").

**Note:** The alpha cells of the pancreas (located in the islets of Langerhans) secrete a hormone called glucagon, which prevents hypoglycemia by raising the level of sugar in the blood.

**Emotional conflict(s):** A problem related to having to "resist" someone or something perceived as repugnant. For instance, one has a job one can't stand because one feels attacked and disgusted by one's employer's remarks. Symbolically, in this insufferable situation, one resists the opponent, preparing for either imminent combat or escape. In such a case, the insulin level will decrease in order to permit an increase of blood sugar to support the muscles, which stay in a chronic state of tension and readiness for action. The fact that one is postponing the fight will lead to a buildup of sugar in the blood. Diabetes is a conflict of the masculine type, which involves a state of resistance against unwanted circumstances. One feels forced to do something one doesn't want to do.

This condition can also be related to a need for "sweetness." For example, when someone is deprived of affection in their relationship and instead has to bear the authority of another, the subconscious solution is to symbolically bring "sweetness" into his or her life by triggering the insulin levels to drop so that the element of sugar (sweetness) rises.

*Example:* A woman feels repulsed by her alcoholic husband when he solicits her sexually. She endures having sex with him while in a state of fear and disgust, and she triggers diabetes.

## Diarrhea

An increase in the frequency of bowel movements that involves a greater looseness of stool.

**Emotional conflict(s):** Can be related to any conflict that creates fear and a high level of stress. This condition can be linked to a subconscious need to expedite "matter" and complete a project within a short period of time. Sometimes diarrhea can be the expression of not wanting to digest and assimilate a "morsel," thus resulting in the accelerated elimination of it.

*Example:* A person feels obligated to accept a situation, idea, or order but simultaneously denies everything about it, not wanting to allow it within his or her system.

## Drinking

Alcoholism is connected to a conflict of "lacking," and it resonates with the liver, the organ that is associated with a feeling of "deprivation." One drinks to avoid the feeling of "lack." For instance, a lack of money, love, understanding, or success can lead a person to use alcohol as a solution to fill the void and assuage the feeling of emptiness. Taking root at the earliest stage of development, a baby who is abruptly deprived of the milk of his or her mother may feel a deep emptiness and sense of "lacking" that can result in alcoholism later in life.

## Duodenum (except Duodenal Bulb)

The upper section of the small intestine that starts at the pyloric sphincter and precedes the jejunum and ileum sections. Its function is involved in the process of breaking down food for digestion.

*Embryonic origin: endoderm.*

**Emotional conflict(s):** Related to the inability to digest something. This type of conflict is often territorial. It can pertain to a situation between friends or family members that instigate feelings of a lack of understanding and a sense of injustice. This condition can also pertain to a conflict or fear of not having enough or of dying of hunger.

# E

## Eczema

*See Skin (epidermis.)*

## Elbow

The joint where three long bones meet in the middle portion of the arm.

**Emotional conflict(s):** Problems with the elbow are often linked to devaluation pertaining to work. One symbolically feels like one is not able to roll up one's sleeves and work hard enough to get results. Also, one may feel profoundly devalued about having caused someone a bad injury by unintentionally hitting him or her with the elbow.

*Example:* One feels guilty and devaluated after one's elbow injured a teammate and develops elbow problems as a result.

## Endometriosis

*See Uterus.*

## Esophagus

A muscular tube through which food passes from the pharynx to the stomach.

### Esophagus—upper two-thirds section:

*Embryonic origin: ectoderm.*

**Emotional conflict(s):** Not wanting to swallow something. One can't accept a situation in which one feels forced to incorporate a "morsel" (i.e., epithelial cancer). For instance, in a figurative sense, one feels forced to swallow words from a partner that are lies and wants to spit them out in order to remove them from one's throat.

### Esophagus—lower third section:

*Embryonic origin: endoderm*

**Emotional conflict(s):** Wanting to swallow and incorporate a "morsel" so that it can be digested, but being abruptly stopped (i.e., adenocarcinoma). For instance, an individual wants to incorporate and "profit" from an inheritance but is stopped by other family members

## Exophthalmia

Increase in the volume of the tissue behind the eyes, which makes the eyes appear to bulge or protrude and doesn't allow the eyelids to completely close.

**Emotional conflict(s):** Related to a problem of the thyroid that involves a dynamic of paranoia (fear from behind). One needs to expand one's lateral vision to see more, in order to either find a corner in which to hide or to be more efficient in following someone with one's eyes.

❖ ❖ ❖

# F

## Fallopian Tubes

Narrow, muscular tubes that provide a pathway for the sperm to reach the ovum. They also enable a fertilized egg to reach the uterus.

*Embryonic origin: endoderm.*

**Emotional conflict(s):** An issue affecting the genitals and pertaining to an experience that is not clean or ugly sexually, such as violence, rape, or a nasty dispute with a man. The biological meaning of disorders related to the fallopian tubes is to increase secretions in order to clean the "dirt" out of the tubes and reestablish a clean pathway.

## Femur

Bone in the human leg, extending from the pelvis to the knee. The femur is the longest, largest, and strongest bone the body.

*Embryonic origin: new brain mesoderm.*

**Emotional conflict(s):** Pertain to one's conflicts of opposition and feelings of devaluation, as if one were "stopped by a brick wall." One feels obligated to yield to a superior force. A person may experience the distress of moving backward instead of forward in life.

*Example:* A woman fears that she is not healing fast enough and feels she has no future (a feeling of backpedaling). She develops a femur problem as a result.

## Fibromyalgia

A condition that involves the muscles, tendons, joints, and soft tissues and is characterized by body-wide pain. In Greek, "fibro" refers to tissues, "myo" refers to muscle, and "algo" refers to pain.

**Emotional conflict(s):** Related to the felt experience one might have during a stressful event involving movement. One is unable to escape or move, or feels that one cannot defend oneself, literally or figuratively. A merging of four emotional conflicts is linked to this condition: powerlessness associated with movement, combined with feelings of self-devaluation and immense moral pain.

*Example:* A man who lives alone falls down the stairs, and while being unable to move, he experiences a state of devaluation and powerlessness. While no one can attend to him, he is in a state of despair, knowing that his elderly mother, who is bedridden, is waiting for him alone at her house, depending on him to feed her. He develops fibromyalgia as a result.

## Flu

A common virus (influenza), with symptoms that include chills, fever, coughing, and general discomfort.

**Emotional conflict(s):** Related to the recovery phase of what is called a "general human conflict related to territory," such as a threat or dispute within one's territory. During the active phase of such a territorial conflict, microulcerations of the bronchi tubes appear (ectodermic tissue). The flu virus is used by the system to restore the ectodermic tissue of the bronchi tubes after the conflict is resolved. An emotional struggle related to a strong argument or fight with a family member or colleague can be a trigger for the flu. The seriousness of the flu symptoms will be proportional to the intensity of the conflict.

**Note:** It is interesting to notice how the flu is most common during the holiday season (i.e., the Christmas and New Year celebrations), since family gatherings often prompt arguments between members of the clan. The reason why some individuals will contract the flu virus while others won't depends on whether or not they are experiencing the conflict previously mentioned.

## Fungus

Fungal diseases are called mycoses. Cutaneous mycoses or dermatomycoses occur only in the superficial layers of skin, nails, or hair.

**Emotional conflict(s):** Associated with one's tendency toward resentment and self-destruction. Fungus of the big toe is often related to a conflict with the mother and a struggle with authority. Fungus appears during the resolution phase of a conflict but can remain chronic because the conflict is not fully resolved.

*Also see Candida Albicans*

G

## Gallbladder

A small organ that concentrates bile produced by the liver and aids with fat digestion. The most common symptom of gallbladder disease is intermittent pain, called biliary colic.

*Embryonic origin: ectoderm.*

**Emotional conflict(s):** An anger conflict within the territory, often linked to problems with boundaries being crossed. One fears the potential risk of another stepping into one's territory and experiences intense anger. The biliary network will ulcerate to metaphorically expand the territory and create more space to contain the anger, thus prompting biliary colic. During the recovery phase, hepatitis may occur.

Gallstones are particularly related to feelings of resentment or holding a grudge. They may also reflect one's fear of the rage and bitterness that another may have toward one.

*Also see Hepatitis.*

## Gas (Intestinal)

Flatulence originates from air that is swallowed and from the breakdown of undigested food by bacteria in the digestive tract.

**Emotional conflict(s):** An issue related to something that cannot be fully digested and evacuated. Gas allows us to push the morsel of waste toward the outside in order to free the pathway. For instance, one wants to free oneself and is symbolically pushing away recurrent problems in order to open one's path.

## Gingivitis (Gum Disease)

Periodontal gum diseases range from simple gum inflammation to more serious conditions that can result in damage to the soft tissue and bone that support the teeth.

**Emotional conflict(s):** Struggle with being unable or unwilling to verbalize something. One feels that one's words have no impact or is afraid of sounding stupid or ridiculous when expressing oneself.

## Glaucoma

A condition of the eye resulting in optic nerve damage, often associated with increased fluid pressure in the eyes. Optic nerve damage often results in peripheral vision loss, thus creating the sensation of seeing through a narrow tube, a symptom commonly referred to as "tunnel vision."

**Emotional conflict(s):** Related to a fear that is coming from behind or felt at the nape of the neck (since it can't be seen). Symbolically, glaucoma forces a person to look straight ahead when a danger is arising from behind, so that he or she can escape in a forward direction. The veil of "smoke" that glaucoma creates within the peripheral vision is a biological solution that permits one to have a blurred view of a danger that would be too terrifying to see with full clarity. This way, one is able to concentrate on escaping by looking straight ahead. In nature, in order to escape a predator, the prey flees without looking back, allowing it to avoid continuous panic.

*Note:* It is when the danger arrives from the front that a person has time to react, but when one is unable to anticipate a danger (as in an accident), the brain interprets it as if it had come from behind. Often, a prey escaping danger is convinced that the predator is still chasing it, but if it took the time to stop and look back, it would eventually become aware that the danger is gone.

*Example:* A woman is constantly panicked about the unknown and what could happen to her children. Her brain registers danger as coming from behind, and she may trigger glaucoma as a result.

## Goiter

*See Thyroid.*

## Gout

A disease that results from an overload of uric acid in the body, leading to the formation of tiny urate crystals of deposit in tissues, especially the joints.

**Emotional conflict(s):** An issue related to not having enough resources to survive (a struggle with existence), and therefore not wanting to let go of or lose a single "crumb." One is symbolically experiencing a conflict with existence related to not having enough, and one retains liquid in one's body, including the elements that should be evacuated (the "garbage").

*Example:* A woman feels that her life is crumbling down around her, as she is losing her job and realizes that she won't be able to provide for herself. She develops gout as a result.

*Also see Kidney.*

## Graves' Disease

*See Thyroid.*

# H

## Hair Loss

Loss of hair from the head or body.

**Emotional conflict(s):** Often related to a conflict of separation (correlating to the scalp). After a relationship ends, one might miss the intimate contact that one felt when one's partner touched one's head. Hair loss can also be linked to a conflict of intellectual devaluation.

*Example:* One feels incompetent at work and devalued intellectually for not understanding the functioning of one's computer and starts losing hair.

**Note:** Dandruff is linked to a sense of intellectual incomprehension, combined with a feeling of abandonment.

*Also see Alopecia.*

## Headache

*See Migraine.*

## Heart (including Myocardium and Pericardium)

A muscular organ located behind and slightly left of the breastbone. The heart pumps blood through the network of arteries and veins called the cardiovascular system.

**Myocardium:**
The contractile middle layer of the heart, made of muscular tissue. The function of the myocardium is to contract the heart and push the blood out.

*Embryonic origin: new brain mesoderm.*

**Emotional conflict(s):** Self-devaluation regarding the capacity of one's own heart to perform properly.

**Pericardium:**
Double-layered sac that surrounds the heart and the bases of the pulmonary artery and aorta. The function of the pericardium is to protect the heart.

*Embryonic origin: old brain mesoderm.*

**Emotional conflict(s):** Fear of attack toward one's heart or the heart of another, such as being afraid of heart disease or heart surgery. A territorial conflict that involves verbal attacks that one feels are directed figuratively toward one's heart.

## Heart Attack

*See Coronary Arteries.*

**Note:** For more information related to the cardiovascular system, also see the following sections: Aorta, Carotid Arteries, Coronary Arteries, and Coronary Veins.

## Hemorrhoids

Swelling of veins inside the anal canal or near the opening of the anus.

**Emotional conflict(s):** An issue linked to territory and not being able to mark it. For instance, one has difficulties finding one's position in society. Also, hemorrhoids may be related to experiencing an identity conflict linked to a lack of recognition in the clan. One may suffer from not being acknowledged by one's father or not knowing who one's father is, and therefore lack a sense of self.

## Hepatitis

Inflammation of the liver, related to a few specific viruses, including hepatitis A, B, and C.

**Emotional conflict(s):** An issue that specifically concerns the bile ducts (ectodermic tissue) and reflects a conflict associated with holding a grudge. Hepatitis A reflects a grudge conflict associated with a fear of lacking something, such as food or money (sustenance tonality). Hepatitis B relates to a grudge conflict associated with a fear of being infected or being forced to be injected with an unwanted substance, such as a vaccine. Hepatitis C is a grudge conflict linked to a struggle about something that is unknown and hidden. For instance, one feels a sense of injustice due to a story that one's parents are withholding from one.

## Herpes

Viral skin disorder that generally appears around the mouth or the sexual organs. Herpes involves the epidermis, the mucous membrane, and the sensory nerves.

**Emotional conflict(s):** An issue related to lack of sexual contact or intimacy. The virus appears during the recovery phase of such a conflict, since its role is to accelerate the reparation of the microulcerations of the skin. Figuratively, a person might feel the stress of a separation of a sexual nature during a last kiss (herpes of the lip) or experience the frustration of a final sexual encounter (genital herpes). Herpes of the cornea can symbolize a separation experienced in visual terms, such as "seeing someone for the last time."

One may be waiting for a kiss that will never come. This relates to having the project (nerve) of having intimacy with someone in the future, while feeling unable to make that contact happen.

*Example:* A young man kisses a girl for the last time before she moves away. That kiss represents the last contact before separation. He develops herpes of the lip shortly after her departure.

**Note:** When the viral infection persists, it means that a certain percentage of the conflict is still active.

## Hiatal Hernia

A condition in which part of the stomach protrudes upward into the chest through an opening into the diaphragm.

**Emotional conflict(s):** Distress linked to an unfulfilled need for tenderness and wanting to receive it. A feeling of emptiness (hunger) relating to the need for affection. This condition can reflect an old conflict related to the relationship with the mother, felt in terms of a lack of affection (e.g., the mother never said the right words to provide emotional comfort). Hiatal hernia can also relate to a feeling of wanting to express something but being unable to. One swallows one's words instead of expressing them.

## High Blood Sugar

*See Pancreas.*

## Hip

The joint where the thigh bone (femur) meets the pelvis bone.

*Embryonic origin: new brain mesoderm.*

**Emotional conflict(s):** One is experiencing a strong opposition in regard to someone else (possibly the mother or mother figure). When one feels inferior, devalued, and in opposition with another, it is as if one has to push against a wall with one's entire body. In this case, the hips are the bones that symbolically absorb all the pressure, thus leading to either wearing, loss of bone density, decalcification, or osteolisis.

## HIV

A virus that may lead to AIDS (acquired immunodeficiency syndrome). AIDS is an infectious disease of the human immune system, which can lead to progressive and life-threatening conditions.

**Emotional conflict(s):** Problem often related to not being wanted as an offspring. One has been conceived in a climate of shame (rape, incest, child out of wedlock) and subconsciously wants to disappear as a way to be loyal to one's parents' wish of the nonexistence of their child. In other words, the parental project associated with HIV may be expressed by the offspring through the metaphor "I am born to die." For instance, parents who are ashamed about conceiving a child out of wedlock give their offspring away for adoption, wishing that the offspring had never been conceived.

Also, one may feel incapable of giving oneself recognition at a deep level or unable to protect oneself (often related to a lack of protection from the father during childhood).

**Note:** The role of the immune system is to combat the "nonself," meaning to destroy what is not recognizable within the system. When one has no self-recognition, AIDS symbolizes a program of auto-destruction. One may be prone to attract circumstances that will put one in contact with the virus, based on the subconscious programs described above.

## Hives

A skin rash, also called urticaria, which is notable for its dark-red, raised, itchy bumps.

**Emotional conflict(s):** related to one's desire to separate from another person or a situation, accompanied by a state of profound disapproval and rejection.

## Hypercalcemia

A condition of too much calcium in the blood. The main cause of hypercalcemia is overactivity in one or more of the parathyroid glands, which regulate blood calcium levels.

**Emotional conflict(s):** An issue related to devaluation and feeling weak and unimportant. Having a need to reconstruct one's internal structure in order to exist again and have a role to play in the clan or in life. Wanting to be strong enough in facing others, in order to be able to resist potential tensions.

*Also see Parathyroid Glands.*

## Hyperglycemia

*See Pancreas.*

## Hypertension (Arterial)

Also called "high blood pressure." A condition in which the arterial blood pressure is elevated. Blood pressure is a measurement of the force against the walls of the arteries as the heart pumps blood through the body.

**Emotional conflict(s):** Distress related to far territorial issues (conflicts with someone or something at a distance). Tension with a member of the family where one feels dominated and forced to do something. Conflict related to submission and being unable to express anger. One has to accept an order or a rule, although one would like to react against it. Conflict related to one's need

269

to close one's heart (arteries) and not feel love, in order to avoid emotional attachment and the pain of losing a loved one. Hypertension can also occur when one feels that one must apply "more pressure" in order to succeed.

**Note:** In addition, high blood pressure can be correlated with a problem of the kidney parenchyma. It is a biological compensation that momentarily ensures adequate urine production.

## Hypotension (Arterial)

Also called "low blood pressure." This condition occurs when blood pressure during and after each heartbeat is much lower than is usual or normal for a person. Subsequently, certain parts of the body do not get enough blood, particularly the heart and brain.

**Emotional conflict(s):** An issue related to powerlessness in relation to a loss of distant territory (one feels too weak to fight). Also, this condition may correspond to the recovery phase after one's fight to preserve one's territory. Orthostatic hypotension is connected to a feeling of not wanting to confront reality and instead staying in a horizontal position (i.e., staying in bed).

**Note:** Another reason for hypotension may be decreased activity of the adrenal cortex, which relates to a feeling of powerlessness in terms of staying on track, following a path that is too hard, and trying to achieve objectives that seem unattainable.

## Impetigo

A skin condition characterized by an infection that presents with distinct, thin-walled pustular vesicles.

**Emotional conflict(s):** Feeling that one's integrity is being attacked, accompanied by a feeling of separation.

## Inner Ear

A series of internal canals embedded in the temporal bone of the skull, which form the organ of hearing and balance.

*Embryonic origin: ectoderm.*

**Emotional conflict(s):** An issue related to wanting or not wanting to hear something. One may feel that one doesn't hear enough kind words or that the information one receives is too much to take in, i.e., "too much to hear." Also, an issue with having to deal with too much silence may affect the inner ear.

*Example:* An older woman who rarely hears from her children suffers from their silence and triggers an inner-ear problem.

## Intestine (Small)

The longest section of the digestive tract that is divided into three segments: the duodenum (see page 260), jejunum, and ileum. Each of those segments performs different digestive functions. This entry pertains specifically to the jejunum and ileum sections. The function of both is paramount in the digestive process, as the small intestine is the area where most of the nutrients from ingested food are absorbed. The majority of nutrient absorption takes place in the jejunum. The food that remains undigested and unabsorbed passes into the large intestine.

*Embryonic origin: endoderm.*

**Emotional conflict(s):** Issues related to a fear of "lack" and not being able to assimilate the "morsel." Issues linked to the mucosal lining of the small intestine are related to conflicts of not being able to deeply benefit or profit from the "morsel," as if it could be taken away before being absorbed into the blood. Conflicts of the small intestine can also pertain to the inability to integrate a situation because of indigested anger toward someone or something.

*Example:* One feels unable to profit from a house that one just bought, because the old tenant does not want to move out and develops intestine problems as a result.

# J

## Jaw

Upper and lower bony structures forming the framework of the mouth and containing the teeth.

*Embryonic origin: new brain mesoderm.*

**Emotional conflict(s):** Can reflect one's self-devaluation about verbal expression. One feels that one has not been listened to and that one's words don't matter.

*Example:* A woman who is one year away from retirement feels that her colleagues no longer validate her ideas during staff meetings, and she triggers temporomandibular joint disorder (TMJ).

*Also see Temporomandibular Joint Disorder (TMJ).*

## Joints

The locations at which two or more bones make contact.

*Embryonic origin: new brain mesoderm.*

**Emotional conflict(s):** Relates to self-devaluation about movement. Depending on the type of self-esteem issue, different joints can be affected. Joints issues often reflect regrets or shame about a gesture associated with the location of specific cartilage.

# K

## Kidney

The kidneys are made up of three parts: the parenchyma (the functional tissue of the kidney), the urinary collecting tubules, and the lining of the renal pelvis. The role of the kidneys is to filter the blood, remove wastes (which are diverted to the urinary bladder), and regulate the body's liquid balance. As the kidneys filter blood, urine is collected in the renal pelvis before being drained through the ureter to the bladder.

### Kidney parenchyma:

The parenchyma contains the nephrons, which regulate the concentration of water and soluble substances (like sodium salts) by filtering the blood, reabsorbing what is needed and excreting the rest as urine.

*Embryonic origin: new brain mesoderm.*

**Emotional conflict(s):** Related to the parenchyma are issues with water or liquid. For instance, a fear related to water, such as drowning or being overwhelmed by a situation involving a flood or broken water pipes, can be expressed through a kidney problem (which is meant to metaphorically avoid the risk of overflow). In general, such a conflict can be associated with any type of liquid, such as alcohol, oil, ice, or snow. An outflow of money (liquidity) can also figuratively represent a conflict with liquid.

*Example:* A farmer has an accident driving his truck and, experiencing the stress of spilling onto the road all the milk he had collected from his cows, subsequently triggers a kidney condition.

### Kidney collecting tubules:

The kidney collecting tubules collect the urine created by the parenchyma and conduct it to the renal pelvis.

*Embryonic origin: endoderm.*

**Emotional conflict(s):** Related to struggles for existence, having lost everything, and feeling abandoned or isolated from others. Problems of the kidney tubules relate to an ancestral conflict of the species when still living in the ocean. When accidentally thrown out of water onto dry land, the life of living beings was threatened. The biological solution enabling survival out of water was for the collecting tubules' excretions to be stopped, so that water would be held inside the organism (water retention). For instance, one may figuratively feel like a "fish out of water" when away from one's clan (a refugee or immigrant), or an individual may have lost all means of existence because of a financial collapse. The brain's solution is to retain water until existence becomes possible again in the environment. Tumor growth between the kidney collecting tubules and the calyces may occur as a means to retain water.

**Kidney renal pelvis:**
A funnel-shaped sac within the kidney that collects the urine.

*Embryonic origin: ectoderm.*

**Emotional conflict(s):** Linked to problems of the renal pelvis is a feeling of invasion of the territory and the inability to mark boundaries (similar to the conflict of the bladder). In this case, the conflict may relate to internal territory or distant external territory.

*Example:* A man may feel invaded at his workplace when he has to share his office with a new colleague and develop kidney renal issues as a result.

**Kidney stones:**
Solid pieces of material that form in the kidney and that can potentially block the flow of urine.

**Emotional conflict(s):** Issues related to having to retain water, figuratively associated with a struggle in marking territory, such as when one feels invaded and unable to create clear boundaries. One feels unable to define the limits of a distant territory.

*Example:* A woman can't be present to survey the renovation of her vacation home, and she worries about the presence of workers in her house. She develops kidney stones as a result.

# Knee

The joint between the thigh and the lower leg. It is made up of bone, cartilage, ligaments, and fluid.

*Embryonic origin: new brain mesoderm.*

**Emotional conflict(s):** An issue related to not wanting to "kneel down" (bend the knees) to an authority. Also, conflict linked to not wanting to move forward in a certain direction. Problems with the knee can reflect one's sense of devaluation when one can no longer participate in an activity or sport that one used to enjoy.

❖ ❖ ❖

# L

## Larynx

The air passage that connects the laryngopharynx to the trachea. It contains a set of elastic vocal cords that play a major role in sound production and speech. Also called the voice box.

*Embryonic origin: ectoderm.*

**Emotional conflict(s):** An issue related to an unexpected and intense fear that abruptly cuts off the breath. One is surprised by a menace in the territory—an emotional crisis in which one feels unable to scream or express the shock of one's trauma.

## Leukemia

A condition that is related to an increase of white blood cells.

**Emotional conflict(s):** The symptoms of leukemia are related to conflicts of deep self-devaluation. The loss of self-esteem is so profound that it affects the bone. Disorders of blood production will manifest according to the level of self-depreciation felt by the individual. The illness is chronic when healing cannot be completed, because the person keeps falling back into the habituated conflict of self-devaluation.

*Example:* A woman who was born fourth after two sisters and one brother always felt devalued because she looked very different from them. Her parents frequently pointed out that they could not understand how they made her. Her appearance—she was the only redhead in the family—was markedly different from everyone else's. As an adult, she is reminded of this sense of deep worthlessness when her boyfriend breaks up with her, saying that he could not marry her and risk having redheaded children. She then triggers leukemia.

**Note:** Children may be affected by a condition called acute lymphocytic leukemia, which can occur when they feel completely worthless or if they subconsciously fear a danger associated with growing up.

## Lipoma

A benign, soft-tissue tumor that is composed of adipose tissue and is usually painless.

**Emotional conflict(s):** An issue related to physical appearance and one's concern about one's figure. Devaluation and dissatisfaction related to the look, shape, or size of a body part. Also can be associated with the need one has to protect a part of one's body that one disapproves of or that others criticize.

*Also see Skin (Hypodermis).*

## Liver

A vital organ that lies on the right side of the abdominal cavity beneath the diaphragm. The main function of the liver is to produce substances that break down fats, and to convert glucose to glycogen. It is divided into four lobes of unequal size and shape. Approximately seventy percent of its main tissue consists of hepatocyte cells, which are involved in the synthesis and storage of protein, as well as the transformation of carbohydrates. Hepatocyte cells also initiate the formation and secretion of bile.

*Embryonic origin: endoderm.*

**Emotional conflict(s):** Related to deprivation or lack of what is essential in order to survive. For instance, the biological meaning of liver cancer is to extract the maximum nourishment from a limited amount of food, as if one is in a state of famine. Hepatic tumor cells (hepatocytes) enhance food stocking and maximize digestion. There are four specific types of conflicts related to the liver:

1. A conflict directly related to the liver, such as fear of having a weak liver based on family problems with this particular organ

2. A conflict related to both the family and money. For example, a family issue in which an inheritance is being split and the individual fears not getting enough of it (i.e., symbolically "eating each other's livers" for a piece of inheritance)

3. A conflict related to a "lack" of any vital element an individual might need, such as food, money, shelter, love, respect, and so on

4. A conflict related to the fear of dying from a serious intestinal illness, with a stress related to absorption, meaning a concern that the intestine won't function well enough to ensure proper nourishment of the body (in such cases, the hepatocyte cells will mutate and proliferate as a way to compensate for intestinal failure)

**Note:** When the biliary network, including the bile ducts of the liver, are affected (ectodermic tissue), the emotional conflict pertains to anger in the territory and boundary issues.

## Lou Gehrig's Disease

*See Amyotrophic Lateral Sclerosis (ALS).*

## Lungs

A pair of organs that permit the act of respiration. The two main functions of the lungs are to transport oxygen from the inhaled air to the bloodstream and to remove carbon dioxide from the bloodstream before releasing it to the atmosphere.

**Alveoli:**
Gas exchange of oxygen and carbon dioxide takes place in the alveoli, which are tiny air sacs at the termination point of the respiratory tract.

*Embryonic origin: endoderm.*

**Emotional conflict(s):** Fear related to being unable to breathe or fear of death. Innately, we know that without oxygen we cannot survive. For example, when one fears death because of a negative prognosis, it can create a "death fright," which emotionally resonates with the need to grasp more oxygen to stay alive. A cell proliferation in the alveolar tissue provides a solution for attaining greater respiratory function. The same biological solution may apply to a fear of suffocating or feeling unable to find a way out of an insurmountable situation. In this case, it is as if one cannot adapt to the environment in which one lives. An adenocarcinoma of the lung may appear as a biological expression of such a struggle.

**Bronchi:**
Branching off the trachea (or windpipe), the bronchi are the tubes that carry air to the alveoli of the lungs.

*Embryonic origin: ectoderm.*

**Emotional conflict(s):** Struggles with the bronchi are related to potential threats in the territory, such as human conflicts. The ulceration of the bronchi during the active phase of a conflict allows one to have a heightened ability to detect the presence of the predator. The diameter of the bronchial tube will expand, thus allowing a greater intake of air. Bronchitis is linked to a feeling of being aggressively pursued in the territory. One feels as if the menace in the territory is imminent. Also one may feel that one doesn't want to share one's air with another, feeling as if one is suffocating when the other person is around. In this type of situation, a person might say, "It's as if you suck up all my air."

*Examples:* A man feels that his boss might show up in his office at any time and attack him about his work. In another example, a man may feel that he cannot express himself in the presence of his wife and experiences the feeling of a "lack of air." He develops bronchial issues as a result.

### Asthma:

An inflammatory condition that causes the airways of the lungs to swell and narrow, leading to symptoms such as chest tightness, shortness of breath, coughing, and wheezing.

**Emotional conflict(s):** Stress related to refusing to breathe bad air and wanting good air instead. A struggle related to wanting to be in two different places at the same time. Similarly, feeling conflicted about breathing the same air as others; having alternating thoughts about wanting and not wanting to share the space with others. Asthma can also relate to a fear in the territory. Bronchial asthma arises when the conflict is of a territorial nature. Laryngeal asthma is triggered when fear is predominant.

*Examples:* A little boy triggers asthma as soon as he has to share a bedroom with his younger brother. In another example, a child is afraid of being hurt by a parent, whether physically or emotionally, and triggers laryngeal asthma.

### Pneumonia:

An infection of the lungs that causes inflammation in the air sacs of the lungs, also known as alveoli.

**Emotional conflict(s):** Pneumonia is a symptom of the repair phase of a conflict linked to the fear of death or the fear of suffocating.

*Also see Alveoli (above).*

## Lupus

A disease that can manifest in purely cutaneous forms (pertaining to the skin), or that can also create symptoms that affect many different organs, including kidneys, blood cells, joints, heart, and lungs.

**Emotional conflict(s):** The conjunction of four specific conflicts is at the origin of lupus: a conflict related to devaluation, associated with a feeling of being soiled, as well as a stress related to liquids (see kidney conflict) and an emotional conflict directly linked to the organ most affected by lupus. Individuals affected by lupus usually express the deep feeling of having lived a disappointing life, where they have felt emotionally and/or physically abused and taken advantage of.

## Lyme Disease

A bacterial infection that features a skin rash (often resembling a bull's-eye), swollen joints, and flu-like symptoms. The outward trigger of this infection may come from the bite of an infected tick. Symptoms include fever, headache, muscle pain, and the swelling of knees and other large joints.

**Emotional conflict(s):** An issue related to a parenting conflict that is linked to separation in the clan and a feeling of devaluation.

*Example:* A women struggles with memories of her childhood, when she had to take care of her younger siblings because her busy parents gave her the role of parenting them (although she needed to be parented herself). She always felt separated from her parents, who were frequently absent. She also felt unable to fulfill the role of a grown-up and devalued in her attempt to do so. As a result of such emotional distress, Lyme disease was activated in her body.

**Note:** The phenomenon of emotional conflict applies in relation to the type of bacteria or virus to which one may be most susceptible.

## Lymph Nodes

Small rounded or bean-shaped masses of lymphatic tissue that are located throughout the body and are part of the lymphatic system. Lymph fluid (often simply referred to as lymph) is a clear fluid that contains white blood cells known as lymphocytes, along with a small concentration of red blood cells and protein. The function of the lymph nodes is to filter the lymphatic fluid and trap unwanted substances. They play a vital role in the proper functioning of the immune system.

*Embryonic origin: new brain mesoderm.*

**Emotional conflict(s):** Fear related to feeling attacked and unable to protect someone or something. The lymphatic system figuratively represents our defense mechanisms. When one feels attacked and devalued, a necrosis (cell decrease) within the lymph nodes permits a greater pathway for lymphocytes and monocytes to operate and "defend" the organism. Enlarged lymph nodes appear during the restoration phase of the emotional conflict (replenishment of the nodes' tissue through mitosis). It's important to note that one may vacillate between active and restorative phases for as long as the emotional conflict is not resolved.

The location of the affected lymph node will correspond to the part of the skeleton linked to the conflict. For instance, lymph nodes of the head and neck originate in the branchial arches. Problems with the upper-body nodes are related to a frontal fear, such as a bad prognosis, treatment, and illness in general. Another example would be a woman who has one or more enlarged lymph nodes under the armpit as an expression of a conflict of powerlessness and self-devaluation related to the offspring—that is, the one "under her wing" (also see Breast).

**Lymphoma:**
A cancer of the lymph nodes and lymphoid tissues.

**Emotional conflict(s):** Linked to an experience of powerlessness and defenselessness in a context that creates fear. Lymphoma can appear during the resolution phase of a conflict related to such a struggle.

*Example:* A man feels criticized, powerless, and devalued by his wife for not being competent enough in taking care of their newborn child. He develops lymphoma under his armpits as a result of feeling inadequate in protecting his offspring.

# M

## Macula (Macular Degeneration)

An oval-shaped and highly pigmented yellow spot, near the center of the retina of the eye, which provides the most detailed central vision. Macular degeneration is a condition resulting in a loss of vision in the center of the visual field because of damage to the retina.

*Embryonic origin: ectoderm.*

**Emotional conflict(s):** A struggle related to having to see someone or something for the last time. For instance, one is subjected to an acute visual stress, such as witnessing the death of a loved one before one's eyes. One may also feel the need to eliminate the visual aspects of certain details related to the progressive degeneration of a close family member.

## Marijuana consumption

Smoking or ingesting marijuana is related to an identity conflict linked to the father. One lacks a sense of knowing who they are because they were not accepted or wanted by their dad. This memory can be imprinted during gestation if the father did not accept the pregnancy. A lack of understanding and connection between father and son or daughter can be at the origin of such a habit. Adopted children will often use marijuana to escape a reality in which they lack a sense of identity due to not knowing who their biological father is.

## Mediastinum (Branchial Arches)

The middle section of the chest cavity (between the lungs). It contains lymph nodes, important nerves, and the branchial arches, among other organs. The function of the branchial arches and the mediastinum that houses them is related to our capacity to breathe.

*Embryonic origin: ectoderm.*

**Emotional conflict(s):** Symptoms of the branchial arches in the mediastinum pertain to a conflict of panic and fear for oneself (or another). For instance, a person having to face the news of a bad prognosis may manifest symptoms within the mediastinum. During the active phase of the conflict, the biological purpose of tissue ulcerations is to increase breathing capacity during intense fear. Cysts (or tumors) in the mediastinum appear during the resolution phase of the conflict.

# Melanoma

*See Skin (dermis).*

# Meningitis

An inflammation (or infection) of the protective membranes (meninges) surrounding the brain and spinal cord.

**Emotional conflict(s):** A struggle related to feeling immense fear and a lack of security. Meningitis can arise from a conflict related to a fear of an attack toward the head and the need to protect it. It can also be related to a concern of having a psychiatric illness, brain tumor, or neurological problem.

# Middle Ear

The middle portion of the ear, consisting of the tympanic membrane and an air-filled chamber lined with mucous membranes. Conveys vibration communicated through compression waves to the inner ear.

*Embryonic origin: endoderm.*

**Emotional conflict(s):** Distress related to not being able to catch a "morsel" of information with the ear or not liking the way a "morsel" of information is presented. Sometimes issues related to having too much information to ingest, literally or figuratively, may trigger problems with the middle ear. Also, children may experience middle-ear problems when they feel unsafe and desire subconsciously to return to the safety of the uterus.

**Note:** In the early stages of the evolution of the human species, the middle ear and the mouth constituted a "gullet."

# Migraine

An intense and painful headache that is often accompanied by nausea, vomiting, and increased sensitivity to light and sound.

**Emotional conflict(s):** A struggle related to intellectual devaluation. Migraines can reflect one's doubt about one's intelligence or mental capacities, often in the context of work or spirituality. One may feel that one is not thinking well enough or clearly enough to resolve a problem. Violent migraines can be related to being unable to face the fact that there is no solution for something and to having to confront reality.

# Mouth

The first portion of the alimentary canal.

### Oral Submucosa:
A layer of loose connective tissue beneath the mucous membrane.

*Embryonic origin: endoderm.*

**Emotional conflict(s):** Related to being incapable of catching or possessing a "morsel," literally or figuratively. One feels unable to get a hold of someone else's words or secret.

### Oral Mucosa:
Epithelium that lines the inside of the mouth.

*Embryonic origin: ectoderm.*

**Emotional conflict(s):** A struggle related to digestion, with a tonality of wanting to reject something from the mouth (literally or figuratively) so that it won't be incorporated.

# Multiple Sclerosis (MS)

A disease caused by the deterioration of the myelin sheath, the protective covering that surrounds nerve cells in the brain and spinal cord. When this nerve-cell covering is damaged, nerve signals slow down or stop.

**Emotional conflict(s):** An issue related to being unable to escape or move. Feelings of self-devaluation experienced in a vertical movement, such as the fear of falling. Multiple sclerosis is the perfect solution to the fear of falling, since it counteracts the stress of movement through the deterioration of the myelin—therefore stopping the transmission of nerve impulses. Also, multiple sclerosis can correlate to the following conflicts or struggles: the inability to follow (which affects the legs); the inability to hold onto or defend (affecting the arms or hands); or the inability to escape (which affects the back and shoulder muscles).

*Example:* A woman is extremely afraid of falling while mountain climbing and feels devalued in comparison to her friends, who are scaling up the mountain with ease. She develops MS and has her first symptom shortly after that event.

**Note:** MS can also be linked to an experience perceived as a social "fall," such as the loss of a job, money, or status. The brain does not differentiate between what is real and symbolic, and, in this case, multiple sclerosis prevents future movement, such as moving up the ladder of success only to fall down again.

## Myopathy

A disease of the muscle tissue (rather than the nerves), resulting in weakness, inflammation, tetany (spasms), or paralysis.

**Emotional conflict(s):** Distress associated with self-devaluation and powerlessness in relation to horizontal movement. Emotional conflict related to wanting to stop a movement that has already been initiated (literally or figuratively). The destruction of the muscle stops the movement from being carried out. In relation to a child's project purpose, a child may express the subconscious project of his or her mother, who conceived him or her for the purpose of stopping the father from going back and forth (movement) between her and someone or somewhere else. For example the child may have been conceived with the intention of stopping the movement that has already been initiated by the father who is regularly visiting his mistress and in order to have him "stuck at home" instead. Myopathy can also relate to being forced to stay in one place or being forbidden any kind of movement.

*Example:* A person has a gun pointed at him or her and is forced to stay immobile in order to stay alive—to "not move a muscle."

**Note:** The conflict linked to myopathy relates to a movement that has already been initiated through the nerve impulse, so the only way that the body can express a solution to this conflict is through muscle wasting, thus stopping the movement in present time. It is important to make a distinction between MS and myopathy. In the case of MS, the conflict concerns future movement(s), and the problem will involve the nerves (unlike myopathy, which involves the muscle).

## Myopia

A condition of the eye, also known as nearsightedness, in which objects at a distance appear blurry and difficult to identify. The person is able to clearly see objects that are close.

**Emotional conflict(s):** A problem related to the fear of danger that is "close by." One has to clearly see what is nearby, at the cost of their ability to see distant objects or events.

*Example:* A boy living with an abusive father who drinks alcohol may trigger myopia after receiving an unexpected slap. In such a case, the boy subconsciously feels the need to develop hyperperformance of the eyes within the context of proximity, so that he can see the slap coming and avoid it.

## Myxedema

*See Thyroid (Hypothyroidism).*

❖ ❖ ❖

# N

## Nail Biting

Nails are similar to claws in other animals. Nail biting is a behavioral disorder with an onset usually occurring in childhood and adolescence.

**Emotional conflict(s):** Linked to a need to hold back aggressiveness and metaphorically "declaw" oneself to avoid hurting another. One feels that it would be unsafe to attack or respond to the aggression of another. Nail biting can also be related to one's inability to keep a hold on something. This habit may be linked to a subconscious fear of having to dig the earth to bury someone (explore ancestral memories).

## Nausea

An uneasy sensation of discomfort in the upper stomach, which often precedes vomiting.

**Emotional conflict(s):** Struggle related to wanting to give back something that feels unacceptable or unfair. A feeling of rejection toward an unpleasant situation.

## Nerve

A cord-like structure that contains many axons (nerve fibers). A nerve provides a common pathway for the impulses that are transmitted along each of the axons to peripheral organs.

**Emotional conflict(s):** Issue related to a "fear by anticipation." One feels scared about the consequences of an action and apprehensive in regard to the future. Nerve pain can also relate to the fear of hurting another with one's movement, literally or figuratively.

## Nephritic Colic

Condition associated with disorders affecting the kidney.

**Emotional conflict(s):** Distress linked to a struggle with existence and a conflict of annihilation (total defeat). This condition can also represent a struggle associated with territorial marking. A kidney stone can be the expression of one's conflict with another, whom one feels is stepping on one's territory.

## Nose (Mucus Membrane)

The area inside the nose made of specialized cells that are responsible for smelling. The sense of smell permits the detection of the odor of prey, food, and sexual hormones, as well as danger.

**Emotional conflict(s):** Distress linked to wanting to get rid of the odor of the enemy. A problem of the mucous membrane of the nose in linked to the archaic conflict of sniffing out the danger of the predator. It can also be related to the fear of toxic gas, chemicals, or smoke. One may have one's nose run or have sinusitis when worrying about what others are saying behind one's back, and have thoughts such as "this situation stinks!"

**Note:** Nasal polyps correspond to a conflict of stench. One feels that something stinks badly, literally or figuratively.

## Nystagmus

Involuntary, fast, and uncontrollable eye movements.

**Emotional conflict(s):** Related to a fear of danger that can come from many directions. Fast ocular movements (from side to side or up and down) permit one to see and avoid danger that could show up from anywhere. This condition allows one to visually check a larger scope of the territory at once.

*Example:* During a battle, a soldier is going through tremendous stress, running away from bombs that come from every side. One of his descendants may express his stress by manifesting nystagmus.

## Obesity (Fat)

Excess fat tissue affecting the hypoderm, which is the deepest layer of the skin (subcutaneous tissue).

*Embryonic origin: new brain mesoderm.*

**Emotional conflict(s):** Obesity is generally linked to a survival mechanism in relation to a conflict of abandonment.

Weight gain and water retention relates to the archaic conflict of the species when still living in the ocean. At this time of evolution, when accidently thrown out of water onto dry land, the living beings depended on the ebb and tide cycle, which would take them back to their element. The life of the species was threatened when being out of the water. The biological solution enabling their survival outside of their element (in this case the ocean) was for the kidney to retain water inside the organism. Figuratively if one feels out of one's element, like a "fish out of water", or being away from one's clan (i.e.: refugee or immigrant), the brain's solution is to retain water until existence becomes possible again. Struggles for existence, having lost everything, and feeling abandoned or isolated from others can therefore be a trigger for water retention and weight gain.

Obesity can also be linked to a fear of starvation. Generally related to a survival mechanism in relation to a conflict of abandonment. In nature, when an offspring is abandoned, it faces the danger of death, mainly from starvation. In order to survive, it is essential to eat. One who feels abandoned can tend to throw oneself at food when it is available, thus metaphorically increasing one's chance of survival. In certain cases, the brain will command the organism to metabolize food into lipids, thus creating greater reserves of fat. That is why obese individuals oftentimes gain weight even though they eat small amounts of food. Metaphorically, being fat also enables one to protect oneself by creating a distance between one and the environment. Being overweight also allows one to appear physically imposing to potential predators, in order to intimidate them (investigate potential memories of sexual abuse in the clan).

*Also see the following examples:*

**Water retention:**
Related to the conflict of the kidney, in terms of feeling isolated and abandoned.

**Weight gain in the stomach area:**
Pertains to a need to protect the offspring.

**Weight gain in the thighs:**
Related to issues about femininity and a need to protect the sexual organs and what is most intimate.

**Weight gain in the neck, shoulders, and upper body:**
May relate to the necessity to be strong in order to support others.

# Omentum

A fold of peritoneum extending from the stomach to the adjacent abdominal organs. It functions as a "shock absorber" and protects the abdominal viscera from physical injury as well as temperature changes. It also facilitates the smooth motion of visceral organs over each other.

*Embryonic origin: old brain mesoderm.*

**Emotional conflict(s):** Feeling unprotected and soiled in relation to the abdomen. One feels that one could not protect oneself in a situation that one perceives as dirty and indigestible.

## Osteoporosis

A condition in which bone mineral density is reduced and bone microarchitecture deteriorates.

**Emotional conflict(s):** A struggle related to self-worth that often affects women after menopause, once the capability to procreate is terminated. This condition can also relate to an all-encompassing conflict of self-devaluation. For instance, one feels worthless because one can no longer measure up to what or whom one used to be when one was younger. Osteoporosis can reflect a sense of nostalgia and sadness about no longer feeling useful.

## Ovaries

A pair of organs in the female reproductive system; each is the size and shape of an almond. They are located in the pelvis, with one on each side of the uterus. The function of the ovaries is to produce eggs and female hormones.

### Ovaries (germ cells):

Germ cells are cells that eventually mature into sperm or ova. Ovarian germ cell tumor is a cancer that forms in the reproductive cells of the ovary.

Often affecting young women, ovarian germ cell tumors (OGCT) are a type of ovarian neoplasm that forms in the reproductive cells of the ovary. Disorders related to germ cells in the ovaries include teranoma, seminoma, and dermoid cysts, and represent only a small percentage of ovarian problems.

*Embryonic origin: endoderm.*

**Emotional conflict(s):** Concern related to the offspring, in terms of "profound loss." There is nothing worse for a living being than the loss of an offspring; for a human being, the loss of a child. This type of conflict resonates with the archaic program of perpetuation of the species and is in relation to one's lineage. The solution to the loss of an offspring is to create another offspring, thus soliciting the production of more ovarian cells. The death of a child might trigger an ovarian tumor in a woman who deeply struggles with her "loss." Also, a woman might figuratively "lose" her son or daughter after the occurrence of a fight and suffer from not knowing if she will see him or her again. Ovarian disorders can sometimes relate to a profound loss other than the immediate offspring and may be linked to the death or departure of a grandchild, parent, friend, or pet. Similarly, a feeling stemming from the anticipation of a loss can trigger the proliferation of ovarian cells as if the loss were happening in the present.

*Example:* A woman who is taking care of her elderly mother lives with the expectation that her mother could die at any time. She triggers ovarian cancer as a result of her chronic stress.

**Note:** Testicular teranoma in men is related to the same emotional conflict (i.e., "profound loss conflict").

**Ovarian cysts (stromal cells/interstitial tissue):**
Ovarian cysts are related to hormone-producing cells within the ovaries.

*Embryonic origin: new brain mesoderm.*

**Emotional conflict(s):** Relates to a conflict of "loss" experienced in a milder form than the loss related to problems with the germ cells discussed above. The undertonality of the conflict associated with ovarian cysts is that of guilt and devaluation. During the active phase of such a conflict, the tissue of the ovary will become necrotic and the ovary will shrink as if it needed to be eliminated. Such conflict can be related to a woman's feelings of unworthiness to reproduce because she was unable to take care of her lost offspring (for instance, after a miscarriage). This conflict can also be linked to a woman's devaluation based on not being able to seduce a man (as in, "he is too good for me"). This condition might also express the distress of an unpleasant conflict with a man. Once the emotional conflict is resolved, the necrosis is repaired and a cyst will appear, thus increasing the production of female hormones and the expression of femininity.

*Example:* A woman is having arguments with her husband and feels that he puts her down and denigrates her. During that phase, irregular periods may occur. Once the conflict is resolved, an ovarian cyst may appear.

**Polycystic ovary syndrome:**
A hormonal disorder involving numerous small cysts along the outer edge of each ovary.

**Emotional conflict(s):** Metaphorically pertains to a conflict about maturation and not being able to grow up, resulting in the absence of ovulation (the egg is not expelled out of the ovary). This condition might also pertain to having a difficult time making mature and definite decisions.

*Example:* A woman might have feelings of wanting to remain a child and not become a woman. She develops polycystic ovary syndrome as a result.

# P

## Palate

The roof of the mouth that separates the oral cavity from the nasal cavity in humans and other mammals.

*Embryonic origin: endoderm.*

**Emotional conflict(s):** In a broad sense, linked to losing the "morsel" after having caught it. The archaic conflict relates to a situation in which the prey could not be held and incorporated in the mouth. A problem related to the soft palate often pertains to a situation in which someone was momentarily in contact with the "morsel" but lost it. Such a conflict includes a notion of separation with the "morsel."

*Example:* A woman gets a raise that is abruptly taken away two months later, and she develops a condition in her soft palate as a result.

**Note:** An issue linked to the hard palate pertains to one's devaluation and fear of not being able to seize and catch the "morsel." An example of a hard-palate conflict could be about feeling incapable of "catching" a promotion.

## Pancreas

A large gland behind the stomach, that is connected to the small intestine. It is both an endocrine gland producing important hormones and an exocrine gland secreting pancreatic juice. The function of the pancreas is to secrete the hormones (mainly insulin and glucagon) that regulate the level of glucose in the blood and produce enzymes designed to digest food.

**Hyperglycemia** *(also see Diabetes)*:
Hyperglycemia is the technical term for high blood sugar. This condition involves beta cells in the pancreas, which are located in the islets of Langerhans (the hormone-producing region of the pancreas). Intermittent hyperglycemia may be an indication of a prediabetic state.

**Emotional conflict(s):** An issue related to high blood sugar involving a situation of attack/defense, reluctance, and resistance. One may feel pushed to act against one's will and is preparing for action. Since muscle power is likely to be needed in order to attack or escape, sugar is made available in the arteries. Insulin secretions are inhibited to keep sugar available in the blood for potential combat. If the person resists and stays in the unpleasant situation, sugar will not be used and will therefore build up. The conflict related to hyperglycemia can also pertain to a deep need for softness in a relationship when one has to frequently exert and bear a position of authority.

**Hypoglycemia:**
Hypoglycemia is related to an abnormally diminished content of sugar in the blood.

**Emotional conflict(s):** A conflict of a feminine type that pertains to a feeling of fear in a situation that is imposed and perceived as disgusting. One feels that one can no longer "fight" and is subconsciously withdrawing the sugar from one's blood. During the active phase of a conflict, one is subjected to glucagon insufficiency (functional impairment of alpha islet cells). In order to compensate for a lack of glucose in one's blood, one is always hungry *(also see Bulimia)*.

### Pancreas (enzyme cells):

Pancreatic adenocarcinoma typically arises from pancreatic enzyme cells and is a secretory type of tumor.

*Embryonic origin: endoderm.*

**Emotional conflict(s):** An issue related to having to give up something that was symbolically already digested. A conflict of dishonor, shame, and humiliation related to family and a struggle over a "morsel."

*Example:* A man who was sure that he would inherit as much as his brother winds up with nothing and cannot digest the situation, thus leading to a problem of the pancreas.

### Pancreatic duct:

Duct joining the pancreas to the common bile duct, that delivers bile from the liver and gallbladder to the small intestine. The function of the pancreatic duct is to carry the enzymes from the pancreas to the small intestine.

*Embryonic origin: ectoderm.*

**Emotional conflict(s):** Intense resentment and rancor in relation to a situation that is perceived as an injustice. A conflict related to territorial anger and a feeling of betrayal in which money might be involved.

## Parathyroid Glands

Small endocrine glands located in the neck behind the thyroid gland that produce parathyroid hormone (PTH), which increases the concentration of calcium in the blood. The parathyroid glands control the amount of calcium in the blood and the bones, maintaining adequate levels of calcium in the body for proper functioning of the muscular system.

*Embryonic origin: endoderm.*

**Emotional conflict(s):** An issue related to the need to improve muscle contraction in order to properly incorporate food and slide the "morsel" down the digestive tract. In a figurative sense, one may have a struggle related to work and ingesting a lot of information properly. During the active phase of such a conflict, the parathyroid hormone levels are increased so that calcium can improve muscular contractions. This conflict can also relate to a need to build oneself up, metaphorically strengthening one's structure.

## Parkinson's Disease

A degenerative disorder of the central nervous system that causes a decline in the ability to control the movements of the body.

**Emotional conflict(s):** An issue related to movement, especially expressing a need to "hold and keep" something or someone. For instance, after recently being reunited, a man discovers that his father is dying and cannot let him go. An emotional struggle having to do with a movement that is repeated without result, as in being figuratively unable to break through a wall. Also, this condition can relate to a subconscious need to unblock a movement that has been blocked for a long time. An emotional conflict related to wanting and, at the same time, not wanting to engage in a certain movement (i.e., stealing).

## Pelvis

Large, bony structure that connects the sacrum region of the spine to the femur bones of the legs.

*Embryonic origin: new brain mesoderm.*

**Emotional conflict(s):** An issue related to a reduced sense of self-worth, in terms of not being able to conceive or to perform sexually. Also, symptoms of the pelvis can reflect one's difficulty with coping with overwhelming insults.

*Also see Hip.*

## Peritoneum

The membrane that forms the lining of the abdominal and pelvic cavity, and that also envelops the visceral organs and the retroperitoneal organs, such as the kidney and the pancreas. It is composed of a mesothelium layer that is further supported by a thin layer of connective tissue. The function of the peritoneum is to protect and support the internal organs.

*Embryonic origin: old brain mesoderm.*

**Emotional conflict(s):** Distress related to an attack against the abdomen, whether literal (i.e., the fear of being cut open during surgery) or figurative (one feels attacked verbally, as if one were being stabbed in the abdomen). In either instance, the thickening of the peritoneum provides protection against further attacks.

## Pharynx

The membrane-lined cavity connecting the nose and mouth to the esophagus. It permits the passage of air and food.

*Embryonic origin: endoderm.*

**Emotional conflict(s):** An issue related to being unable to catch or spit out the "morsel," or a conflict of losing the "morsel" that was just caught. One wants to put the "morsel" out of reach, farther than the back of the throat, so that it will be kept and ultimately digested.

*Example:* A woman is about to get engaged when one of her friends starts flirting with her future fiancé. She symbolically wants to put her catch (the fiancé) out of reach, and she triggers cancer of the pharynx (hyperperformance of the pharynx that allows the morsel to slide down faster).

## Pituitary Gland (Anterior Lobe)

A secretory organ situated at the base of the brain. Its function is to send signals to regulate various hormones that have dramatic effects on reproduction, growth, and stress.

*Embryonic origin: endoderm.*

**Emotional conflict(s):** Linked to feeling incapable of accessing something and being overwhelmed by it. The content of the conflict will determine the type of imbalance affecting the pituitary. For instance, in a situation where a woman fears not being able to feed her child, an increase of prolactin may manifest to allow her to produce more milk and nourish her offspring. In another example, a man desires a higher position in his company but perceives it as unattainable; therefore, the secretion of human growth hormone (HGH) may occur as a result of obsessively wanting "to grow" professionally (symbolically representing an intense need to reach higher, grow, and expand). A person who feels incapable of pursuing the right direction and sticking with a plan of action may have an imbalance involving the secretion of the ACTH hormone

## Pneumonia

*See Lungs.*

## Presbyopia

Affecting the lens of the eye, presbyopia is the gradual loss of the ability to focus actively on nearby objects.

**Emotional conflict(s):** Reflects one's fear of the future or of a danger at a distance. One often triggers presbyopia in relation to thoughts about aging and/or a fear of illness. The biological meaning of presbyopia is linked to symbolically increasing visual performance in relationship to what is at a distance versus what is near (to clearly see the danger that is coming). One can become farsighted when one is deeply concerned with unavoidable "dangers"

291

such as death, realizing that time has passed and that one may not have enough time left to realize one's dreams. Such thoughts often manifest after the age of forty, when one feels that one has already lived half of one's life.

## Prostate

An exocrine gland located between the bladder and the penis, just in front of the rectum. It has two main functions. It secretes fluid that nourishes and protects the sperm. It also generates natural antiseptics produced by enzymes that clean the genital ducts. During ejaculation, the prostate squeezes this protective fluid into the urethra, where it is expelled with sperm and semen.

*Embryonic origin: endoderm.*

**Emotional conflict(s):** An issue pertaining to two types of conflicts. There can be a sexual conflict about an unclean genital situation (since one of the prostate's functions is to clean the genital ducts). For instance, a married man may be aroused by the idea of sexual experiences with younger women and feel that his thoughts are outside of the sexual norm and are dirty (related to the notion of sin).

The second type of conflict is linked to the prostate's function of nourishing the sperm. Problems with the prostate can be triggered by worries about the children or grandchildren, in terms of loss or family crisis. In order to perpetuate the species, a grandfather who is worried about his children not being able to have their own offspring may subconsciously want to act as a genitor (symbolically providing a solution for the perpetuation of the clan), thus overstimulating his prostate function. This conflict may be at the root of a prostate cancer. In another example, a man may feel that his relationship with his wife or partner is a mismatch, such as being with a much younger partner. He may struggle with his sexuality, wanting to perform like a young man and thus subconsciously overstimulating his prostate to create more sperm.

## Psoriasis

A skin disease that causes itchy patches of thick, red skin with silvery scales.

**Emotional conflict(s):** There is a double conflict of separation—that is, an individual is subjected to the emotional struggles of two different conflicts related to separation. Psoriasis happens when one conflict of separation is resolved while the other is still active, thus soliciting the epidermis in two opposite fashions simultaneously. There are active microulcerations concurrent with the inflammation related to cell replenishment.

*Example:* A woman gets married and moves out of her parents' home, relocating to another country where her military husband is stationed, thus triggering a first separation conflict. A few months later, her husband is deployed to a war-torn region, thus triggering a second separation conflict. Since she is pregnant, her husband proposes that she return to her parents' home for a period of time; therefore, the woman begins to resolve the first separation conflict. However, the separation with her husband is ongoing (an active separation).

**Note:** Eczema appears when there is only one separation conflict, during its resolution phase (also see Skin/Epidermis).

❖  ❖  ❖

# R

## Rectum (Sigmoid Colon)

Part of the digestive system involving the submucosal layer of the sigmoid colon and the submucosal layer of the upper two-thirds of the rectum. The function of this lower part of the digestive system is to enable the stool to move toward the outside and be expelled.

*Embryonic origin: endoderm.*

**Emotional conflict(s):** An issue related to a conflict of not being able to expel what one perceives to be a filthy, disgusting "morsel." The matter is too ugly to be eliminated, and one cannot evacuate the dirtiness that has been done to one. Figuratively, it is impossible for someone to let go and forgive a perceived wrong action, which is seen as despicable and dirty.

## Rectum (Lower)

The lowest part of the digestive system. The anus is the opening of the rectum, at the far end of the digestive tract through which stool leaves the body. The rectum's function is to move the bowel in order for the stool to be defecated through the anus.

*Embryonic origin: ectoderm.*

**Emotional conflict(s):** An identity conflict related to territory and the inability to find and define one's position (territorial conflict of a feminine type for both women and men). The biological expression of such a conflict allows increased defecation through an ulcerative widening of the rectum, figuratively enabling an individual to "mark" his or her position in the territory.

*Example:* A man's role as a father is compromised after a divorce and separation from his family. He no longer holds his position within the clan, since he feels replaced by a stepfather. He develops Hemorrhoids as a result of his perception. In another example, a woman loses her position as a manager to another worker and no longer knows where she belongs within the company. Feeling that there is "no place for her," she triggers a condition of the rectum.

## Retina

*See Detached Retina.*

## Ribs

Long, curved bones forming the cage that surrounds the chest. The ribs serve to protect the heart, lungs, and internal organs of the thorax region.

*Embryonic origin: new brain mesoderm.*

**Emotional conflict(s):** Problems with the ribs reflect difficulties with family members, in terms of feeling devalued by them. It can be linked to a deep need for love or protection. The upper ribs reflect problems with the ancestors, the middle ribs are linked to struggles with the collaterals (such as brothers and sisters), and the lower ribs are connected to issues with the descendants (children or grandchildren).

# S

## Sacroiliac

Refers to the sacroiliac joint (SI joint), which sits between the sacrum and the iliac bone of the pelvis. It is formed by associated ligaments that meet on either side of the lower back.

*Embryonic origin: new brain mesoderm.*

**Emotional conflict(s):** Problem related to sexual frustration. Self-depreciation related to sexuality, in terms of not being satisfied. Devaluation related to having access to profound and sacred knowledge that creates emotional pain, such as stories about the past and the genesis of extreme and far-reaching patterns or circumstances.

## Sacrum

A bone structure that is connected to the pelvis and located at the base of the lumbar vertebrae.

*Embryonic origin: new brain mesoderm.*

**Emotional conflict(s):** An emotional struggle related to what is sacred. Problems with the sacrum can pertain to memories of incest, sexual abuse, pedophilia, or other sexual deviations. Conflicts of the sacrum often relate to notions of sacrifice and guilt.

## Salivary Glands

Exocrine glands with ducts, including the parotid glands and the sublingual and submandibular salivary glands of the mouth. Their function is to produce saliva.

### Sublingual salivary gland and parotid glands:

*Embryonic origin: endoderm.*

**Emotional conflict(s):** A feeling of not being able to grab and incorporate enough nourishment. Subconsciously, a cancer of such glands allows one to incorporate food faster with more saliva in order to assimilate it and store it in case of deprivation. This conflict can relate to one's inability to keep what one thought that one had already secured, such as a job, money, and/or a promotion.

### Salivary gland ducts:

*Embryonic origin: ectoderm.*

**Emotional conflict(s):** Distress related to not having the right to absorb food or not wanting to incorporate something. When nourishment is not allowed, one may express one's need for the desired food with a watering mouth. For example, in a literal sense, one can suffer from being forbidden to eat and not allowed to mix the wanted food with one's saliva. Figuratively, one can refuse to absorb and incorporate the orders of one's boss or other authority figure and can subconsciously block absorption by manufacturing a calculus in one of the gland ducts.

## Scleroderma

An autoimmune disease of the connective tissues, that creates a thickening of the skin and spontaneous scarring.

*Embryonic origin: ectoderm.*

**Emotional conflict(s):** Stress related to an abrupt separation with a tonality of devaluation, and often associated with a feeling of being soiled.

## Scoliosis

A condition that causes a sideways curve of the backbone or spine.

**Emotional conflict(s):** Scoliosis can be the expression of one's need to negate oneself or to avoid being touched by another (such as with molestation or incest). It can also allow one to metaphorically "move aside" from the other when feeling devalued.

*Example:* A young boy develops scoliosis because he feels less important than his brother, symbolically putting himself aside from his sibling.

**Note:** This conflict is also known as the "collateral" conflict.

## Scrotum

The sac, located between the penis and the anus, that contains the testicles. Its function is to protect the testes and keep their temperature slightly lower than the rest of the body. The scrotum also contains blood vessels and part of the spermatic cord.

*Embryonic origin: old brain mesoderm.*

**Emotional conflict(s):** Issues related to a fear of the testicles being unprotected and possibly hurt.

*Example:* A man is worried about being injured during contact sports or martial arts, and he develops a condition of the scrotum.

## Shingles

A virus that creates a skin rash that grows into small blisters filled with fluid. This condition is usually confined to one region of the body and affects the epidermis, dermis, and sensory nerves.

**Emotional conflict(s):** A separation conflict (epidermis) with a tonality related to the violation of one's integrity (dermis) and the need to cease contact (nerves). The body is affected in the region that felt "stained." For instance, being beaten, molested, or raped can trigger such a conflict. Figuratively, a verbal insult can also elicit a feeling of being soiled.

## Shoulder

The upper joint of the human arm, comprising the collarbone, shoulder blade, and upper arm bone.

*Embryonic origin: new brain mesoderm.*

**Emotional conflict(s):** For a right-handed person, a problem of the left shoulder reflects feelings of a lack of self-worth as a parent or as a daughter or son. For instance, a father feels responsible for his son's drug abuse and thinks that if he had been more present as a father, his son would not have adopted this limiting behavior.

The right shoulder (again, for a right-handed person) symbolizes the reduction of self-worth in relation to a partner, sibling, friend, or coworker. For instance, a woman feels that she is not being a good spouse as she is often absent (working the night shift as a nurse), and she develops an extensive decalcification of the shoulder.

**Note:** For a left-handed person, the meaning of the above conflicts is reversed. The offspring conflict is expressed in the right shoulder, and the partner conflict is expressed in the left shoulder.

## Sinus

Space (or cavity) within the bones of the face, connecting with the nasal cavities. The mucosa of the sinus is an extension of the nasal mucosa.

*Embryonic origin: ectoderm.*

**Emotional conflict(s):** An issue pertaining to something that "stinks." One feels that something smells bad, literally or figuratively, stemming from a latent fear of being criticized. Distress related to having a hard time foreseeing future events or understanding what might currently be occurring behind the scenes.

*Example:* A woman feels that her work colleagues may be gossiping about her, and she is affected with chronic sinus infections.

## Skin

The body's soft outer covering, also known as the largest organ of the body. Functions of the skin include gathering sensory information from the environment and acting as a protective barrier that interfaces with a sometimes hostile environment. It is also involved in maintaining proper body temperature.

**Epidermis:**
The outer layer of the skin and the principle barrier to the outer environment.

*Embryonic origin: ectoderm.*

**Emotional conflict(s):** Conflict generally related to separation and loss of touch. The epidermis permits physical contact. When one feels separated, the biological solution to alleviate such stress is to numb the skin through microulcerations. This way, one does not feel the loss of contact with the absent person or thing (a parent, friend, lover, house, or anything to which one is attached). Skin disorders such as eczema appear during the resolution phase of such separation conflicts.

**Dermis:**
The middle layer of the skin, composed of two layers—the papillary and reticular dermis.

*Embryonic origin: old brain mesoderm.*

**Emotional conflict(s):** An issue related to an attack against one's integrity. For instance, a melanoma can be the expression of a "dirtying conflict" and a feeling of violation related to one's body, such as rape, sexual abuse, inappropriate physical contact, a verbal attack, or another transgression.

**Hypodermis:**
The innermost and thickest layer of the skin, which consists primarily of loose connective tissue and lobules of fat.

*Embryonic origin: new brain mesoderm.*

**Emotional conflict(s):** Linked to self-devaluation about the physical appearance of a specific part of the body. For example, a lipoma can be the expression of wanting to protect an area of the body that is being criticized and perceived as unattractive by oneself or others.

**Note:** For related skin issues, also see Acne, Alopecia, Hair Loss, Herpes, Hives, Impetigo, Lupus, and Psoriasis.

## Smoking Cigarettes

The act of smoking gives an individual the illusion of getting more air into his or her lungs. Those who smoke give themselves emotional relief each time they inhale—a momentary respite from their worries or dread.

Smoking allows one to draw in and experience a sense of inner safety, calming the sensation of loneliness one may be enduring. Smoking gives the impression of bringing more oxygen inside the lungs and is related to a fear of not being able to breathe in the environment. One feels unable to adapt to their surroundings.

## Snoring

Often a loud, guttural sound, snoring is the vibration of respiratory structures when one's breathing is partially obstructed while sleeping.

**Emotional conflict(s):** Relates to metaphorically being unable to catch a "morsel" with the nose. In opposite fashion, it can also reflect a desire to distance oneself from something. For example, one wants to "catch the breath" of the person one wishes to be close to sexually, or instead, one wants to distance oneself from an odor, smell, or danger (whether literal or figurative). Snoring can also relate to a need for attention, care, or protection while sleeping.

## Spine

In human anatomy, the vertebral column is divided into three major sections: the cervical, the thoracic, and the lumbar spine. The sacrum is situated below the lumbar spine and is part of the pelvis. The spine is made up of individual bones called vertebrae. There are seven cervical vertebrae, twelve thoracic vertebrae, and five lumbar vertebrae.

*Embryonic origin: new brain mesoderm.*

**Emotional conflict(s):** See each vertebra and its corresponding conflicts.

**Cervical spine:**
In general, cervical vertebrae relate to communication, as the nervous system impulses travel through the neck before being distributed throughout the body.

*C-1 (Atlas):* A conflict related to communication and feeling unable to express deep thoughts. Problems with C-1 can reflect one's tendency to ruminate and contemplate ideas rather than expressing them.

*C-2 (Axis):* A conflict related to the integration and deep understanding of information. C-2 problems can be associated with feeling resentful when obligated to incorporate ideas with which one does not agree.

*C-3:* A conflict that pertains to contact with another. One chronically experiences a state of opposition toward someone else and feels rancor toward the other.

*C-4:* A conflict of being unable to communicate an opinion and be heard. Distress correlated with auditory issues.

*C-5:* A conflict related to being unable to have a voice. One feels that one's opinion is unimportant. Being forced to compromise in a situation that feels unfair because communication could not occur from both sides. Distress correlated with the vocal cords and the pharynx.

*C-6:* A conflict pertaining to not wanting to "bow down to" an authority (in literal terms, this translates to not wanting to bend the head). Distress related to having to give up childhood dreams because they are inaccessible. Distress correlated with the muscles of the neck, thyroid, and tonsils.

*C-7:* A conflict related to an unwillingness to submit to someone's authority. Feelings of injustice; having to tolerate being under someone's power. Distress correlated with the neck and shoulders.

*C-7/T-1:* Conflict related to immediate danger and fear. For instance, one fears that one won't wake up after having anesthesia.

**Thoracic spine:**
Thoracic vertebrae generally express one's feeling of "being responsible for all" and having to be the pillar of a structure that holds everything for oneself or the clan.

*T-1:* A conflict related to one's feeling that the order of things is not being respected. Also conflict linked to the fear of dying. Distress correlated with the esophagus and the trachea.

*T-2:* A conflict related to the loss of territory. Distress associated with self-devaluation within the nest and not being able to stand as a pillar for others. Distress correlated with the heart and coronary arteries.

*T-3:* A conflict corresponding to a threat within the territory. Lack of affection related to the mother (real or symbolic). Distress correlated with the lungs, breasts, and ribs.

*T-4:* A conflict related to feelings of bitter resentfulness, stubbornness, and adhering to a position of being right. Distress correlated with the gallbladder.

*T-5:* A conflict related to a feeling of a lack of integration within the clan (such as feeling rejected or treated like an outsider). Distress correlated with the liver and blood.

*T-6:* A conflict related to a recent struggle in the territory that is felt as indigestible, accompanied with a feeling of devaluation. Distress correlated with the stomach.

*T-7:* A conflict of resistance in an emotional climate of repugnance. A feeling of profound disgrace. Something was done that felt foul or disgusting. Distress correlated with the pancreas.

*T-8:* A conflict related to the bloodline, such as filiation (descendent relationships). Can be correlated to problems with blood disorders or hemorrhage.

*T-9:* A conflict related to one's struggle to find direction, or difficulty making decisions. Distress correlated with the adrenals.

*T-10:* A conflict related to a feeling of annihilation or collapse within the territory. Distress correlated with the kidney.

*T-11:* A conflict related to territorial marking and an associated sense of devaluation. Distress correlated with the urethra.

*T-12:* A sexual struggle often related to the partner, frequently stemming from an unclean genital conflict. Distress correlated with the pubis.

**Lumbar spine:**
Lumbar vertebrae relate to preservation of the self and the species, in terms of the structure that is in place. For instance, being the pillar within the clan and/or having to count only on oneself to survive.

*L-1:* A conflict related to a "disgusting story" stemming from a situation with family members or friends, possibly related to a violation such as incest or molestation. Distress correlated with the colon.

*L-2:* A conflict related to having to let go of a reserve or safety net (e.g., money). Devaluation pertaining to not having enough reserves due to a "dirty story." Distress correlated with the appendix.

*L-3:* A conflict related to sexuality. Self-devaluation linked to not being able to conceive. For example, one feels unable to "mark" one's sexual territory (to have sex) because one's spouse has had an affair. Distress correlated with the testes or ovaries.

*L-4:* A conflict related to feeling outside of the sexual norm. One feels that one is a mismatch with one's partner. Devaluation related to being different from others (outside the norm), in relation to finances, work, or lifestyle. Distress correlated with the prostate or uterus.

*L-5:* A conflict about having sexual fantasies that are believed to be outside of the norm. Devaluation related to siblings or friends (collaterals). Fear of being judged by others.

*L-5/S-1:* A conflict related to a feeling of sacrifice due to being the pillar of the family for the purpose of survival. Distress related to sexual self-devaluation (such as sexual abuse or sexual assault).

## Spleen

An organ located in the upper abdomen, that is an important part of the lymphatic system. Among other functions, it filters and removes old red blood cells and helps control the amount of blood in the body.

*Embryonic origin: new brain mesoderm.*

**Emotional conflict(s):** Corresponds to a struggle related to blood, when, for instance, one is unable to function because of a wound that bleeds abundantly, externally or internally (e.g., after an accident). The brain does not differentiate between a hemorrhage and a blood transfusion; therefore, a problem with the spleen can be prompted by a blood transfusion. A spleen disorder can also pertain to any other feelings of devaluation related to blood, such as receiving the diagnosis of leukemia.

## Stomach (Greater Curvature)

The primary organ of digestion, which is a muscular, elastic, pear-shaped bag located between the esophagus and the intestine. The function of the stomach is to secrete protein-digesting enzymes and strong acids to permit food digestion.

*Embryonic origin: endoderm.*

**Emotional conflict(s):** An issue related to recent anger and frustration, and difficulty in digesting something that is too big to be accepted. For instance, one has a concern related to money or an inheritance with a family member (or close member of the clan). A cell increase (tumor) of the secretory type (production of gastric juices) allows the stomach to figuratively break down the "big morsel."

## Stomach (Lesser Curvature)

The lesser curvature of the stomach contains the duodenal bulb and the pyloric canal. Its function is to pass the mixed-food bolus to the duodenum.

*Embryonic origin: ectoderm.*

**Emotional conflict(s):** An issue related to territorial frustration. A conflict linked to the violation of boundaries, such as a problem with a neighbor or an unfaithful partner. The ulcerative widening of the pylorus symbolically creates the space for the "morsel" to pass through when one has no choice other than having to digest it.

**Note:** Problems related to the greater curvature correspond to a situation that is "too big to digest," while problems of the lesser curvature pertain to a situation one is "forced to digest."

## Stroke

An ischemic stroke is most often caused by a blood clot that blocks or plugs a blood vessel in the brain. A hemorrhagic stroke is caused by a blood vessel that breaks and bleeds into the brain.

**Emotional conflict(s):** An intellectual struggle related to being unable to find a solution to a problem that is perceived as enormous. During the active phase of the conflict, an increase of dopamine and adrenaline will occur. The overproduction of such hormones will raise the blood pressure and heart rate. It is during the resolution phase of the emotional conflict that a stroke takes place.

*Example:* A CEO fears that his company may crash at any time. The unmanageability of the situation forces him to stay in survival mode while he tries to save his empire. He experiences a stroke as a result of his perception.

# T

## Teeth

Bone-like structures rooted in sockets in the jaw that are used for biting or chewing food or as a means of attack or defense.

*Embryonic origin: ectoderm.*

**Emotional conflict(s):** In general, problems with the teeth are related to being unable to "bite back" in a situation of attack/defense. One feels devalued and frustrated in a situation in which one forces oneself to keep one's anger and aggressiveness inside.

## Temporomandibular Joint Disorder (TMJ)

Refers to acute or chronic pain of the temporomandibular joint, which connects the jaw to the skull.

**Emotional conflict(s):** A problem related to communication, in which one feels that one cannot argue well enough to be heard or to win a debate. One feels that one's words are not "polished" (well chosen) or powerful enough to either get through to the other or to contradict the other.

## Testes

The male sex glands, located in a pouch of skin called the scrotum. The function of the testes is the production of sperm, as well as male hormones (primarily testosterone).

*Embryonic origin: endoderm.*

**Emotional conflict(s):** Testicular cancer (seminoma) is the result of an emotional stress related to the loss of an offspring. The biological program that pertains to the continuation of the species always prevails. There is nothing worse for a living being than to lose an offspring, and the perfect solution provided by the brain for such a conflict is to replace the loss as quickly as possible. A pathology of the ovaries for women, or of the testes for men (endodermic tissue,) is directly related to procreation and the replacement of the loss. As always, a conflict can be experienced literally or figuratively, and a profound loss may relate to someone or something other than a child.

*Example:* A man loses his best friend, who dies in a car accident. He develops a testicular cancer shortly after the loss.

**Note:** Problems related to the part of the testes that is linked to the new brain mesoderm layer pertain more specifically to an ugly conflict with a sexual undertonality in which a female partner is involved. It can also reflect a conflict of loss accompanied with self-devaluation. The formation of a cyst will occur during the recovery phase of such a conflict.

## Tetany

A disorder involving the involuntary contraction of muscles.

**Emotional conflict(s):** A problem related to movement in a context in which one feels blocked and unable to act according to one's desires. Emotional distress related to feeling unable to protect oneself with either the right gesture (symptoms on the left) or the right words (symptoms on the right).

## Thalamus

The structure within the brain composed of two masses of gray matter that are situated between the cerebral cortex and the midbrain. Its function includes relaying sensation, motor signals, and spatial sensing to the cerebral cortex. The thalamus also regulates sleep and alertness.

*Embryonic origin: ectoderm.*

**Emotional conflict(s):** An issue related to feeling misjudged by others (right side) or pertaining to the judgment one may direct toward oneself (left side). For instance, the conflict of the thalamus often resonates with a woman's despair, such as feeling disregarded by a man after giving her virginity away to him. A condition of the thalamus may pertain to one's gestational memory (project purpose) of the profound disappointment of one's mother, who was treated roughly by her husband sexually, or who sensed that they were not sexually compatible (such as on her wedding night or very soon after getting married). Also, an ancestral memory could be at the root of thalamus problems in the offspring or descendants, such as the shame that was experienced by a woman in the clan who felt judged by the family after conceiving a child out of wedlock. A conflict related to complete discouragement, such as that expressed in the statement "I wish I were dead."

## Throat

The portion of the digestive tract that lies between the rear of the mouth and the esophagus.

**Emotional conflict(s):** In general, throat problems relate to having difficulty swallowing something metaphorically or being unable to express oneself verbally. Sometimes throat pain can reflect the stress of a child who can't kiss his mother. Also, one may experience feelings of being threatened, as if one had "a knife to one's throat," and one may trigger a throat condition.

- *Endodermic tissue*—wanting to swallow and incorporate something but being unable to do so.
- *Ectodermic tissue*—being forced to swallow something and not wanting to, or feeling forced to hold words inside.

## Thyroid

One of the largest endocrine glands in the human body. This butterfly-shaped gland is controlled by the hypothalamus and pituitary glands. The function of the thyroid is to "run" our metabolism, producing two hormones (T3 and T4) that have important actions throughout the body and that regulate many aspects of our metabolism. The thyroid monitors the rate at which food is converted into energy. The hormones it produces also have direct effects on most organs. Problems of the thyroid gland can be related to overactivity (hyperthyroidism) or underactivity (hypothyroidism).

**Thyroid gland (acinous part):**
The secretory part of the thyroid that is shaped like a grape. A hot nodule corresponds to the active phase of a thyroid conflict, which elicits the production of more thyroxin (the main hormone produced by the thyroid gland), thus causing hyperthyroidism. A cell proliferation (tumor) allows for the production of more thyroid hormones (T3 and T4), in order to accelerate the metabolism.

*Embryonic origin: endoderm.*

**Emotional conflict(s):** Extreme stress related to not being fast enough to "catch the morsel" in relation to a vital need for sustenance (i.e., food, money, job). Figuratively, an individual wants to "catch" a promotion before another gets it. This archaic conflict can be illustrated by the "flying fish" that attempts to capture an insect but is not fast enough to catch it before a bird does. A thyroid conflict may be linked to an intense need for accelerating action in order to do everything there is to do. For instance, one might need to become "faster" in order to manage one's work schedule, go to school, and raise a child at the same time.

**Thyroid ducts:**
The thyroid ducts are related to the excretory part of the gland. They are the passageways that deliver thyroid hormones into the bloodstream. An ulcerative widening of the ducts will enable more thyroxin to pass through into the bloodstream.

*Embryonic origin: ectoderm.*

**Emotional conflict(s):** Issues related to powerlessness and the feeling that something is not being done fast enough to prevent a problem. One does not have the capability to act quickly enough on one's own, and no one is helping one. A conflict related to the fear of facing a situation that one has possibly waited too long to address (for instance, an issue with a boss or coworker). Emotional distress created by delaying a task or goal and feeling that there is not enough time left to accomplish it.

*Example:* A woman waited too long to get pregnant and is now too old to conceive. In another example, a man waited too long to go see his father at the hospital and did not have enough time to tell him that he loved him before his father died. In both cases, a hyperfunction of the thyroid may be triggered.

**Note:** The types of emotional conflicts associated with the thyroid ducts are more intellectual in nature than those pertaining to the endodermic thyroid gland.

**Special note:** The following discussion pertains to specific thyroid conditions.

**Hyperthyroidism:**
A condition in which the thyroid gland produces too much of the hormone thyroxin. The heart beats faster and harder under the influence of thyroid hormones. The body's metabolism is accelerated and may cause sudden weight loss, an irregular heartbeat, sweating, and nervousness or irritability.

**Emotional conflict(s):** An issue related to a need to catch the "morsel" quickly, which expresses a sense of urgency. The presence of more thyroxin allows an increase in the metabolism and provides more energy to act fast or to flee in the face of danger. In a case where the thyroid ducts are concerned, one perceives that it would be possible to achieve one's task, providing that one acts quickly enough.

*Example:* In order to get ahead at work, a woman constantly feels the need to hurry to prepare documents for the weekly staff meeting. She develops hyperthyroidism as a result.

**Hypothyroidism:**
The sign of an underactive thyroid. Such a disorder causes slow metabolism and weight gain, sensitivity to the cold, fatigue, dry skin, and various other symptoms.

**Emotional conflict(s):** Fear of moving too fast and having to slow down in the face of danger (primal fear). A conflict related to being overwhelmed by the magnitude of an event or the number of things to do. One needs to accomplish a task quickly but feels inundated, knowing that one won't be able to make it happen. In the case of myxedema (skin and tissue disorder), the emotional conflict is related to long-term hypothyroidism, which could be the result of recurring conflicts that damage the thyroid.

**Note:**

- Low levels of TSH (thyroid stimulating hormone) can be associated with one's incapacity to follow up on what one intends to do, because one doesn't believe that it will really happen.

- A cold nodule on the thyroid that does not produce thyroid hormones may occur during the healing phase after hyperthyroidism.

- Thyroid nodules or goiters can be associated with a fear of strangulation (such as a memory of strangulation within the clan).

**Hashimoto's disease:**
An autoimmune disease in which the thyroid gland is targeted and progressively destroyed. At the early stage of this disorder, a goiter (an enlargement of the thyroid gland) may appear.

**Emotional conflict(s):** A problem related to the need to eliminate the aspect of rapidity in oneself because it interferes with the well-being of someone or something important. One wants to gain time and push against one's own nature of going fast (notion of self-destruction) and subconsciously needs to slow down, thus leading to the destruction of the organ responsible for one's speed (thyroid gland).

*Example:* A man wants to spend more time with his kids every morning, but he is out the door for work before he can even have breakfast with them. As a subconscious solution to his conflict, he develops Hashimoto's disease in order to figuratively eliminate that which allows him to speed up, so that he can spend more time with his children.

**Graves' disease:**
A condition in which the thyroid is overactive and produces an excessive quantity of thyroid hormones. A compact cellular proliferation can bring about a Basedow's goiter.

**Emotional conflict(s):** An issue related to not having been fast enough to catch and swallow the "morsel." In an emergency situation, the production of thyroxin accelerates the metabolism so that the individual can act more rapidly. For instance, this conflict can metaphorically relate to a situation in which one arrived too late to prevent someone's death.

# Toe

Any of the five digits at the end of the human foot.

*Embryonic origin: new brain mesoderm.*

**Emotional conflict(s):** Problems with the toes often relate to issues with the mother or relatives, mainly in terms of territorial or sexual issues.

# Tongue

The fleshy muscular organ in the mouth. We use the tongue to "catch" food: it moves the food as an aid in chewing and swallowing. It also allows us to pronounce words.

*Embryonic origin: ectoderm.*

**Emotional conflict(s):** Distress symbolically related to the inability to "throw the mouth" on prey. Sometimes the conflict is related to the necessity of keeping words "inside the mouth" and to not tell a secret. The conflict can also be related to difficulty expressing oneself properly. A person may feel that he or she has a "dirty tongue" and should not have said certain things. Tongue cancer is most often of the epidermoid carcinoma type. Therefore, the conflict associated with this condition involves a notion of separation from the "morsel."

## Tonsils

Small masses of lymphoid tissue situated on either side of the throat at the back of the tongue.

*Embryonic origin: endoderm.*

**Emotional conflict(s):** An issue related to the "morsel," in terms of not being able to swallow it (right side) or not being able to spit it out (left side). Metaphorically, the "morsel" is experienced as vital and can represent the love of a parent, a favorite toy, money, or a promotion. The "morsel" may represent words that could not be fully expressed during a fight. One feels that one did not respond fast enough to win an argument.

## Torticolis

A twisted posture of the neck in which the head is tipped to one side while the chin is turned to the other.

**Emotional conflict(s):** Problem related to a devaluation in movement while feeling subjected to a double constraint that is experienced from front to back. One wants to turn the head away from a situation or event but feels morally unable to do so. Since the brain is subjected to a double constraint, the solution becomes the contracture that will immobilize the neck.

*Example:* A man does not want to see his mother die, but he feels a moral obligation to stay with her while she deteriorates before his eyes. He develops torticolis as a result.

## Ulcers (Duodenal Bulb)

A condition affecting the lining of the stomach.

**Emotional conflict(s):** An issue pertaining to territorial anger, such as a situation with a friend or coworker, and related to the respect of boundaries. This territorial conflict can also be linked to a problem with an unfaithful partner.

## Ureters

The tubes that propel and transport the urine from the kidneys to the urinary bladder.

*Embryonic origin: ectoderm.*

**Emotional conflict(s):** Linked to one's struggle in finding the limits within one's own territory.

*Example:* A man resents the presence of his mother-in-law, who is visiting for several weeks. He wants her out of his territory, and he triggers a condition in one of his ureters.

## Uterus

A female reproductive organ, which is also referred to as the "womb." It is composed of three layers: the endometrium, the innermost layer (the lining of the uterine cavity); the myometrium, the middle layer (smooth muscles); and the perimetrium, the outer layer (loose surrounding tissue). The function of the uterus is to enable the development of the fertilized ovum, which is implanted into the endometrium lining. The uterus plays a major role in the female reproductive system, from the moment of conception to childbirth.

### Endometrium/uterine mucosa:
Secretory- or resorptive-type growth.

*Embryonic origin: endoderm.*

**Emotional conflict(s):** Concern related to conception and difficulties getting pregnant. More secretions are needed to improve the chance of conception. A thicker mucosa will also optimize the chances of implantation of the ovum. Problems in the mucosa of the uterus can express a concern for the offspring. For instance, it is possible that a mother or grandmother fears sexual dangers around her offspring, and she manifests an endometrial tumor. The uterus can also be the expression of a woman's sexual struggle, if she feels that her partner's conduct toward her is unpleasant, or if she thinks that her sexuality with him is "out of the norm" or a mismatch (i.e., he is too old or too young for her). In this case, she may feel that it would be impossible for her to create a family with him. A problem related to an unclean situation with a man may also apply to the uterine mucosa.

### Endometriosis:
A condition of the endometrium in which the cells from the lining of the uterus overproduce and grow. This can lead to pain, irregular bleeding, and infertility.

**Emotional conflict(s):** Trouble related to wanting to have a child but not being able to do so because of circumstances. For instance, a woman has a profound desire for pregnancy that cannot be fulfilled because of a financial struggle or a living situation that is not adequate for a child. Also, a woman may feel that she is away from her home and from the kinds of surroundings that would support her ability to safely give birth and raise her child.

**Myometrium/smooth muscles:**
Fibroid tumors.

*Embryonic origin: new brain mesoderm.*

**Emotional conflict(s):** A struggle related to a woman's difficulty around giving birth. A woman may feel devalued by the fact that she had an abortion or a miscarriage. It is also possible that a woman carries the subconscious memory of her own birth, which was difficult because her mother could not push hard enough and produce strong contractions at the moment of delivery. Fibroid tumors can also express a woman's frustration with not being able to conceive (due to sterility, menopause, or the absence of a partner).

**Cervix:**
The lower portion of the uterus that provides the opening to the top of the vagina.

*Embryonic origin: ectoderm.*

**Emotional conflict(s):** An issue associated with a woman's sexual frustration when her partner is passive, not present enough, or possibly not interested in her. A woman may feel a lack of satisfaction stemming from not being wanted enough by a man who she wishes would desire her. On the other hand, problems with the cervix can manifest when a partner is too demanding of a woman and perceives her as inadequate sexually (often related to her lack of drive). The biological meaning of cervical cancer often pertains to a feeling of being separated from a partner. During the active phase of such a conflict, the ulcerative widening of the uterine cervix symbolically allows more sperm to reach the uterus when the chance to have intercourse presents itself.

# Vagina

The muscular canal of the female reproductive system that is lined with mucous membranes and connects the uterus to the outside of the body. It provides lubrication and receives the penis during sexual intercourse.

*Embryonic origin: ectoderm.*

**Emotional conflict(s):** A sexual need to be "taken" (possessed or claimed) by a man. Frustration about being unable to have intercourse with someone.

*Also see Bartholin's Glands.*

## Veins

Blood vessels that carry the blood toward the heart. Most veins carry deoxygenated blood from the tissues back to the heart. (The exceptions are the pulmonary and umbilical veins, both of which carry oxygenated blood to the heart.)

*Embryonic origin: new brain mesoderm.*

**Emotional conflict(s):** Self-devaluation within the clan (blood related). One feels that one represents "bad blood" oneself because of one's failures and shortcomings.

**Special note:** The following discussion pertains to specific vein conditions.

**Varicose veins:**
Enlarged and twisted veins near the surface of the skin. Emotional conflict associated with a feeling of dragging a heavy load ("ball and chain" conflict).

**Raynaud's disease:**
A disorder that causes a discoloration of the fingers because of vasospasms that decrease blood supply. Struggle often related to self-devaluation arising from not being able to hold on to someone who has died.

## Vertebrae

*See Spine.*

## Vertigo

A balance disorder in which a person experiences a perception of spinning and tilting. This condition is often accompanied by nausea.

**Emotional conflict(s):** Associated with conflicts of the inner ear, vertigo relates to being unable to stand hearing something. It can also be linked to a fear of moving forward in life. One can have vertigo after losing a loved one, thus symbolically being forced to stay in the same place (to avoid a spinning motion) so that one can be "found" by the person that one lost.

## Vitiligo

A chronic disorder that causes depigmentation of certain areas of the skin. This condition is linked to the death of melanocytes, which are the cells responsible for pigmentation.

**Emotional conflict(s):** An issue related to one's need to clean and purify what has been soiled. Also, the white patches of skin may express the unfulfilled need for deep connection to another without protection (e.g., sex without a condom). A conflict linked to an intense feeling of separation that is perceived as sudden and atrocious (feeling ripped apart from someone).

## Vomiting

A symptom involving the forceful expulsion of the contents of one's stomach through intestinal motor function. Food is not accepted into the system and is purged back out.

**Emotional conflict(s):** A problem related to the rejection of what is imposed, such as an idea or an order. One wants to reject a proposition and does not want to allow any of it to move through one's system. A conflict related to the fear of being forced to do something.

*Example:* A child has to finish the food on his or her plate and will be punished if he or she doesn't. The child vomits as a result.

## Warts

Small tumors that only grow in the top layer of skin (epidermis) and do not have "roots."

**Emotional conflict(s):** An issue involving self-devaluation, shame, and a feeling of being soiled in relation to a specific area of the body. Sometimes warts can develop in the pubic area as an expression of feeling soiled by an inappropriate thought or a shameful situation of a sexual nature. This conflict is often triggered by an emotional state of low self-esteem, especially when comparing oneself to another who is more talented and successful at doing something.

*Example:* A boy feels that he does not play soccer very well and is not as agile on his feet as the other kids are. He puts his attention on the soles of the feet of his teammates, who are running fast and kicking the ball with flair. He will develop plantar warts as a result of his feelings of inadequacy in comparison to others.

## Water Retention

*See Kidney (collecting tubules) and Obesity.*

## Weight

*See Obesity.*

## Wrist

The joint connecting the hand with the forearm. It is made up of eight small bones known as carpals.

*Embryonic origin: new brain mesoderm.*

**Emotional conflict(s):** Issues related to dexterity or the inability to accomplish a manual task satisfactorily.

*Also see Carpal Tunnel Syndrome.*

*Closing note:* This edition of the *Bio-Breakthrough Dictionary* represents a work in progress. An expanded edition will soon be available. For more information, please contact the BioReprogramming® Institute:

Phone: (323) 717-6107

Web: www.bioreprogramming.net

# The Bio-Breakthrough Dictionary Index

# Conclusion

Thank you for allowing me to share with you this enriching part of my life—the experience and knowledge base that have changed many lives. It is an honor to connect with you through these writings.

We are living in one of the most fascinating eras of humankind, in which revelatory knowledge regarding illness is finally surfacing and becoming available to everyone. I believe that one day, not long from now, the new findings described in this book will revolutionize the field of health and healing. We will soon witness the emergence of a new style of medicine that will combine modalities for emotional healing with adequate remedies. Addressing the impact of our emotions will cease to be a side note and will instead become a central focus.

In the meantime, healing will continue unabated as more and more individuals access a profound new awareness, which is the intention and promise of this book. By making use of the processes offered here, you, and those you care about, will benefit in mind, body, and spirit.

It is my hope that this information has provided insight, changed your opinions about disease, alleviated some of your fears, and given you cause for optimism. Perhaps now you can look at your life as an epic unfolding that makes sense at the deepest level, a story that you have the power to modify in any way and at any time. Always remember that when something unpleasant happens to you, it is possible for you to change your perception and recognize it as a blessing in disguise.

Finally, I hope that you are inspired to break free of any opinions, ideas, and beliefs that may be hindering your ability to flourish and enjoy the adventure of your life. Your independence from these impediments is the first step to healing. Remember: the power to create health is within you.

With passion,
*Isabelle Benarous*

# Index

# About the Author

Isabelle Benarous is an international lecturer, consultant and author. She is the founder of the BioReprogramming® Institute, which is dedicated to teaching and disseminating BioReprogramming®, a master tool for the resolution of emotional conflicts.

Her extensive experience as a trainer in biological decoding and neuro-linguistic programming led Isabelle to create a comprehensive, transformational approach to emotional conflicts based on the science of human evolution and the processes of the mind. This is the BioReprogramming® method, which aims to provide lasting solutions to emotional conflicts related to health disorders and other life challenges, optimizing the prevention of illness and allowing transformation from within.

Isabelle is acclaimed for her clear explanations, creativity and strategic intellect during live interventions. Her goal is to educate and inspire others to become the masters of their own healing, and to offer therapists and health-care practitioners a new vision for approaching illness. She has built an outstanding reputation through her work running workshops and training sessions with companies and health organizations worldwide.

❖

Printed in Great Britain
by Amazon